TRIPHASIC
TRAINING

A Systematic Approach To Elite Speed And Explosive Strength Performance

Cal Dietz
&
Ben Peterson

BYE DIETZ SPORT ENTERPRISE
322 Gandydancer Circle
Hudson, WI 54016

First Bye Dietz electronic edition February 2012

Illustration credit goes to Kait Peterson

Cover Designed by Kait Peterson

Created in the United States of America

3 5 7 9 10 8 6 4 2

Library of Congress Cataloging-in-Publication Data is available.

ISBN: 978-0-9851743-1-6

On the eighth day, of the second month, of the twelfth year, of the twenty-first century, I dedicate this book to my family — wife Karyn , children Tatum and Brody, Mother, Father, brother Andy, Grandparents — and friends that helped me in my journey.

- C.D.

To the three men who gave rise to my fascination with human performance and inspired me to pursue my passion — Coach Mac, Coach Lilja, and Coach Nick.

- B.P.

TABLE OF CONTENTS

SECTION 5
HIGH FORCE AT HIGH VELOCITY
(55 TO 80 PERCENT)

SECTION 6
HIGH VELOCITY PEAKING
(BELOW 55 PERCENT)

SECTION 7
PUTTING IT ALL TOGETHER

FOREWORD

Triphasic Training is a game changer! It becomes clear how the University of Minnesota Olympic sport programs have achieved such high levels of success after reading this book. I first began communicating with Coach Dietz in 2008. After watching Coach Dietz teach these principles, I came to the realization that his method was sound because it applied complex scientific principles in a practical manner for people to understand. This combination has established a "blueprint for success" and helped Coach Dietz's athletes accomplish great feats both at the collegiate and professional level. I integrated the *Triphasic Method* with many collegiate and professional athletes at IMG. The results were outstanding! I will continue to utilize and integrate this very effective method throughout my tenure as a coach in this great profession. I've often heard that success leaves clues. After reading this book, you'll have a blueprint for success and a greater knowledge of the training process. Loren Seagrave always says, "Educate people! Train animals!" This book will help you understand the "Why" and not just the "How." It's a "must have" for anyone trying to get better!

— **Jeff Dillman**
Director of Strength and Conditioning
University of Florida

AUTHOR'S NOTE

Co-authoring a book presented a unique challenge that neither of us expected. The book is a compilation of stories, personal experiences, and knowledge of two individuals. As such, a conventional writing style would have us write the book in a manner that distinguishes which author is contributing to a specific story or anecdote. It would require us to preface sentences with, "Cal remembers when..." or "Ben worked with an athlete who..." When we were finished with sections of the book and went back to read what we had written, we found the constant quoting hindered the flow of the book and prevented the reader from making connections between examples that came off as separate story lines.

To solve this perceived flaw to the book, we came up with a simple solution. We wrote the book from the first person view of a third party narrative. Instead of stating which one of us is involved with a story, we say "I remember" or "I worked with." In essence, we created an imaginary person who is the culmination of both of our life experiences, knowledge, and stories. We beg the readers indulgence with this style choice and say that it is in no way meant to deceive or misguide the reader as to the source of information, but rather to improve the consistency and readability of the book. We feel that this allows for one clear voice to present the information and will maximize the usefulness of the material to the reader.

PREFACE

WHAT THIS BOOK IS NOT

Right off the bat, I want to make a huge confession. I want to tell you what this book is not. This book is not the Holy Grail of training! It isn't the only way to train athletes, nor does it promise to turn every athlete who uses these methods into an All-American. Even with the most advanced training methods, scientific knowledge, and vast array of sports supplements the twenty-first century has to offer, sport coaches, athletic directors, general managers, and parents must realize that in order to win, you must have the best athletes. That means you must recruit the best athletes in college and you must pay for the best athletes in the pros. No method in existence currently used by any strength coach can make up the gap between the genetics of a superior athlete to that of an inferior one.

So what does that mean? Are superior genetics the sole factor in determining success? Without getting into any physiology or neurology, let me explain using a real life example of two hockey players I coached several years ago. We will call them Fred and Walter. Fred and Walter grew up playing hockey together in a small town in northern Minnesota. From the very beginning, they were inseparable. To call them rink rats would have been an understatement. If they weren't at the local rink working on their slap shot or playing pick-up games, they were at the rink that Fred's dad made every year in the backyard working on stick handling and skating. Both households even had the same rule—if you were watching television, you had to work on your stick handling at the same time. (Both boys had small plastic sticks they practiced with on the floor during commercial breaks.)

Based on the amount of practice and work the two boys invested since the age of six, it shouldn't be any surprise that they were All-State selections in hockey and that both accepted scholarships to play for the University of Minnesota Golden Gophers (U of M). I remember when Fred and Walter arrived. They were virtually identical. Both stood six feet tall and weighed 175 lbs. During their four-year careers, they both went through the exact same strength and conditioning routine every off-season. Their one rep max (1RM) for the bench and squat were within 15 pounds of each other. They ate the same meals at the training table, lived in the same house, and even dated the same girl (though not at the same time). I will add, and personally attest, that both Fred and Walter gave 100 percent to everything they did surrounding Gopher hockey. They attacked every workout and skated every shift like it was their last. For all intents and purposes, Fred and Walter were the exact same athlete, the only difference being their genetic makeup— they had different parents.

Here is where the story takes a drastic turn. During their time at the U of M, Walter continued to excel while Fred seemed to struggle at times on the ice. By their senior season, Walter was a pre-season All-American who would eventually go on to play in the NHL. Fred, meanwhile, was an average third line player. Why? How could two essentially identical athletes end up at such different levels?

The answer was genetics. Genetically speaking, Walter had a higher end sympathetic nervous system (SNS) and superior hormonal profile than Fred. The SNS is part of the electrical wiring grid of the body, relaying instructions from the motor cortex to the muscles of an athlete to perform coordinated muscle movements—hand eye coordination, force production, balance, and reactive ability to name a few. In addition, the SNS stimulates the endocrine system and hormonal response of the body under stress, controlling the release of epinephrine and norepinephrine (commonly known as adrenaline) and the mobilization of energy substrates through glucogon secretion as well as levels of other hormones associated with athletic performance such as testosterone (muscle building), T3 and T4 (metabolism), insulin-like growth factor-1 (muscle building), and insulin (anabolic recovery). In short, the SNS is the "fight or flight response," the most powerful response of the human body. The better the wiring or the quality of the cable used in that wiring, the faster and more efficiently a signal will travel through the grid. Similarly, an athlete's hormonal profile dictates his ability to respond to the rigors of competition—stress, performance, and recovery. An athlete who can process and respond to stimuli more quickly as well as orchestrate the body's hormonal response efficiently will have a decisive advantage over other athletes. In Walter's case, both processes were superior.

Think of Fred and Walter as sports cars. Let's be patriotic and go with Ford Mustang GTs. Both rolled off the assembly line as stock models, but over the years, the cars were overhauled and upgraded. All the hours practicing stick handling and skating were like putting on a better air filter and upgraded exhaust. The hours spent in the weight room squatting and jumping on Russian plyometric boxes were like putting in a new engine block chip that allowed the cars to shift faster and accelerate more quickly. In the end, both cars were far superior to what they had been when they originally rolled off the assembly line over twenty years earlier. The only difference—one that I failed to mention at the start—was that when these cars first rolled off the line, Walter had a V-10 turbo engine while Fred had a V-8. From the very start, Walter had greater potential because his engine could inherently generate more horsepower. As long as both cars received the same upgrades, the V-10 turbo would always be the better, faster car.

Getting back to Fred and Walter, this doesn't mean that a person with a superior nervous system and hormonal profile will automatically be a better athlete. If Walter stayed home watching television and playing his Playstation 3 all day while Fred was off working out and practicing, I guarantee only Fred would have been offered a scholarship to play Division I hockey. Being blessed with the genetic gift of a superior nervous system, a V-10 turbo engine, doesn't guarantee a person athletic greatness. It merely gives him a better chance of reaching greatness if he puts forth the effort.

I don't know if you, as a coach, are lucky enough to have an entire weight room full of turbo V-10 engines or a bunch of V-8s. You might not have Mustangs at all but instead are sitting with a lot of Toyota Corollas. The main thing I want you to understand is that this is not a book about turning a Toyota Corolla into a Mustang GT. That is impossible. Every athlete has limited potential, a ceiling defined by his genetics. At the same time, no athlete is confined to a certain level of performance; every athlete can improve.

WHAT THIS BOOK IS

Every strength and conditioning coach is, to an extent, a mechanic. Not to beat the car metaphor to death, but you have to look at every athlete as a complex engine with thousands of moving parts. And you, the coach, are trying to squeeze every single drop of horsepower you can out of that engine. This book is a method of training that will turn you into a master mechanic, showing you how to improve the horsepower and performance of any make or model car that walks into your weight room. The tri-phasic undulating block model can be applied to any athlete at any time during his training cycle and achieve the same results—improvements in power, rate of force development, and neuromuscular coordination.

At this point, I would guess that some of you are holding up red flags to question that last statement. "How can one training model be applied to such a wide range of sports with the same results?" That is a fair and legitimate question, a question that I will answer in this book. While on the surface sports like hockey and basketball may seem very different, they are identical at their physiologic core. Bear with me a second—the "ah ha!" moment is only minutes away.

First, let's agree on a couple things:

❖ All athletes use muscles. This is self-explanatory. Moving on...

❖ Every sport requires dynamic movement of those muscles. Remember, dynamic muscle action refers to the active movement of a muscle through a partial or complete range of motion (swinging a baseball bat, jumping for a rebound, or sprinting up a sideline).

I know that neither of those points are groundbreaking. Coaches often have a very good understanding of the dynamic movements used most frequently in the sports they train. This is where you can cite the importance of specificity of training until the cows come home. Coaches will often tailor their workouts to try and improve those specific neural pathways and muscle actions in their athletes, with the goal of creating more explosive, powerful, efficient athletes at that movement pattern. The problem doesn't lie with this approach to training at all. In fact, taking this approach to training is dead on accurate *one-third* of the time. The problem lies with the other two-thirds.

Remember that "ah ha!" moment I promised you? Well, here it is:

ALL DYNAMIC MUSCLE ACTION IS TRIPHASIC!

That one simple sentence is what ties every sport together and allows all athletes to be trained using the same method, yielding the same results. It is what this entire book is about. Understanding the physiologic nature of muscle action taking place during dynamic movements gives you, the coach, a foundational training method that can be applied to every sport. Couple this method with a periodization schedule that can be altered to fit with any training time frame and you have the tri-phasic undulating block method.

In a very brief and basic explanation that will be expanded upon at length in later chapters, the triphasic nature of all dynamic movement can be broken down into three phases:

1) **Eccentric phase:** This is the deceleration or lowering portion of the movement. It is associated with muscle lengthening. During this phase, kinetic energy is absorbed and stored in the tendons of the muscle structure to be used during the stretch reflex.

2) **Isometric phase:** This is where the mass, or athlete, comes to a complete stop before being reaccelerated in a new direction. (This is actually governed by Sir Isaac Newton's Laws of Motion. More on that and physics later.)

3) **Concentric phase:** This is the acceleration of an athlete or mass. It is associated with muscle shortening.

As the adage goes, a chain is only as strong as its weakest link. If your training program consists solely of methods that train the concentric portion of dynamic muscle action, your athletes are heading into the season with a chain consisting of one strong link and two weak links. This book is designed to show you how to develop the other two phases of dynamic human movement within a periodization model that will make all three links strong and optimize the performance of your athletes. Remember that:

ATHLETIC MOVEMENT = DYNAMIC MOVEMENT = TRI-PHASIC MOVEMENT

WRAP UP

I'm sure by now I have peaked your interest and forced you to rethink, in part, the training model you currently use with your athletes. When you are done reading this book, you'll not only be able to write programs that produce explosive, powerful athletes, but you'll also be able to spot flaws in the various movement patterns pertinent to their sport. These flaws tend to develop over time, especially during yearly training phases or macro-cycles. Keep in mind, these issues can develop even with the use of the best training methods. Any time an athlete develops a specific aspect of his performance (strength, speed, or power), it likely causes a deficit in a separate but related performance quality. For example, let's say you make an athlete faster with concentric only focused training. Great! The problem, however, is that you neglected to train the athlete's eccentric decelerator in tangent to be able to absorb the higher levels of force now placed on him by the athlete's improved speed. When the athlete decelerates to make a cut or jump on the field/court, he can't change direction as quickly due to a undertrained eccentric phase—the inability to absorb the increased force. This book will give coaches and/or trainers an understanding of how to address those qualities and fix and spot these issues to help your athletes reach a new level.

Now that you have a better idea of what this book *is* and *is not*, it is time to get to work. At this point, you've read the course outline. Now, it's time to get into the nitty gritty details and learn the tools that you, the master mechanic, will take back to your garage, the weight room, to start tuning up your athletes.

Note to the Reader

The digital edition of this book contains over 3,000 hyperlinks to video clips that demonstrate how to properly perform every exercise, as well as six hours of video lectures by Coach Dietz from his national speaking tour. In this book, these hyperlinks are indicated by words or phrases that are underlined. In order for you to take advantage of these features, the pages which have these links can be downloaded for free at:

http://www.xlathlete.com/xl/events/Triphasic%20Training%20Hard%20Copy%20Hyperlinks%20Underlined%20in%20Blue.pdf

When you come to a page in the book that has a hyper/video link (denoted by underlined text) simply scroll to that page in the downloaded PDF file and click the link.

SECTION 1

BASIC PRINCIPLES & THEIR APPLICATION TO TRAINING

1.1: BASIC PRINCIPLES

The program outlined in this book and the methods used to execute it work. Period. After over twenty years in the field of strength and conditioning, I've been able to test, refine, and implement a training methodology that gets results (28 Big Ten/WCHA titles, seven national championships, and over 375 All-Americans in numerous different sports). Now, don't get me wrong—I'm not saying that I'm responsible for or that my training methods are responsible for all those accolades. The accolades are due to two things—great recruitment efforts on the coaches' part and great work ethic on the athletes' part. I've been lucky to work with groups of very athletically gifted, dedicated young men and women. Conversely, because I've been fortunate to consistently work with such high caliber athletes year after year, it has allowed me to formulate, implement, tweak, and refine a system of training that gets results.

This system, and its success, is based on a set of three principles that I've adopted and stick with when writing programs for my athletes. These are 1) stress the human body, 2) stress it often, and 3) stress it differently each time. To accomplish all three, you have to be a little creative. The ultimate purpose of this book is to teach you how and when to apply different methods of stress with your athletes to not only improve performance but engage the athletes and get them excited about training.

1.2: STRESS, STRESS, STRESS!

If the athlete isn't being physically stressed, you're wasting your time. I honestly believe that. This philosophy—one of constantly applying stress to the human body—is the single most important component of any training program. Let me say it again—you must *constantly* be stressing the athlete. I was lucky because early in my own playing career as a wrestler and football player at Findlay College in Ohio, I was exposed to literature and training methods that showed me the value of stress and its initial negative, though eventually positive, effects on performance (more on that in a minute). Since my playing days, I've continued to learn everything I can about programming and training the human body to perform at its highest levels. I've looked at and dissected every successful training program I could get my hands on (and by "successful," I mean world record setting), and they've all had one common theme—high levels of stress.

Taking those early lessons about stress that I learned at Findlay and combining them with what I've learned since through research and experimentation, I'm convinced that stress is the essential factor that must be a constant in athletes' training in order for them to maximize their athletic potential. That said, this isn't a book about stress. It's a book about how a coach should apply stress to the athlete to maximize performance. Yes, I'll discuss triphasic muscle action, undulation, the block system, and a host of other things, but you have to realize that these are all different methods of applying stress to the human body. Before a coach can effectively apply these methods to elicit performance benefits for an athletic population, a coach needs to have a firm grasp on the foundations on which those methods are built. Specifically, in this case, a coach must understand stress—its cause and effect relationship on the human body and how that relationship influences adaptations that improve sport performance.

Stress and the human body's mechanisms to cope with it are amazing things. Stress is caused by anything and everything the human body encounters. From the bumps you feel while driving to work in your car to the apprehension you feel on a first date to the sheer terror of stumbling across a grizzly bear in the woods, stress is your body's way of interpreting and cataloging the world around you. The idea of stress as an all-encompassing stimulus was first presented as the general adaption syndrome (GAS) by Dr. Hans Selye in the 1950s.[1] Often referred to as the "Grandfather of Stress," Selye discovered that everyone interprets the world around them through stress.

By definition, GAS is the manifestation of stress in the human body as it builds over time. What this means is that stress isn't a single, isolated event. It must be thought of as a fluid stimulus that the human body must constantly deal with. Think of stress as a wave. When you're in the valley, you're experiencing low levels of stress. When you're at a peak, you're experiencing high levels of stress. The important thing to understand is that regardless of your place on the wave, you're always under stress.

Selye understood the interaction between stress and the body to be a battle to reach homeostasis. The human body doesn't like change, which is why it doesn't like stress. Stress is the signal to the body that something has to change, something must adapt to reduce the amount of stress exerted by that stressor on the body if it were to come across it a second time. If the stressor is large enough, it triggers adaptation. The brain will then signal the body, through hormonal response, to adapt to that stressor. The body's thinking is that while it doesn't want to change, it is better off adapting to the stress so that if encountered a second time, it will be dealt with by the new mechanisms put in place for its facilitation and not have any negative effects on the body.

IMAGE 1.1 - HANS SELYE

---

[1] Image 1: Used with permission from Steve Berczi and the *Hans Selye Institute*.

Think about this in terms of running because it is both the easiest and most relatable example. Imagine you haven't been out for a run for several months. Maybe you live in Minnesota like I do and outdoor running is difficult from January through March. Anyway, you go out for a run. The next morning you roll out of bed and almost fall over. Your feet are killing you, your quads are on fire, and your lower back feels like you slept on a concrete floor. After a brief analysis of the situation, you conclude that you're getting old and incredibly out of shape, but you're pretty sure that it won't kill you if you go run again. This process continues for a week or so. Each time you wake up, you're a little less sore than the previous day even though the number of miles you ran each subsequent time increased. Why? The simple and clear answer might seem to be that you're in better shape, but that isn't the real reason "why." The real reason is because your body has adapted to a new stressor—running. During the first run, your body was screaming at you, "What the $@!*% are you doing?!?!" Your body had adapted to a state of homeostasis that didn't involve running. It was happy. By throwing in a new stressor, it forced the body to adapt, to change, so that the next time you went running, it said, "Oh, this again? I knew this was coming. It's easy." The human body is lazy and wants to be kept in the nice warm blanket of homeostasis as much as possible. As a strength coach, you need to rip that blanket off and dump a bucket of ice water over it to stimulate adaptation!

Entire volumes of books have been written on GAS and its implications since Selye first published his work over a half century ago, none of which I will go into here. For the purposes of strength and conditioning, as well as understanding the undulating model, you only need to understand how it pertains to athletic performance. Selye broke down GAS into three stages— alarm reaction, resistance, and exhaustion. Let's take a moment to examine each stage more closely as it pertains to an athlete.

1) **Alarm reaction** (workout): This is the athlete's "fight or flight" response. A strong training stimuli, elicited by workloads of high stress, mobilizes the athlete's energy resources in amounts that far exceed the metabolic level necessary for homeostatic response. It can also be thought of as an immediate, or acute, training effect that leads to the degradation of muscle

tissue and energy substrates. These increased demands trigger profound endocrine responses (i.e. the secretion of stress hormones such as cortisol, epinephrine, and norepinephrine, as well as human growth hormone (HGH)). This is a catabolic response.

2) **Resistance** (recovery): This stage begins after the workout and is the body's attempt to return to homeostasis, repairing the damage from the workout through an insulin response (repairing muscle damage and refilling glycogen stores). This is the anabolic stage. Stress hormone levels will return to normal but only if given sufficient time to dissipate. If another stressor returns before the athlete has completely recovered, the athlete will experience another alarm stage response, pushing him deeper into a catabolic state.

3) **Exhaustion** (severe overtraining): This stage is defined by very high levels of stress for the athlete. Other terms used to express this stage are overload, burnout, or adrenal fatigue. In this state, an athlete's endocrine system begins to shut down, as it is no longer able to keep up with the high stress loads placed on it. An athlete in this state will often have a deficient thyroid (low metabolism or constantly tired), severely impaired immune system, elevated cortisol levels, disturbed sleep patterns, and an inhibited insulin response. This stage is associated with decreased sport performance.

When you put the three GAS phases together along with an understanding of the physiological response they stimulate, you'll find that there are three possible results from training.

1) Low-grade stress that produces a mild alarm reaction response. This doesn't result in any positive adaptation because the training stimuli or workloads weren't stressful enough to upset the athlete's homeostatic balance by triggering a resistance stage response. These workouts are pointless and waste valuable training time.

GENERAL ADAPTATION SYNDROME
(UNDERTRAINED ATHLETE)

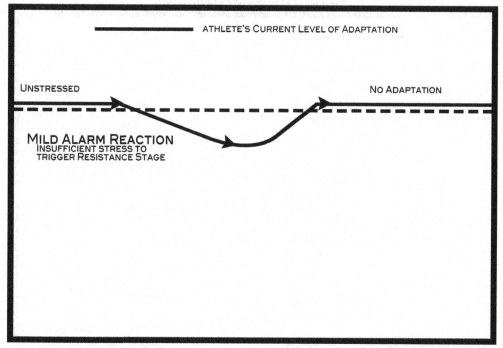

Figure 1.1: Undertrained athlete—workout doesn't provide sufficient stress to trigger a resistance stage (anabolic) response. Doesn't result in any positive adaptation.

2) Long bouts of high-grade stress usually applied over a period of months or even years. Here the stress of numerous workouts compounds itself. Before the athlete's body can begin to build itself back up through the resistance stage, another stressor is applied that pushes the body into a deeper catabolic state. The athlete's body isn't given sufficient time to recover to its previous level of adaptation before another stressor is applied. If more and more stress is applied without adequate time given for recovery, the athlete falls further and further down the proverbial cliff, eventually reaching the bottom of the canyon. Classified as severe overtraining, this consists of extreme exhaustion as well as mental, neural, and adrenal fatigue. If an athlete is allowed to reach this point, it can take months, or even years, to climb back out.

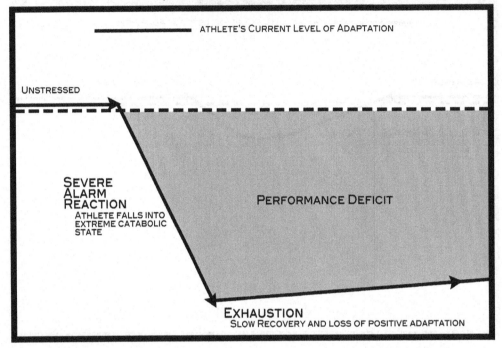

Figure 1.2: Overtrained athlete—excessive stress with little to no recovery time pushes the athlete into an extreme catabolic state or exhaustion. Also known as overtraining, this type of stress pattern produces a performance deficit and can take months, or years, to recover from.

3) Short bouts of exposure to high-grade stress usually applied over a period of weeks or months produces an alarm reaction response, signaling a massive, catabolic hormonal release. This, in turn, forces the body into the resistance stage, where it begins to rebuild the damaged tissue and refill metabolic stores. The result of these workouts is a *supercompensation* by the athlete's body, improving subsequent performance. Here, the athlete isn't allowed to fall all the way to the bottom of the canyon. Halfway down, additional stress (workouts) is stopped, and the athlete's physiological system begins to climb back up and recover.

GENERAL ADAPTATION SYNDROME
(SUPER COMPENSATED ATHLETE)

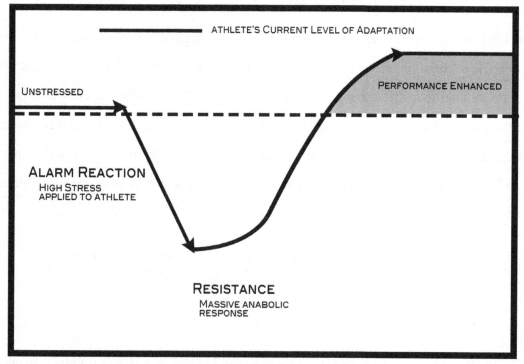

Figure 1.3: Supercompensated athlete—proper application of high-grade stress causes a severe alarm reaction and hormonal release within the athlete. This, in turn, signals a massive resistance stage response, turning the athlete anabolic and leading to positive adaptation.

Where most coaches fail their athletes is in their fear of overtraining them. When coaches think of overtraining, they often think of it only in its most severe form, as outlined by stage three of Seley's GAS—exhaustion. They are so afraid of producing results like the one in option two (see graph) that they never stress their athletes hard enough to see a full supercompensation response. While severely overtraining an athlete will have extremely negative effects on an athlete's performance, a more mild dose of overtraining, known as overreaching, will yield drastic improvements.

Overreaching is characterized by training to a point of fatigue that begins to show performance decrements and overtraining symptoms within the athlete. These symptoms can last anywhere from a few days to several weeks. Exposure to high bouts of stress, when given adequate time to recover, can lead to a delayed training effect, resulting in resynthesis of the damaged muscle tissue and depleted energy substrates to a level above and beyond their previous state. This phenomenon is known as supercompensation.

Overreaching will force the athlete's body to adapt to higher levels of stress than normally obtained by less stressful alarm/reaction cycles. In this case, the athlete's body interprets the extreme stress load as a life-threatening stimulus. The body literally believes it could endure severe injury or even death if it encountered that same level of stress a second time. As a result, the body and its physiological mechanisms go into overdrive to rebuild bigger and stronger than before and make sure that when it meets that level of stress again, it won't just survive but will thrive!

"Only when standing at the brink of destruction does man truly realize his potential."
— ANCIENT SAMURAI MAXIM

Clearly, you must not *severely* overtrain your athletes. However, as I just pointed out, you must overreach them to maximize their performance gains. How does a coach know how far and how hard to push an athlete? That is where the art of coaching and a solid understanding of stress and its application come into play. As a coach, you must not severely overtrain your athletes, throwing them over the proverbial cliff. They will never be able to climb back out. Instead, you need to tie a rope around their waist and throw them over, only letting them fall halfway down. Great coaches are the ones who know how far they can let an athlete fall and still have enough strength to climb back out. Be careful though—once you get good at this, you might not recognize the athletes as they climb back over the lip of the cliff. The athletes you threw over the edge won't be the same ones that climb back out. They will be bigger, stronger, and more powerful than before.

In a sense, there should never be anything fun about a workout, at least not from a physiological perspective. Sure, workouts can be fun in nature—competitive, rowdy, and energized. However, each workout should make your body think that you're trying to kill it. To progress, an athlete's body must constantly be introduced to new, more intense stressors.

A strength coach is a stress manager. In looking at the three possible outcomes stress can cause in an athlete, there is a fine line between spurring positive adaptation and overtraining an athlete to the point of severe physiological damage and performance deficit. Stress is a double-edged sword. It can build an athlete into a dominating force or it can cut him down to an inferior shell of his former self. The strength coach's most important job is learning how to wield that sword to constantly spur positive adaptation. The subsequent sections of this chapter not only show you how to stress the athlete on a daily basis—explaining the volumes, loads, and intensities that should be used—but also how an athlete must be stressed on a weekly (undulating) and monthly (block system) scale.

1.3: FIVE FACTORS FOR SUCCESS

Understanding that stress is *the* critical component, the question then becomes, "How much stress does an athlete need to maximize performance?" Where is that magic tipping point between undertraining and overtraining an athlete? As I said before, I've researched every world-class caliber program I could find. After much searching, referencing, and translating (some of the programs I obtained were in Russian and French!), I found the answer—a lot! Coaches too often are afraid of severely overtraining athletes. They never stress them hard enough or push them long enough to truly realize their potential. Whether it was cross country, Olympic weightlifting, swimming, powerlifting, throwing, sprinting, or any other sport for that matter, the programs that produced the best results applied the most stress. In looking at these programs and the world-class athletes they produced, I realized that there were five key factors in every program:

1) **High volume:** The total weight lifted per session or workout

2) **High intensity:** The percentage of an athlete's maximum lift during a workout

3) **High frequency:** The number of times the athlete trains per week

4) **High expectations:** The expectations of the athlete (missed workouts, skipped sets, or failed reps are unacceptable)

5) **Overreaching:** The point the athlete is pushed to but not past (adrenal fatigue)

This isn't to say that all five factors were present all the time in every workout. That would be suicidal! These guys were just crazy. Each program blended and combined two or three of these five qualities, cycling them throughout the training year or macro-cycle. When one form of stress began to lose its novelty on the athlete's system (the athlete's body begins to interpret what was formerly a high level of stress as the new level of homeostasis), the coach cycled in a new high-level stressor to spur further positive adaptation.

Let me give you an example of one such program. The Bulgarian National Olympic Weightlifting team was a dynasty during the 1970s. In the 1972 Olympics, the Bulgarian team dominated the competition by taking three gold and three silver medals, leaving the world and favored Soviet Union scratching their heads as to the reason for Bulgaria's success. To put this in perspective for you, the Soviet Union, at the time considered the world's best in this event, covered an area roughly two and a half times the size of the United States and had a population of over 200 million people. Bulgaria, on the other hand, was a country half the size of the state of Minnesota, with a population of about 3.5 million people. It was David verses Goliath, and David dominated.

Going into the games, the Soviet Union was expected to sweep the medal board in the Olympic weightlifting events. Meanwhile, the Bulgarians were relative unknowns on the world stage. The embarrassing loss to the Bulgarians forced the Soviets to rethink their entire methodology of training their athletes. In studying the Bulgarian method of training, the Soviets came to the following conclusion, noted in an issue of the *Soviet Sports Review* in 1974:

> *"The main reason for the better results is the substantial increase in the training load volume to a degree never used in international lifting practice to this time. Indeed, Bulgarian trainers draw on Soviet experience. For example, their means and methods of training are the same that we have in our country. But, Bulgarian athletes have substantially increased their training load in recent years."* [2]

There are two important points to take from the above excerpt. First, the Bulgarians weren't doing anything revolutionary. They didn't have a super secret training protocol or new methods that enabled them to surpass the Soviets. Everyone was doing the same thing. Second, the Soviets concluded that Bulgaria's success was "substantial increases in training load and volume to a degree never used in international lifting competition." The truth was the Bulgarians were outworking everyone else. They were stressing the human body to a level higher than anyone thought possible.

---

[2] Roman RA (1974). The training of Bulgarian weightlifters. *Soviet Sports Review* 1:41–42.

Table 1 summarizes the comparison of the two teams and their training protocol going into the 1972 Olympics.[3] As you can see, the Bulgarians lifted higher volumes, heavier percentage loads, and more often than the Soviet athletes.

TABLE 1.1: SOVIET UNION VS. BULGARIAN WEIGHTLIFTING PROGRAM (BASED ON 106KG LIFTER)		
	SOVIET UNION	BULGARIA
VOLUME (LIFTS/MONTH)	1,000	1,500
LOAD (TONS/MONTH)	106	135
WORKOUTS (PER WEEK)	4	15

When the Soviet analysis was completed in early 1974, they instantly changed their training protocol to resemble that of the Bulgarians. What were the results? In the 1976 Olympic games, only two years after making the modifications to the program, the Soviets were back on top as a world power in Olympic weightlifting (winning seven gold medals), an event they would continue to dominate until the fall of the Soviet Union in 1991.

Interestingly, the Soviets decided to make similar modifications to the training protocols for many of their other Olympic sports teams including swimming, track and field, wrestling, and hockey. In the 1980 Summer Olympics, the Soviet Union won a record setting eighty gold medals. The next closest country was East Germany with forty-seven. In 1984, the Soviet Union boycotted the Olympic Games in Los Angeles, deciding instead to host their own Friendship Games in Moscow for all the Eastern Bloc Countries. Of the eighty-three gold medals won by the United States at the Los Angeles Olympics, over half of them would have been silver or bronze performances if they had competed against the Soviet athletes. Meanwhile, the Soviets did fairly well at their Friendship Games, winning 126 gold medals. The adaption of the

---

[3] Roman, R.A.; (1974). The training of bulgarian weightlifters. *Soviet Sports Review*, 1:41-42.

Bulgarian training method of high stress, high volume, and high intensity lifting turned the Soviet Union into a superpower until the dissolution of the Soviet Union in 1991, which divided up the team and resulted in severe budget cuts that made it impossible to continue such a rigorous training schedule for its athletes.

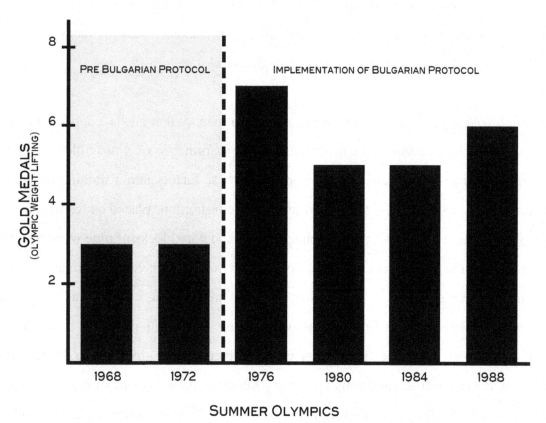

GOLD MEDAL COUNT - SOVIET UNION

Figure 1.4: Graph depicting the number of gold medals won by the Soviet Union during the Summer Olympic Games before (light bars) and after (dark bars) implementation of Bulgarian lifting protocols.

Now, I'm not advocating the use of this specific type of training for high school or college athletes. A training protocol like the one used by the Bulgarian National Team is definitely outside the realm of NCAA regulations. I'm giving you an extreme example of the amazing capacities of the human body and how far it can be pushed with extreme levels of stress. While I don't think the same type of training should be used with most populations, I believe one hundred percent that the methods behind their approach are essential and will result in positive sport performance improvements in any population who chooses to adopt and apply them.

Just to give you a visual, at the end of this section you will find an example program that would have been followed by a Bulgarian Olympic lifter leading up to competition. If your jaw drops as you go over it, that's normal. I did the same thing when I first saw it. The workout consists of nine training sessions per day, four days a week, for a total of thirty-six weekly sessions. You heard me right. The lifter performs nine separate training sessions on Monday, Wednesday, Friday, and Saturday. Each session was to be completed by the lifter in under forty-five minutes without any more than ninety minutes to recover between each session. There is absolutely nothing fancy about this workout at all. There aren't any bands, chains, or fancy tempos. Just high volumes, high loads, and high frequency—high stress!

As a strength coach, you must learn to apply stress in a manner that elicits a supercompensation effect by overreaching if you want to maximize the performance of your athletes. Both high school and collegiate settings are ideal to implement these factors into a training program that can push an athlete to the brink. Due to the training time restrictions placed on teams imposed by the school calendar, it gives a strength coach specific mandatory blocks of time when the athletes must rest. During the school year, there are times when you don't have access to athletes (finals week, Christmas vacation, etc.). The goal of many of my training cycles is to overreach my athletes before they leave for break. That way, during training, I put their body through a maximal stress load, using the five factors to stress them before giving their bodies time to completely recover. As an example, my goal every May is to have as many of my hockey players sick with a cold or the flu going into finals week. I know that sounds terrible, but a sick athlete is an early warning sign of an overtrained athlete. When athletes are severely stressed and overtrained, their immune system is compromised and they get sick. During finals, there is a ten-day period when I'm not allowed to train the hockey players at all. Therefore, I overreach them going into finals (they are tired, sick, and miserable). Coming out of finals, however, when they get back to training ten days later, it isn't uncommon to see twenty- to thirty-pound increases in most of their major lifts as well as faster sprint times.

TABLE 1.2: BULGARIAN NATIONAL OLYMPIC TEAM TRAINING PROGRAM

SESSION 1 — 8:30-9:00AM — BACK SQUAT

SET	LOAD	REPS
SET 1	30%	x 2
SET 2	38%	x 2
SET 3	42%	x 1
SET 4	54%	x 1
SET 5	63%	x 1
SET 6	70%	x 1
SET 7	88%	x 1
SET 8	96%	x 2
SET 9	98%	x 1
SET 10	96%	x 1
SET 11	96%	x 1
SET 12	92%	x 2
SET 13	92%	x 2

SESSION 2 — 9:15-10:00AM — SNATCH

SET	LOAD	REPS
SET 1	30%	x 2
SET 2	38%	x 2
SET 3	50%	x 2
SET 4	56%	x 1
SET 5	69%	x 1
SET 6	75%	x 1
SET 7	81%	x 1
SET 8	91%	x 2
SET 9	86%	x 1
SET 10	91%	x 1
SET 11	81%	x 2
SET 12	81%	x 2
SET 13		

SESSION 3 — 10:30-11:15AM — CLEAN & JERK

SET	LOAD	REPS
SET 1	36%	x 2
SET 2	46%	x 2
SET 3	56%	x 2
SET 4	67%	x 1
SET 5	77%	x 1
SET 6	87%	x 1
SET 7	92%	x 1
SET 8	97%	x 1
SET 9	95%	x 1
SET 10	97%	x 1
SET 11	95%	x 1
SET 12	97%	x 1
SET 13	92%	x 1

SESSION 4 — 11:45-12:30PM — SNATCH

SET	LOAD	REPS
SET 1	38%	x 1
SET 2	50%	x 1
SET 3	56%	x 1
SET 4	69%	x 1
SET 5	75%	x 1
SET 6	81%	x 1
SET 7	84%	x 1
SET 8	88%	x 1
SET 9	84%	x 1
SET 10	88%	x 1
SET 11	84%	x 1
SET 12	88%	x 1
SET 13	81%	x 1

SESSION 5 — 2:00-2:45PM — FRONT SQUAT

SET	LOAD	REPS
SET 1	30%	x 2
SET 2	38%	x 2
SET 3	42%	x 1
SET 4	54%	x 1
SET 5	63%	x 1
SET 6	70%	x 1
SET 7	88%	x 1
SET 8	96%	x 2
SET 9	98%	x 1
SET 10	96%	x 1
SET 11	96%	x 1
SET 12	92%	x 2
SET 13	92%	x 2

SESSION 6 — 3:30-4:15PM — SNATCH

SET	LOAD	REPS
SET 1	38%	x 1
SET 2	38%	x 1
SET 3	44%	x 1
SET 4	44%	x 1
SET 5	50%	x 1
SET 6	56%	x 1
SET 7	69%	x 1
SET 8	75%	x 1
SET 9	81%	x 1
SET 10	86%	x 1
SET 11	91%	x 1
SET 12	94%	x 1
SET 13	97%	x 1
SET 14	94%	x 1
SET 15	97%	x 1
SET 16	94%	x 1
SET 17	88%	x 2
SET 18	88%	x 2

SESSION 7 — 4:45-5:30PM — CLEAN & JERK

SET	LOAD	REPS
SET 1	36%	x 1
SET 2	36%	x 1
SET 3	46%	x 1
SET 4	46%	x 1
SET 5	56%	x 1
SET 6	67%	x 1
SET 7	77%	x 1
SET 8	82%	x 1
SET 9	87%	x 1
SET 10	92%	x 1
SET 11	97%	x 1
SET 12	100%	x 1
SET 13	95%	x 1
SET 14	100%	x 1
SET 15	97%	x 1
SET 16	95%	x 1
SET 17	95%	x 1

SESSION 8 — 7:00-7:45PM — SNATCH

SET	LOAD	REPS
SET 1	44%	x 2
SET 2	50%	x 2
SET 3	56%	x 1
SET 4	69%	x 1
SET 5	75%	x 1
SET 6	81%	x 1
SET 7	88%	x 1
SET 8	91%	x 1
SET 9	94%	x 1
SET 10	91%	x 1
SET 11	94%	x 1
SET 12	88%	x 1
SET 13	88%	x 1

SESSION 9 — 8:15-9:00PM — SNATCH

SET	LOAD	REPS
SET 1	36%	x 2
SET 2	46%	x 2
SET 3	56%	x 1
SET 4	67%	x 1
SET 5	77%	x 1
SET 6	82%	x 1
SET 7	87%	x 1
SET 8	92%	x 1
SET 9	95%	x 1
SET 10	97%	x 1
SET 11	95%	x 1
SET 12	97%	x 1
SET 13	95%	x 1
SET 14	92%	x 1
SET 15	92%	x 1

1.4: RESULTS SPEAK LOUDER THAN WORDS

I base all my theories and methodologies in this book on things that are measurable. By comparing the methods employed in the weight room to the results in competition, it will become instantly apparent whether or not a specific training method or protocol has resulted in improved sport performance. You *must* measure and evaluate everything that you do as a strength and conditioning coach. Sports like track and field, swimming, and weightlifting allow you to consistently measure performance-based results so that you can evaluate the methods you applied, see their transferability (how efficiently the athlete's gains in an exercise transferred to his improvement during competition), and then implement those methods to other sports.

Throughout my coaching career, I've been very fortunate to have coached at a school with a track and field team. Some coaches may view this as more of a curse than a blessing because track usually has dozens of athletes all competing in different events with unique needs. Add in the fact that the track season seems to run twelve months a year with athletes needing to peak every other meet, and it can turn into a program writing nightmare! If you can get past all that, however, you will find that a track and field team is the single best place to develop and test training methods and programs that can then be applied to a much wider athletic base.

The great thing about track and field events is that they are all one hundred percent performance based. Everything in track and field is measurable—how far the discus flies or how fast the sprinter runs. From one competition to the next, the extent of each event stay the same (except for weather conditions in outdoor competitions). There is very little variability within the track model compared to skill-based anaerobic sports such as hockey or basketball where no two games are ever the same. Variability in these sports is very high and thus any direct training effect is lost. I'm not saying that you can't see improvement in an athlete's performance from a training program. What I'm saying is that there isn't any way to show, definitively, that those improvements can be attributed to training.

If a basketball team has a horrible regular season but goes on to win their conference tournament, beating two ranked teams and gaining an automatic bid to the NCAA tournament, a strength coach could pat himself on the back and attribute it to having peaked his athletes at the right time. I will concede that is a possibility, but what if I told you that the team was young and it took them the majority of the season to learn to play as a team? Or that two of the wins in the conference tournament came off half-court buzzer beaters? These are examples of the two biggest reasons why a strength coach can't evaluate the validity of a program from team-based anaerobic sports—teamwork and luck (printed in bold in the table1.3). When you add those two variables into the equation, it completely discredits any correlations that could be drawn from your training methods. A thrower never gets lucky on a good throw. A high jumper doesn't rely on a teammate to give him a push off going over the bar. Both are the result of perfect technique gained through thousands of hours of practice and proper strength training methods.

TABLE 1.3: THE VARIABILITY OF SPORT			
	TRACK AND FIELD	HOCKEY	BASKETBALL
OUTCOME MEASURE	DISTANCE	WIN/LOSE	WIN/LOSE
CONTROL VARIABLES	STRENGTH POWER NERVOUS SYSTEM	STRENGTH POWER NERVOUS SYSTEM	STRENGTH POWER NERVOUS SYSTEM
RANDOM VARIABLES	TECHNIQUE WEATHER	TECHNIQUE ICE CONDITIONS AWARENESS GOALTENDING EXECUTION DEFENSE OFFENSE COACHING STRATEGY SHIFT STRENGTH LINE MATCHING SKILL OF COMPETITION **TEAMWORK** **LUCK**	TECHNIQUE PASSING DRIBBLING DEFENSE OFFENSE CLOCK MANAGEMENT COACHING STRATEGY INBOUNDING AWARENESS SKILL OF COMPETITION **TEAMWORK** **LUCK**

Table 1.3 shows all the variables that go into factoring the outcome measure of different sports. Notice that team sports, such as hockey and basketball have exceedingly more random variables (variability) in their outcome measure. This increased variability makes it hard to find correlation between training and performance.

By using the training methods outlined in this book, you're getting a leg up on the competition because the methods have been tried and measured at the highest levels of competition and proven to be reliable in delivering sport performance gains. While you, as a strength coach, will never be able to stand up and take credit for a conference championship or national title, you can take pride in knowing that the methods you used with your athletes undoubtedly aided in their success.

1.5: VARIATION IS KEY

Finally, a quick word about variation. A program that doesn't change is an ineffective program. It is imperative that the five factors discussed previously are constantly rotated through the training cycle. Again, the factors are:

1) **High volume**
2) **High intensity**
3) **High frequency**
4) **High expectations**
5) **Overreaching**

The first three factors (volume, intensity, and frequency) can all be adjusted by altering the loading parameters (changing exercises, the weight on the bar, the method of movement being applied, or the number of training sessions per week). Below in table 1.4 is one example using horizontal pressing that shows the large spectrum coaches have to pick from when choosing how to stress an athlete. This is not a complete list, and only shows some of the possible loading parameters for a horizontal pressing exercise, the combination of which make a lifting method.

TABLE 1.4: LOADING FOR HORIZONTAL PRESSING VARIATIONS			
EXERCISE	LOAD ON BAR	METHOD OF MOVEMENT	FREQUENCY
	55%	ECCENTRIC	
SUPINE BENCH PRESS	60%	ISOMETRIC	1 DAY/WEEK
INCLINE BENCH PRESS	65%	CONCENTRIC	2 DAY/WEEK
CLOSED GRIP BENCH PRESS	70%	REACTIVE	3 DAY/WEEK
DB BENCH PRESS	75%	CHAINS	4 DAY/WEEK
INCLINE DB BENCH PRESS	80%	BANDS	5 DAY/WEEK
DIPS	85%	WEIGHT RELEASERS	6 DAY/WEEK
	90%		

Again, if the athletes aren't constantly being forced to adapt to stress, you're wasting their time. This isn't to be mistaken for simply returning to the previous stimuli. You must come up with novel ways to stimulate and stress your athletes to spur change and see performance improvements. This serves a dual purpose—it keeps the athletes interested and engaged in the training and continually pushes their bodies to adapt. No one likes to go to work every day and do the same old routine over and over.

Keep in mind that new or increased levels of stress must be given to the athlete all the time to see continued increases in training effect. When I speak about training effect, I'm referring to results from continued training such as an increase in the key performance measures needed to benefit the demands of an athlete's sport. An example for a football player would be an increase in the ten-yard dash or vertical jump.

1.6: SUMMARY AND REVIEW

At first, this may seem like a lot to keep track of. Stress is a very complicated task, especially when you realize that its application, modification, and implementation can have either beneficial effects or detrimental effects on athletic performance. Just look back at the horizontal pressing table with just six exercise variations per lift, eight different percentages that can be used to load them, and seven different methods with which the load can be moved (not counting the dozens of variations and ways these can be manipulated). That's over 330 ways you can perform one single compound exercise. And that's just choosing the exercise! We haven't even considered how heavy the load should be on the bar, the volume or total reps that should be lifted, or the frequency of times the athlete should perform that pressing movement per week. Are you concerned yet? You should be. It's a daunting task.

That, right there, is why I decided I needed to write this book—to create a format that would simplify the application of stress and the tri-phasic undulating block system. Remember—as a coach, you must be a stress manager. You not only need to know what tools are out there (bands, chains, eccentric loading, high volume), but you must also know how to use them to elicit the greatest possible training effect for your athletes.

You know the old proverb, "Give a man a fish, he eats for a day. Teach a man to fish, he eats for a lifetime." I didn't want to just write a programming book for coaches to take and simply rip out programs and throw at their athletes. I want coaches to be able to understand and apply sound, knowledge-based training principles in the sincere effort to improve the performance of the men and women they train.

The undulated block system will allow you to implement the *Five Factors of Success*. However, to truly learn how to "fish," there is one more idea that you must grasp before we dive into the actual programs that will help develop explosive, powerful athletes. It is the one, single variable of training that ties all sport together, an integral piece to the puzzle that if missed or neglected will sabotage the potential gains of even the most gifted athlete. That variable is the triphasic nature of all muscle action.

SECTION 2

PERIODIZATION:
THE IMPLEMENTATION OF STRESS

2.1: MICROCYCLE: UNDULATING MODEL

Stress is the key. Without stress and its derivatives, athletic performance stagnates. However, simply understanding that stress is the most important component to training will get you nowhere if you don't have a structured system in place that gives guidance and organization to its application. Simply walking into a weight room every day to have an athlete perform ten sets of ten reps on the back squat, six days a week for six months straight will not make him a better athlete. In fact, a reckless application of stress such as this will be more detrimental to athletes in the long run than if you didn't stress the athletes enough because it will lead to severe overtraining—complete adrenal and psychological fatigue. Instead, a coach needs a periodization method that allows for the application of high levels of stress within a framework that gives optimal recovery time between workouts to ensure proper, continuous adaptation to stress.

To achieve that goal, I use a microcycle method known as undulated periodization. Undulation can be defined as *the acute variation of volume and intensity on a weekly (microcycle) or daily basis*. It is the most effective means of applying stress to the human body within the athletic model. The value to an athlete of using a model such as this, using variation of load and volume on a workout to workout basis, became apparent to me when I stumbled across an article published by Dr. Anatoly Bondarchuk in the 1970s. In the study, he performed an experiment with a very simple goal—find which loading method for the back squat would have the greatest positive impact on vertical jump scores over a training period of six weeks. The vertical jump is often considered to be the best marker of explosive, athletic performance. In this study, there were three groups. Group one used loads equaling 50 percent of their maximum loads, group two used 90 percent of their maximum loads, and group three used a combination of 90 percent and 50 percent of their maximum loads. As you can see by the chart below, the combination group outperformed the 50 percent and 90 percent groups by a large margin.

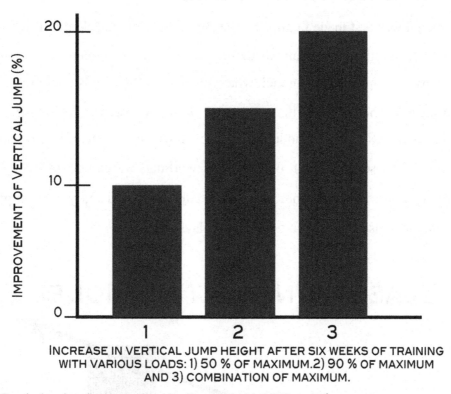

INCREASE IN VERTICAL JUMP HEIGHT AFTER SIX WEEKS OF TRAINING WITH VARIOUS LOADS: 1) 50 % OF MAXIMUM. 2) 90 % OF MAXIMUM AND 3) COMBINATION OF MAXIMUM.

Figure 2.1: Graph showing the results from Dr. Bondarchuk's 1970 study.[4]

The brilliance of this study and its implications for programming lies in its simplicity—pre-test the vertical jump, allocate lifters into three groups, squat for six weeks, and retest. There is little room for confounding factors to influence results. And even better, the variable marker in the study, the vertical jump, showed the transferability of each loading method to dynamic, explosive movement as would be required in sport. The study found that using a combination of various loads elicited the best results, resulting in a higher vertical jump. Undulation not only allows for a wide range of variability within the microcycle but also allows for changes in load and intensity on a daily basis, ensuring that the athlete is constantly stressed at a level sufficient enough to promote proper, constant adaptation. This model will work for athletes in any sport that requires dynamic muscle movement.

---

[4] Bondarchuk, A (1970). Effect of mixed load training on vertical jump performance. *Soviet Sports Review.*

CLASSIC UNDULATING MODEL

The undulating model was first made famous by the Bulgarian National Weightlifting team in the 1970s. Their coach during this time, Ivan Abadzhiev, is to sport performance what Einstein is to physics. The man was a genius. In this model, what you essentially have is a progressive increase in intensity throughout the week with a decrease in total volume. To make simple the understanding and application of the undulated model, I will use a three-day, weekly training schedule (Monday, Wednesday, Friday) to explain its workings. Once you understand the basic principles and foundations of this method, you will be able to use and apply them to programs of varying training day lengths (six days, five days, four days, etc.).

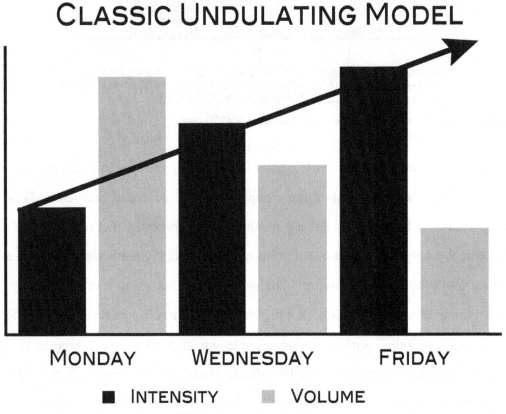

Figure 2.2: Graph depicting a three-day classic undulating model. It shows a parametric relationship. As intensity increases throughout the training week, volume decreases.

Table 2.1 depicts the loading schemes for three different mesocycles that would have typically been applied during training. As you can see, the loading percentages (intensity) increase as the week progresses. This, in turn, requires a decrease in associated volume.

TABLE 2.1: THREE-DAY CLASSIC UNDULATED MODEL LOADING			
MESOCYCLE	MONDAY (% 1RM)	WEDNESDAY (% 1RM)	FRIDAY (% 1RM)
STRENGTH METHOD: ABOVE 80%	HIGH VOLUME 75%–80%	MODERATE INTENSITY 82.5%–87.5%	HIGH INTENSITY 90%–97.5%
SPEED STRENGTH: BETWEEN 55%–80%	HIGH VOLUME 55%–65%	MODERATE INTENSITY 65%–72.5%	HIGH INTENSITY 80%–75%
PEAKING METHOD: BELOW 55%	HIGH VOLUME 25%–35%	MODERATE INTENSITY 40%–45%	HIGH INTENSITY 50%–55%

For all the success that this periodization model had for Bulgarian weightlifters, I found it didn't work at all for my collegiate athletes. In fact, the first year that I changed my programming model to an undulating one, most of my track athletes' performance declined. It dawned on me fairly quickly what the problem was. The Bulgarians had been very open about their use of anabolic steroids within their training schools during the 1970s and 1980s to promote "faster recovery" for their athletes. Simply put, my collegiate, drug-free athletes, could not recover from the high volume on Monday's training day according to the model; it beat them up. As a result, they couldn't come back and do quality work on Wednesday. Furthermore, the added work from Wednesday simply prolonged their adrenal and neural fatigue through Friday, again inhibiting the athletes' ability to do quality work during the workout. It took them through the weekend, when they had 72 hours of rest between workouts, for their bodies to recover. Consequently, I was only getting one good lifting day out of my athletes each week—Monday, the high volume day.

What I was seeing in my athletes was the manifestation of what I had known for years—drug-free athletes have a hard time recovering from high volume workouts. High volume workouts, as compared to high intensity workouts, cause an enormous amount of physiological damage to muscle tissue and severely depleting muscle and liver glycogen. The only way to repair and refill the damage done to the muscles is through a hormonal response. In addition, anabolic hormones fortify tendons and ligaments as well as aid in increasing bone density. Hormones such as testosterone or growth hormone do a fantastic job of repairing and rebuilding tissue, but they have one huge drawback—they take a long time to work.

A typical 18- to 25-year-old male will have somewhere between 19 to 23 nmol/L of testosterone in his body at any one time[5]. The anabolic effect of exercise will increase that number by 20–30 percent. (It should be noted that the percentage increase in testosterone found in women would be similar to that of males. However, overall levels are much lower.) The problem with the classic undulating model was that it wasn't giving my athletes enough time to take advantage of this anabolic surge to repair and grow from the damage done by the initial workout before they had to deal with the stress of a second or third workout. Do you remember the four possible outcomes of Seley's GAS from the previous section? In using the classic undulating model, I was overtraining my athletes each week, leading to decreased sport performance as outlined in figure 2.3.

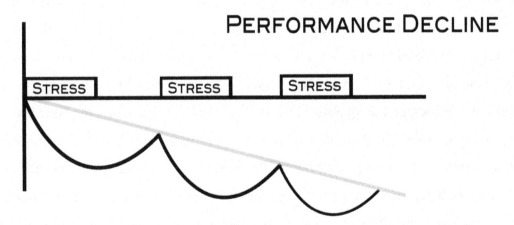

PERFORMANCE DECLINE

Figure 2.3: Overtrained performance response. The repeated application of stress, without sufficient time for the body to adapt during Selye's recovery stage, leads to a performance decline over time.

When the human body encounters a stressor that it believes justifies an anabolic hormonal response such as a high volume leg day, it initiates a long series of signals that must first take place before the hormone has any beneficial effect. This signaling begins with Seley's *alarm stage*, culminating with a massive hormonal release during the *recovery stage*. Let's take

---

[5] Vermeulen A (1996) *Declining Androgens with Age: An Overview*. New York: Parthenon Publishing.

testosterone as an example. Testosterone takes fifteen steps from onset of stress to protein synthesis for it to have any positive anabolic effect. Looking at the figure 2.4, you can see that testosterone actually requires two hormones—the follicle stimulating hormone (FSH), which is released from the hypothalamus, and the leutinizing hormone (LH), which is released from the anterior pituitary. Then testosterone (T) is released from the adrenals and testicles (or ovaries in women).

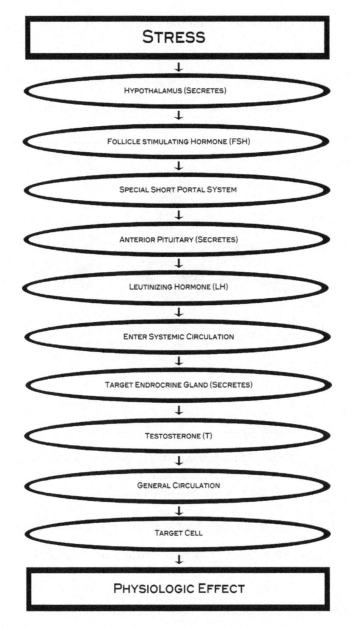

Figure 2.4: Figure showing the twelve extracellular (outside target cell) steps in testosterone production.[6]

---

[6] Sherwood L (2010) *Human Physiology: From Cells to Systems*. 7th Edition. Belmont, CA: Brooks/Cole Publishing.

Once the testes (or ovaries) receive the signal, they release T into the blood stream to find cells that require protein synthesis. But the story doesn't end there. Once the T hormone finds a target cell, it still must go through three more steps before the process of protein synthesis can commence:

1) Transition through the lipid bilayer through osmosis

2) Bind to a hormonal receptor

3) Enter into the cell's nucleus to signal the formation of new proteins

The Bulgarians and Soviets could make incredible gains on this classic model because they were cheating. They could skip steps one through twelve. By artificially increasing their free testosterone pool through the use of anabolic steroids, their bodies could immediately begin protein synthesis, repairing the structural damage done from the workout the instant they set down the barbell. For my drug-free athletes, there was simply too much high volume, low stress work at the onset of the training week to allow their natural hormonal

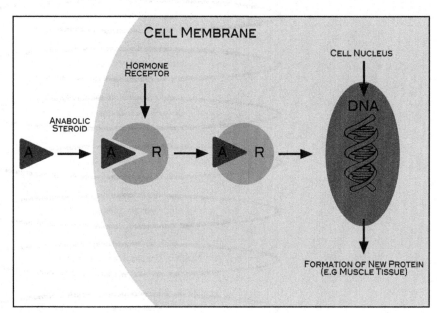

Figure 2.5: Image depicts process by which testosterone diffuses across the cells lipid bilayer, activating intercellular hormone receptors that travel to the cells' nucleus to signal protein synthesis.

response to repair the physiological damage that was done. If this is repeated for several weeks, it compounds itself and leads rather quickly to an overtrained, underperforming athlete.

From an evolutionary perspective, the human body has evolved to deal with short, acute bouts of high stress very well. For example, imagine a hunter gatherer living 10,000 years ago who is out collecting berries and nuts when he stumbles across a Saber-toothed tiger. He needs a physiological mechanism that will allow him to either fight the tiger or run away from it. In either case, the response only needs to last ten to thirty seconds. By then, our caveman is either safely up a tree or lunch. Because we have already seen the amount of time a hormonal response takes to facilitate action, the human body had to develop a second mechanism, a faster one, to mobilize the body for action.

The system that evolved is known today as the "fight or flight" response. Unlike our hormonal pathways, the fight or flight response is initiated through the sympathetic nervous system (SNS). Traveling with the speed of an internet signal through a cable line, the SNS signals the release of catecholamines (better known as epinephrine and norepinephrine or adrenalin), dilates the pupils, releases glucose into the bloodstream, increases the heart rate, and diverts blood from the internal organs to the muscles. In short, it gets the human body ready for war in the blink of an eye.

The fight or flight response is the most powerful mechanism the human body possesses. It is a very effective, efficient way to deal with high intensity, short-term stress. The only drawback to it is that it weakens fairly quickly. Because it is such a violent shock to the system, the system can't maintain such a high state of readiness for a prolonged period of time. On the bright side, the central nervous system doesn't require a lot of rest between responses to recover.

The way the body deals with long-term stress is very different. Prolonged levels of high stress (like that brought about by the high volume work in the classic undulating model) lead to elevated cortisol levels that can act like a toxin in the athlete if they remain high for an extended period of time, leading to muscle breakdown, poor sleep patterns, decreased metabolism, and an inhibited hormonal response.

I still believed that undulated loading was the best method to elicit change in my athletes. However, I had to come up with a variation that would account for both the duration required to benefit from the hormonal response while maximizing the use of their fight or flight mechanism and central nervous system. In looking at the classic model, I knew that Wednesday and Friday weren't my issue. I had to find a way to adjust the volume from Monday.

MODIFIED UNDULATING MODEL

I'm always hesitant to admit to people how I fixed the undulating model to work for athletes. I would love it to be some great stroke of genius, a story the likes of Newton's apple or Einstein's elevator. But to be honest, the solution was so 'slap you in the face' simple, I'm embarrassed to say that it didn't come to me sooner. It took several microcycles through that first off-season trying other, more complicated remedies before I realized a true solution. True to form, Occam's razor prevailed—the simplest solution was the best.

Backtracking for a moment, I began using the undulating model with my track athletes in 2003. As I stated before, it took me several weeks to realize that the classic model was hurting my athletes—the volume was too high for a drug-free athlete to handle. To fix the problem, I came up with the very complex, arduous, and intricate (please note tone of intense sarcasm) solution—

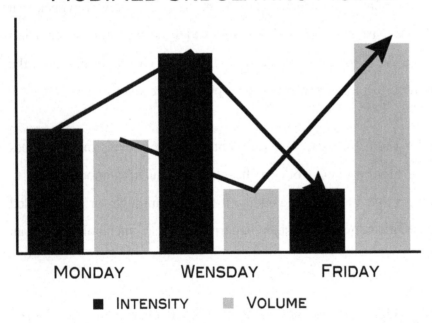

I shifted all the training days one slot to the left. Ta da! In the new modified undulating model, Monday is now the medium heavy day, Wednesday is the high intensity day, and Friday becomes the high volume day (Figure 2.6). I don't want to demean the importance or significance that this small change has on athletic performance. I sit here and poke fun at myself thinking back on my revelation. However,

Figure 2.6: Graph depicting a three-day modified undulating model. High volume work is pushed to the end of the training week (Friday), allowing for sufficient time to recover over the weekend. High intensity work is placed on Wednesday to take advantage of the neural priming that the moderate intensity work plays on Monday.

no one up to that point had thought to shift the undulating model in that way. So I guess I'm half genius, half lucky.

Below is the same table you saw before with the classic model in table 2.1. However, now the loading scheme has shifted to place the volume at the end of the training week.

TABLE 2.2: THREE-DAY MODIFIED UNDULATED MODEL LOADING			
MESOCYCLE	MONDAY (%1-RM)	WEDNESDAY (%1-RM)	FRIDAY (%1-RM)
STRENGTH METHOD: ABOVE 80%	MODERATE INTENSITY 82.5%–87.5%	HIGH INTENSITY 90%–97.5%	HIGH VOLUME 75%–80%
SPEED STRENGTH: BETWEEN 55%–80%	MODERATE INTENSITY 65%–72.5%	HIGH INTENSITY 80%–75%	HIGH VOLUME 55%–65%
PEAKING METHOD: BELOW 55%	MODERATE INTENSITY 40%–45%	HIGH INTENSITY 50%–55%	HIGH VOLUME 25%–35%

The new model allowed for 72 hours between both higher volume workouts, Monday and Friday, giving the athletes' hormonal response sufficient time to pass through Selye's *recovery stage*, fixing any musculoskeletal damage as well as replenishing muscle and liver glycogen stores. In addition, the moderate intensity of Monday and subsequently higher intensity of Wednesday didn't have any detrimental effects on the athletes' performance on Friday, as they could recover from these shorter, high bouts of stress much more easily with their fight or flight response. Finally, the high volume on Friday that used to kill my athletes physiologically at the start of the week now had enormous benefit for two very important reasons.

First, the higher volume took on a small role as an active recovery day, forcing blood and nutrients into the muscles to help speed recovery. Secondly, and more importantly, it enabled me to push them a little past their physical limits. Some weeks I pushed more than others, but with 72 hours to rest before their Monday morning workout rolled around, I could employ an even higher level of stress than I could have previously with the classic model, pushing them to the point of overreaching each week. I found that if I pushed like this for four to six weeks and overreached just a little bit each week, the athletes, coming back from a *download week,* would supercompensate at a level I had never seen. They could leave their last plyometric jump workout of the training block (more on blocks in the next section), just barely clearing the hurdles, only to come back ten days later and jump over them like they were the Easter bunny on speed. Again, the undulating model is the perfect fit for high school and collegiate athletes because it forces them to take periods of rest away from the gym. Knowing this fact, a strength coach must increase the stress loads of an athlete as much as possible to allow this supercompensation to occur.

Below are two figures. The first, figure 2.8, displays the physiological response my athletes were having to the classic undulating model used by the Bulgarian and Soviet national teams. In this instance, the volume from Monday was pushing them so far down the rabbit hole that they couldn't climb back to the surface before they had to repeat Monday the following week. After only three weeks in this model, as shown in the graph, you can see that the athletes are severely overtrained.

PERFORMANCE DECREASE

Figure 2.8: Shows the effect of the classic undulated model. High volume work incurred largely physiological stress, accumulating metabolites and inhibiting full recovery during the week.

In sharp contrast to figure 2.8 is figure 2.9, which displays the athletes' response to the modified undulating model. Here you can see that the athletes aren't overwhelmed by the higher intensity at the start of the week. While the high volume of Friday (formerly Monday) still pushes the athletes down the rabbit hole, they now have 72 hours to allow their bodies to recover by climbing back to the surface and are able to exceed that through a small supercompensation.

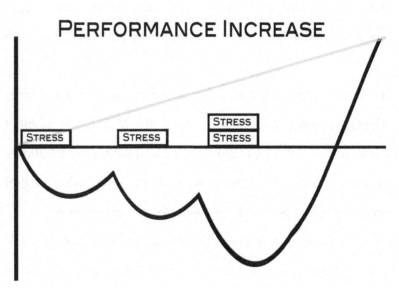

PERFORMANCE INCREASE

Figure 2.9: Shows the effect of the modified undulated model. High intensity work done early in the week is primarily neurological stress, and athletes can recover more quickly due to lack of metabolite accumulation. Volume at the end of the week gives the athlete time to recover over the weekend.

I was also lucky (and again I'm a firm believer that every good idea requires a little bit of luck) that the track coach's running schedule at this time was front end loaded, with higher intensities at the start of the week, and lighter at the back end because he was expecting his athletes to be more beat up. As I would find out later in talking with the coach, Phil Lundin, he had modeled his off-season running program for his athletes after some of the same concepts used by the Soviet team in the 1980s. He was using an undulating type model as well. Go figure! This fit perfectly with the modified undulating model, as the higher volume later in the week then acted as an active recovery day in addition to helping with increased work capacity. After I changed to the modified model, the athletes were able to practice at a high level during the week on the track and train hard in the weight room at the same time. There wasn't any sacrifice on either end. I saw continuous improvement throughout the entire course of that off-season. I knew then that I had found a method of training that could have tremendous benefit for the team that season.

I didn't have to wait very long into that season to see not only one but two justifications that proved to me that my modified undulating model was far superior to its predecessor. At the NCAA Outdoor Track and Field Championships that year, both my 400-meter runners ran the fastest times recorded in the world to date that year! I can't take full credit for this accomplishment. Much of that goes to the athletes themselves for their hard work and dedication, as well as to their coach, Phil Lundin, for his skill and knowledge in peaking them for the meet. However, at that point, I began to realize the undulated model fit very well within many coaching models and was something I needed to apply with all of my athletes.

By simply changing the order of the stressors applied with the classic undulating model, an athlete was now able to handle both the high levels of intensity and volume during a training week. In the end, this new modified undulating model allows an athlete to be stressed at higher intensity levels for longer periods of time using higher volumes, all within a weekly periodization model that allowed for a very high level of variability. Hundreds of hours of research have gone into understanding the undulated model. The results of this research have time and again justified both its means and approach as an effective method of training that maximally stresses the athlete. In simplest terms, I have yet to see a method that creates a state of fatigue that garners greater gains for drug-free athletes than my modified undulating model.

2.2: MESOCYCLE: BLOCK SYSTEM

The undulating model is clearly a potent method of training that generates amazing results. However, athletes train for periods of time that last much longer than one week. As a coach, you must have a plan, a blueprint, that lays out dozens of weeks, months, or even years of consecutive training phases. Great programs are those that are laid out with an end goal in mind with each phase building on the last, increasing and varying the stress placed on the athlete, all while improving their performance measures. The undulating model, while great at applying stress, is broad and needs guidelines. It will not be a very effective approach if, as a coach, you walk into your office, spin the "Undulating Wheel o' Fun," and see what type of workout it lands on for the week. "Oh look! Let's do box jumps!" No, the workout plan must be organized and well thought out. And while this all starts with a weekly microcycle undulating outline, it must be built into a larger mesocycle template.

How do you do that? The best way I have found is to layer the undulating model into a block periodization system. Establishing stress as the foundation on which every training program must be built, it is the job of the strength and conditioning coach to employ a method of periodization that allows for the constant pursuit of stress, a course that relentlessly, consistently, and vehemently stresses the athlete at an optimal level. To ensure success in this endeavor, my athletic undulating model serves as the framework supported by a block training system. Keeping with my analogy of a strength coach as a mechanic, the modified undulating model is a tool (the means) that is used to build the separate parts of the athlete's engine, these parts being speed, strength, power, and sport-specific endurance. The block system, in turn, can be viewed as the method, or instructions, with which a coach actually builds the engine.

CREATION OF THE BLOCK SYSTEM

The origins of the Block Training System can be traced back to the early 1960s in—where else? —the Soviet Union. Two colleagues, scientists by the name of Yuri Verkhoshansky and Vladimir Issurin, were experimenting with a method of training that they, at the time, called the Conjugate

Sequence System.[7] Revolutionary for its time, the Conjugate Sequence System was the first to look at the importance of varying the type and application of stress within a structured system to maximize adaptation, allowing athletes to reach the highest levels of performance. This system laid the foundation from which the theories and practices of the Block System would eventually be built.

Image 2.1 - Dr. Verkhoshansky (Far Left)

Now to fully understand the Block System and its application to training, you must understand some basic vocabulary.

Means: Any form of training stressor applied to an athlete—squats, presses, sprints, or jumps. These are the *five factors* and their derivatives outlined in Section 1.3 (high volume, high intensity, high frequency, high expectations, and overreaching) and the things that stimulate Seley's GAS response.

Parameter: A measurable factor forming one of a set that defines a system. These are the performance measures of an athlete (strength, speed, power, etc.) or the parts of the athlete's engine and the things a coach must focus on improving.

System: A set of connected parameters forming a complex whole, or in particular, a set of parameters working together as part of a mechanism towards a unifying goal. Strength, power, and speed parameters are targeted and laid out in a structured and thoughtful way to ensure the accomplishment of the end goal—improved sport performance.

---

[7] Image 2.1: Used with permission from Natalia Verkhoshansky.

Dr. Verkhoshansky performed research that looked into the amount of stress required to elicit continuous adaptation. What he found with his athletes was that even with high volumes of training, there wasn't any statistically significant correlation that proved an increase in the level of stress resulted in improved sport performance. First of all, we should all be impressed that Dr. Verkhoshansky was using math to prove the validity of training. I had a hard time passing algebra in high school. There isn't any chance that I could ever use it to find validity to a strength training protocol. Secondly, and more importantly, Dr. Verkhoshansky had stumbled onto what, at the time, was a paradox. At the time, he knew what you learned in Section 1—in order to see significant improvements in sport performance, an athlete has to be put through very high levels of stress (high volume, high load, high frequency). Yet, his research couldn't find any correlation to prove that. What he saw in his data was actually the opposite. High stress resulted in decreased sport performance. What Dr. Verkhoshansky soon realized was that this wasn't a paradox but simply an issue of misplaced emphasis. Athletes *do* need to be stressed to the highest levels. (I wasn't lying to you about that.) However, that stress must be focused on a specific performance parameter to ensure maximal adaptation of the athlete. If multiple forms of stress are applied to multiple parameters at once, the level of stress on each declines along with adaptation and performance.

In the early 1960s, Soviet athletes were mostly trained within a system they called the "complex parallel form of training." In more modern terms, this is what we could call a "mixed method of training," where the athlete is exposed to several different means focusing on two or three parameters in each workout. They may start with an explosive movement, such as cleans, and then progress to a strength movement like a back squat and end the workout with hypertrophy work on the leg press. Given what we now know about how the body interprets and adapts to stress, this mixed training approach is a suboptimal way to improve the sport performance parameters of an athlete. Although the "total" stress of a mixed training workout can be very high, the amount of stress placed on each specific training parameter is very low.

Let's say that it takes 15,000 pounds of training volume (stress) in a workout to see a positive adaptation. (This is a completely fictional number, so take it with a grain of salt. I'm just using it to illustrate a point. Don't go to the weight room tomorrow and have your athletes all lift 15,000 pounds worth of volume, please.) Looking at the example below, you can see that the total stress of the different training means is high—over 25,000 pounds. This gives us a clearance of more than 10,000 pounds over what is needed to see an adaptation from stress. However, when the stress placed on each training parameter is examined individually, the means used only elicit a fraction of the total stress from the entire workout. Our stress level required to see positive adaptation, 15,000 pounds, only occurs in the parameter for local muscular endurance (LME). That's great if that was the training goal but terrible if you're trying to build a powerful athlete. However, this is a workout that many coaches would use to try to get their athletes stronger and more explosive in the off-season. The stress placed on the athlete, focusing on LME, decreases the total stress able to be placed on the other parameters, speed-strength and strength, resulting in no positive adaptation. Going back to Seley and GAS, the resulting stress for each parameter incurred only a mild alarm reaction stage and, as a result, a substandard hormonal response and performance adaptation.

TABLE 2.3: MIXED TRAINING WORKOUT				
EXERCISE	PROTOCOL	PARAMETER	TOTAL STRESS (BY VOLUME)	STRESS BY PARAMETER (BY VOLUME)
CLEAN	4x2 @ 275 LBS (85%)	SPEED-STRENGTH		2,200 LBS
BACK SQUAT	5x5 @ 320 LBS (80%)	STRENGTH	29,100 LBS	8,000 LBS
LEG PRESS	4x15 @ 315 LBS (65%)	LOCAL MUSCULAR ENDURANCE		18,900 LBS

When different training parameters are targeted within the same workout they must be seen as having a negative or detractory effect on one another. That is, stress placed on one training parameter detracts from the stress that could be placed on a different training parameter. This led

Dr. Verkhoshansky to believe that the only way to produce significant sports performance improvement was through the use of a specific concentrated loading system, implemented by specific training "blocks," each focusing on one specific training parameter at a time.

Quickly, I want to point out some of the other shortcomings that mixed training methods have on the development of sport performance as compared to the Block System. These concepts will be further drawn out in the next section of this chapter. However, keep these in mind as a frame of reference:

1) Mixed training only allows for one to three peaks per year. Due to the low levels of stress able to be applied to each performance parameter of an athlete, gains are slower and harder to come by. This model used to work better for international competitors when there were only two or three competitions per year (local qualifier, nationals, and worlds) and the athlete had ample time to develop and prepare for each. However, in today's modern sport environment, athletes need to peak more often—sometimes dozens of times per year.

2) Differing neurological signals interpreted by the athlete's body cause confusion within the homeostatic response. With no one stressor clearly signaling for adaptation, the multiple training targets worked during mixed training elicit conflicting responses within the athlete. More on this in a moment when we look at the biological justification for the Block System.

3) Mixed training doesn't provide sufficient stimuli for high level athletes. The more proficient the athlete, the higher level of stress required to spur positive adaptation. Every athlete reaches a point where the stress required to improve one's performance target (i.e. strength) is so high that to try to improve another performance target (i.e. speed) at the same time would be impossible, as the extra stress load it would place on the athlete would elicit negative catabolic effects and lead to overtraining.

Around the time Dr. Verkhoshansky was experimenting with the rudiments that would eventually transform into the Block System, Dr. Issurin was performing similar research into the optimal methods of stressing and adapting an athlete.[8] He observed that every training means he applied to an athlete had the ability to improve only a specific training parameter for the athlete. For example, a heavy back squat would improve an athlete's raw strength while a depth jump would improve an athlete's reactive ability. Performing means not specific to a parameter did not stimulate the correct adaptation. After running further experiments, Dr. Issurin noticed that as the length of application of a specific means increased, the related training parameter improved as well. Inversely, he also noticed that the longer he applied a certain means to an athlete, the positive adaptation seen in that training parameter would decrease. Simply put, it showed that a specific type of stress caused a specific type of adaptation within the athlete. However, as the athlete adapted to that stress, he became less inclined to see continued improvement.

Image 2.2 - Dr. Vladimir Issurin

Figure 2.10 shows a typical response that athletes might exhibit after weeks of training to improve their maximal strength in the back squat. You can see that as the time the athletes are exposed to heavy loads increases, the improvement rate (percentage gain in 1RM) decreases. This isn't to say that the athletes can no longer make gains if they continue to train for the same parameter for extended periods of time. However, those gains will become harder and harder to come by and begin to stagnate.

---

[8] Image 2.2. Used with permission from Dr. Vladimir Issurin.

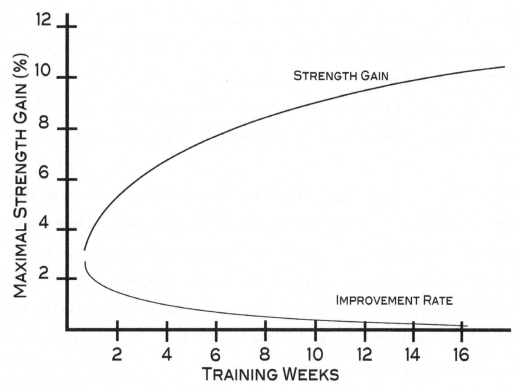

Figure 2.10: Graph shows the rate of diminishing improvement in maximal strength as duration of exposure to unchanging stimulus increases.

This led Dr. Issurin to believe that there needed to be a systematic implementation of training means in order to maximize the adaptation of training parameters and thus performance of an athlete. If one form of training means showed continued adaptation to a training parameter for only a short period of time, then different training means would have to be "strung" together, one after another, to ensure continuous adaptation of the athlete. If an athlete ceased to see substantial gains in his strength-speed parameter after three weeks (for example, as seen by a decrease in gains in the athlete's power clean), then it does the athlete no good to continue training that parameter. No sense beating a dead horse. Instead, Dr. Issurin noted, a coach must change the focus to a different training parameter in order to see continued adaptation.

Knowing that means caused improvements in parameters but that these gains only lasted for short periods of time, he realized that a systematic approach to the application of stress had to be created that constantly changed and varied the means used to ensure continuous adaptation. Furthermore, both Dr. Verkhoshansky and Dr. Issurin understood that in order to see the best possible adaptation in those parameters, their athletes could only train one parameter at a time. Therefore, the systematic approach taken would have to account for the least pertinent parameters (and by least pertinent, I mean those parameters that have the lowest direct transfer to the athlete's sport) to be trained first with the most important parameters trained as close to competition as possible (parameters that directly transferred to improved performance).

Because of the necessity for the high concentrations of stress on a parameter, an athlete can't train for strength, speed, and power all together immediately before a competition or competitive season. The subsequent stress of each would be too low to see maximal improvement, or the total stress would be too great and the athlete would be overtrained. In either case, performance would suffer. Instead, a coach must analyze which training parameters are most vital to athletic success in an athlete's respective sport and make sure those parameters are trained and peaked last or as close to competition as possible.

Looking at this through the wide lens of anaerobic sports (understanding that on a basic level, all anaerobic athletes need to be strong, fast, and above all, powerful), there is a common sequencing of parameters that should be used to allow maximal transfer of training gains. This sequence is usually as follows:

1) General fitness
2) Maximal strength
3) Strength endurance and power
4) Maximal speed

Luckily, the human body lays out the systematic approach to the training of these parameters for us through its own physiological adaptive processes. As you will see shortly, through the adaptive process known as *long lasting delayed training effect (LDTE)* or *residuals*, a coach is able to systematically train all the components required for an athlete to excel in an anaerobic sport (strength, speed, and power) without sacrificing the potential development of any within a training year and ensure that these qualities all peak at the same time!

From the insights and discoveries of Dr. Verkhoshansky and Dr. Issurin, the Block Training System can be summed up in three essential points:

1) **Concentrated loads:** In order to see the highest levels of adaptation, the means used to elicit stress must be highly concentrated, allowing for only one training parameter to be trained at a time to ensure sufficient stimulation of the athlete.

2) **Specificity:** Stress leads to positive adaptation of the athlete through a reaction between specific training means and parameters. These reactions, however, take place for a limited time, as the athlete begins to see diminished returns to training as he adapts to the means being applied.

3) **Systematic implementation of training means:** With only one parameter able to be trained at a time, it is imperative that the application of training means is used in a well thought out sequential manner using LTDE, enabling an athlete to peak the training parameters most pertinent to his sport as close to the competition period as possible.

FOUR ESSENTIAL PRINCIPLES

By today's definition, the Block Training System is the sequencing of specialized mesocycle blocks, a block being a training cycle of highly concentrated, specialized work that serves to improve a specific performance parameter of the athlete. Again, performance parameters refer to one specific part of the athlete's engine—speed, power, strength, or sport-specific endurance. In essence, you're trying to isolate one specific part of the athlete's nervous system or a specific physiological adaptation at a time.

Keeping the limitations of mixed training in mind, the block system, like everything else, is outlined by certain rules or basic principles. This will be a little bit of a review of what you have just read, however, it's essential that you understand these basic concepts before you can fully grasp the methods and correctly implement them with your athletes. Here is a quick overview so you can see how each builds on the previous rule before we look at each in depth:

1) The main principle, the foundation on which block periodization exists, is that maximal performance enhancement can only be obtained through highly concentrated training loads (stress). This should make sense after what you learned about stress earlier in this book—high stress is the key. In order to provide sufficient stimuli to induce a supercompensation effect as outlined by Seley's GAS, the athlete must endure a high level of stress.

2) The second principle is a derivative of the first—if an athlete must endure high levels of stress to improve a specific performance parameter, only a minimal number of those parameters (usually one) can be pursued during a single block without compromising performance enhancement or severely overtraining the athlete.

3) The third principle dictates that blocks must be laid out in such a way as to promote the consecutive development of many training parameters. Due to the fact that anaerobic sports require more than one ability (speed, strength, power, and endurance), the Block System needs a way to ensure that an athlete can develop and retain numerous training parameters without upsetting the second principle.

4) Finally, the fourth principle solves the problem postulated by principle number three through the use of LDTE or residual training effects. The correct order of training blocks is imperative, as it allows for both the assimilation of acute exposures to high stress from previous workouts to spur adaptation within blocks and the superimposition of the residuals of previous training blocks, permitting multiple training parameters to peak at the same time.

Principle #1: High training loads

This first principle comes back to the first point I made in this book—stress your athletes and stress them often! In high level athletes, only highly concentrated training loads provide sufficient training stimulus to generate positive adaptation. I say high level athletes because this principle wouldn't hold true for novice athletes. Early on in an athlete's career, stress, any stress, will be new and likely cause a supercompensation effect, promoting positive adaptation. Multi-targeted training (like that seen in mixed training) still provides enough stress to the athlete's different systems to see improvement in various aspects of performance. When an athlete is young (and by this, I mean a training age of three years or less), it is possible to improve multiple parameters at once because they are all underdeveloped. As athletes mature and as their bodies adapt to higher and higher levels of stress, a coach must continually push the envelope by increasing stressors to ensure that positive adaptation continues.

Let's revisit the stress/volume example from table 2.3. This time we'll compare two athletes performing the same workout:

Athlete A is a second year starting running back at a Division I program. He has been training hard for six years (since his freshman year of high school). He requires 20,000 pounds of volume a day to signal a positive adaptation in a training parameter and see improved sport performance.

Athlete B is a freshman running back in high school. His first exposure to weight training was last summer before football camp (his training age is therefore one) and he's back in the gym this summer trying to win the starting spot on the JV team next fall. Being so young, he only needs 2,000 pounds of volume a day to see improvement in a training parameter.

Based on what you know about these two athletes, which would benefit the most from the training program outlined earlier in table 2.3? If you said Athlete B, you're right! Because his training age is so young, Athlete B doesn't require as much stress as Athlete A to see an adaptation in a specific parameter. Athlete B will see improvement in all three parameters targeted in the workout; speed strength, strength, and muscular endurance. Athlete A, on the other hand, has adapted to a much higher level of stress required to elicit adaptation over his training life span and wouldn't see any improvement from performing the outlined program. This, I believe, is the main reason why mixed training has such a strong hold in western training culture. It starts in high school where most athletes are introduced to a mixed form of lifting. They see great results, not because it's a great method in promoting sport performance improvement, but because their training age is so young that any level of stress will give them decent gains when first starting out. The seed is planted and takes root in their brain that a mixed approach to training produces great results. Many of these young athletes, in turn, grow up to become strength coaches who teach the same methods they used in high school to a new generation. As a result, it is a vicious cycle creating decent high school athletes who will never reach their full potential due to lack of highly concentrated training loads.

Principle #2: Focus on a minimal number of training targets

Due to the high training loads that are required from principle number one, it becomes impossible to train multiple parameters at once. An athlete can't train for strength and power at the same time because the training loads required to elicit positive adaptation for each are too great—the sum of the total stress from the two training targets would severely overtrain the athlete. As a result, each block must focus on one training parameter at a time. In focusing on only one parameter per block, it is important to know the optimal duration for which the athlete should remain in that block. Too little time and valuable adaptation is wasted; too much time and the athlete may regress due to stagnated gains or overtraining.

At the beginning of a block, athletes will see good gains as a result of a high improvement rate—a new stress elicits a massive response of adaptation. As the block progresses, the athlete will continue to see gains. However, these gains will come with smaller and smaller improvement rates. He won't improve as quickly in week three as he did in week one. Figure 2.10 shows a typical response you might see with improvements on the back squat for a football linebacker. Initially, the player sees large gains in strength due to a high improvement rate. As the weeks progress, however, you see that both strength gains and improvement rate begin to plateau.

The duration of a block is essential to ensure that an athlete is maximally stressed, ensuring maximal gains without overworking the specific parameter, which would cause a decrease in performance. Remember, everything must build on itself. For most blocks, this length seems to be two to six weeks because it gives sufficient time for the body to attain and build new physiological, biochemical, and neural adaptations from training.

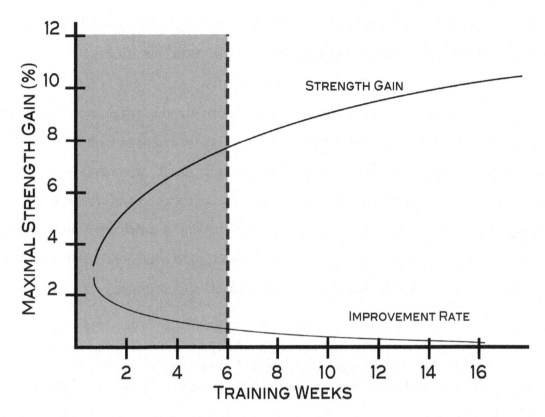

Figure 2.10: Graph shows the optimal training block length of a parameter to ensure maximal gains (gray shaded area). For most parameters this is two to six weeks.

Remember, improvement rate is the level to which the body adapts to a stressor. As the athlete continues to train strength, his strength gains begin to decrease (stagnate) as the improvement rate slows. This decrease is the result of the athlete's body adapting to strength oriented workouts —heavy loads and high intensities. While the athlete would likely continue to make small gains in strength if the block was extended past four weeks, these gains would be so small that they would have little to no positive translation to improved performance on the field. As a result, the athlete is better served to focus on a new block, a new set of stimuli that will use his newly acquired strength to improve a related, albeit, different performance quality.

Principle #3: Consecutive development of training targets
Knowing that each block must entail extremely high levels of stress and the result of those high levels being that only one parameter can be effectively trained at a time, it is imperative that training blocks be laid out in a specific order to ensure the continued development of the athlete. Performance, in any sport, requires the use of several performance abilities to excel. In the case

of the Block System where each block must be laid out using a highly concentrated level of stress, these abilities must be developed consecutively rather than concurrently.

You must keep in mind that whenever you train a specific training parameter or performance quality, you do it at the expense of another parameter. Every time athletes train for strength, they are sacrificing time they could have spent training power, speed, or endurance, the result of which implies that the performance level of these other targets decreases. For that reason, the sequencing of the training blocks becomes extremely important. A coach can't randomly choose a block to have his athletes perform at their peak. He needs to have an understanding of how the training effect of that block will carry over to the next block or competition.

> *"When learning how to cook, an inexperienced chef understands primarily the types of and quantity of the ingredients in a dish. A master chef, on the other hand, understands the way and sequence of their addition to the dish to maximize taste."*
>
> **-DR. VERKHOSHANSKY**
> *"Special Strength Training Manual for Coaches"* (2010)

Principle #4: Long lasting, delayed training effect—residual training effect

As was just pointed out in the previous paragraph, the use of training blocks is associated with the loss of performance in other, non-targeted performance qualities. It is therefore imperative that coaches understand the importance of residual training effects. Residual training effects can be defined as *the retention of changes induced by systematic workloads beyond a certain time period after the cessation of training.* Put another way, a residual training effect is the retention of physiological or neural adaptations after the cessation of training for a certain period of time. Understanding the time period, or residual, that certain performance parameters have is paramount in planning sequential blocks of training to ensure both continuous adaptation of the athlete and the peaking of all his performance qualities before competition to maximize performance.

It is important to understand that not every performance target has the same residual. For example, strength residuals tend to last upwards of thirty days while speed residuals may only last for seven days. The short residual effect seen with maximal speed requires that an athlete must always peak with speed as close to the day of competition as possible. Other factors have shown to influence the length of training residuals as well. Prolonged periods of training, higher level athletes, and parameters associated with physiological and biochemical changes (such as sport-specific endurance or strength) are all associated with longer residual effects. Table 2.4 outlines the average residual training effect of training parameters:[9]

TABLE 2.4: DURATION OF RESIDUAL TRAINING EFFECTS (RTE) FOR DIFFERENT MOTOR ABILITIES		
MOTOR ABILITY	RTE (DAYS)	PHYSIOLOGICAL BACKGROUND
AEROBIC ENDURANCE	30±5	INCREASED NUMBER OF AEROBIC ENZYMES, MITOCHONDRIA, CAPILLARY DENSITY, HEMOGLOBIN CAPACITY, GLYCOGEN STORAGE, AND HIGHER RATE OF FAT METABOLISM
MAXIMAL STRENGTH	30±5	IMPROVEMENT OF NEURAL MECHANISM. MUSCLE HYPERTROPHY DUE MAINLY TO MUSCLE FIBER ENLARGEMENT.
ANAEROBIC GLYCOLYTIC ENDURANCE	18±4	INCREASED AMOUNT OF ANAEROBIC ENZYMES, BUFFERING CAPACITY, AND GLYCOGEN STORAGE. HIGHER POSSIBILITY OF LACTATE ACCUMULATION.
STRENGTH ENDURANCE	15±5	MUSCLE HYPERTROPHY, MAINLY IN SLOW-TWITCH FIBERS. IMPROVED AEROBIC/ANAEROBIC ENZYMES. BETTER LOCAL BLOOD CIRCULATION AND LACTATE TOLERANCE.
MAXIMAL SPEED	5±3	IMPROVED NEUROMUSCULAR INTERACTIONS AND MOTOR CONTROL. INCREASED PHOSPHOCREATINE STORAGE AND ANAEROBIC POWER.

Numerous studies have been done that calculate just how long an athlete is likely to retain a residual effect from training. Let's look at a couple of examples specifically so that you can begin to understand what an athlete's body goes through physiologically in trying to retain a specific performance quality.

---

[9] Table adapted from: Issurin, V. (2001). "Block Periodization: Breakthrough in Sport Training." New York, NY: Ultimate Athlete Concepts.

Figure 2.11 depicts the average loss of strength as measured by a 1RM back squat over a period of twelve weeks. Looking at the figure, you will notice that the slope or decrease in strength from week zero to week four is fairly mild, only dropping off 1–2 percent. From this, we can infer that if an athlete abstained from training strength for up to four weeks, he would have very little drop-off when returning to the strength training a month later. As we move further right on the x-axis, however, you will notice that the slope begins to increase, meaning larger decreases in maximal strength. Between weeks eight and twelve, the athlete's max decreases to between 80–90 percent of what it

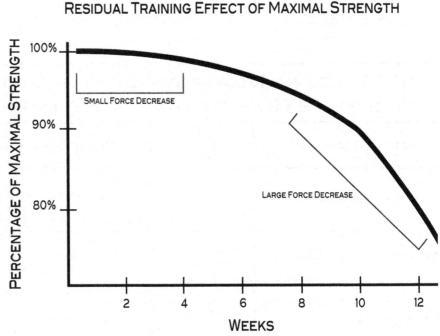

RESIDUAL TRAINING EFFECT OF MAXIMAL STRENGTH

Figure 2.11: Showing the duration of residual training effect for maximal strength. Abstaining from max strength training for a period of up to four weeks only sees a decrease in the parameter of 1–2 percent. Longer durations of detraining a parameter can lead to the accelerated loss of performance.

originally was. That is the entire point of understanding residual training effects—understanding how long an athlete can take between similar blocks without worrying about drastically decreasing that specific parameter. For example, as seen in this graph, the athlete could take four to six weeks to focus on different training targets like speed or power before having to return to a strength block without fear of drastic decreases in strength.

The problem is that most people, coaches and athletes included, believe that if they aren't training something specifically, they're getting worse at it. While this is true to a certain extent (the athlete did see a one percent drop in strength over the four-week time period), the athlete likely saw a 5–10 percent increase in the other training target trained during that month when strength wasn't trained. Training for sport performance is a give and take—three steps forward, one step back. If every time an athlete performs a strength block, he gains five percent on his 1RM and then loses one percent while improving other performance qualities for one or two blocks before returning to a strength block, that's a four percent net increase in strength. If an athlete can get three or four strength blocks in during a annual training cycle (which is entirely possible depending on the sport), that's a 12–16 percent increase in strength. That would equate to a 35- to 48-lb increase per year for an athlete who started with a 300-lb bench press. Not bad!

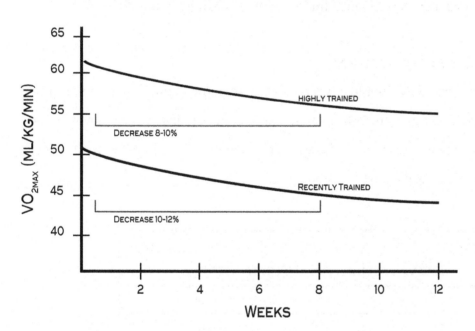

Similarly, aerobic capacity, measured here as an athlete's VO2 max, can be retained by an athlete for just as long, if not longer, than maximal strength. Again this is due to the extensive physiological and biochemical restructuring of the muscle tissue that takes place for this

Figure 2.12: Aerobic capacity has the longest training residual. Regardless if the athlete is highly trained or not, aerobic adaptation decreases at a slow rate; only 2% per week.

type of adaptation (mitochondria creation, increased density of the rate limiting enzyme phosphofructokinase, improved rate of glycolysis, etc.). In the training of my athletes, I assume that they will retain a high enough level of aerobic capacity that I only need to train (or retrain) an aerobic block once every 42 to 56 days (six to eight weeks).

In looking at figure 2.12, a six- to eight-week break might seem excessive as it correlates to an aerobic performance decrease of 10–12 percent, but you must remember that I train predominantly anaerobic athletes—hockey, baseball, and track and field. They don't need to retain such high levels of aerobic fitness to see the improvement transfer to their sport. If, on the other hand, I was training a soccer team or basketball team, sports that require more support of the aerobic system to see success on the field (or court), I would likely have to change my block schedule to train (or retrain) the aerobic component every three to five weeks. This is why you must have a solid understanding of the physical demands placed on your athletes during competition and why you must have a firm grasp on training residuals and their time frames. Without these, obtaining maximal performance for your athletes will be impossible.

BIOLOGICAL JUSTIFICATION

Most coaches are taught that they should always start a workout with speed and/or power movements and then progress to strength movements before ending with higher volume hypertrophy work. As an example, table 2.5 shows a very simple high school football player's off-season leg workout may look like this:

TABLE 2.5: EXAMPLE OFF-SEASON LOWER BODY WORKOUT	
EXERCISE	SETS X REPS
BARBELL CLEAN	4 x 2
BACK SQUAT	5 x 5
ROMANIAN DEADLIFT	4 x 8
LEG PRESS	3 x 12
CONDITIONING	100-YARD SHUTTLE X 6

The physiological basis for this type of training is that the athlete should perform high speed, high intensity movements that place the highest level of stress on the nervous system first, when the athlete is fresh, and then proceed to movements with higher volumes, lower intensities as the athlete fatigues.

I'm here to tell you that this is a poor training method, and I'll tell you why. Mixed training produces mixed results due to conflicting physiological responses. Simply put, your body doesn't know what you're trying to tell it to do. The athlete starts out with cleans, so the body thinks it wants to get more powerful, but then the athlete does heavy back squats. Well, now the body is a little confused. At first it thought the athlete wanted to be powerful, but now all of a sudden the athlete is signaling the body to be strong. To make matters worse, the athlete ends the workout by performing hypertrophy work with high rep sets of Romanian deadlifts and leg presses. By this point, the body is throwing its proverbial hands up in the air, completely confused by the conflicting signals. It asks, "Do you want me to be powerful, strong, big, or what?!"

Ultimately, simultaneous development of many parameters decreases the effectiveness of training. The human body wasn't designed to simultaneously adapt to many forms of stress. One of the most affirming supports for the use of the Block System over any mixed model of training is the human body's biological, evolutionary mechanism to adapt to stress. Remember, the flight or fight response that we talked about earlier was designed to deal with short, acute, high bouts of specific stress. See tiger, and run away from tiger. See heavy weight, and lift heavy weight. If instead the athlete is inundated with numerous varieties of stress (as is the case in any mixed training template), it's harder for the system to cope with and adapt to those stressors. If the athlete is asked to lift a 1RM squat, do leg presses for sets of twelve, and then run a few miles, the nervous system and physiological response don't know which stress they should adapt to or which stress is the most pertinent. The body will always believe the stresses must all be accounted for (evolutionary perspective) and will try to adapt to all stimuli. This, however, will limit the level of adaptation that takes place for each stress. This is not divide and conquer; this is divide and die.

Ask yourself this simple question—do you produce better work when you can focus all your time and effort on one thing, or when you have several things you have to get done all at once? In the eyes of an athlete's nervous system, the block system of training is focused, straightforward stress with only one logical adaptation. Mixed training is seen as chaos. Which do you think will result in improved sport performance? Below is a short excerpt taken from a presentation by Vladimir Issurin, the father of block periodization:

> *"Preparation that entails the use of both types of training concurrently demand energy needs that surpass the limits of homeostatic regulation. Correspondingly, stress reactions become stronger. This more strained metabolic and hormonal body environment suppresses homeostatic responses and has a deleterious effect on workloads intended to develop basic athletic abilities. Such conflicting responses, which are typical of mixed training among high-performance athletes, lead to a decline in general aerobic abilities, a reduction in muscle strength, and cases of overtraining."*
>
> **- VLADIMIR ISSURIN**

The bottom line is that the Block System allows you to avoid sending conflicting signals to the physiological systems of your athletes, exploiting the most appropriate mode of biological adaptation.

BASIC LAYOUT

Using the four principles as the base for the development of the Block System, a macrocycle is generally laid out in three distinct sections or mesocycles—accumulation, transmutation, and realization. Each of these sections, in turn, consists of one to three separate blocks. The rationale for this layout is based upon two rules that result from an analysis of the four principles previously explained—the rule of specificity and the rule of sequential system adaptation.

Here is a quick overview of the three sections so that you see how they work in succession before we look at each in more depth:

1) **Accumulation:** Aims to develop basic motor and technical abilities such as aerobic endurance and muscular strength. This phase is associated with large volumes and medium to high intensities and requires the use of restorative methods to ensure physiological adaptations such as muscle tissue and energy substrates, which need time and materials to rebuild. It is normally the longest of the three phases.

2) **Transmutation:** Aims to develop specific motor and technical abilities specific to the athlete's sport such as anaerobic endurance, strength-specific endurance, and power. This phase is associated with high intensities and increased velocity of movement. Based on studies performed by German scientists, it was found that adaptation in this phase peaked after a three-week block.

3) **Realization:** Aims to develop a pre-competition level of readiness (also known as peaking). This phase is associated with the development of maximal speed and acceleration as well as event specific readiness. It is normally the shortest of the three phases and takes place as close to competition as possible.

TABLE 2.6: MESOCYCLE OVERVIEW			
MAIN CHARACTERISTICS	ACCUMULATION	TRANSMUTATION	REALIZATION
PARAMETERS (MOTOR ABILITIES)	GENERAL ATHLETICISM: AEROBIC ENDURANCE, MAXIMAL STRENGTH	SPORT-SPECIFIC: LOCAL MUSCULAR ENDURANCE, STRENGTH ENDURANCE, POWER	PEAKING: TRANSFERABILITY, MAXIMAL SPEED, EVENT SPECIFIC ACCELERATION
VOLUME/INTENSITY	HIGH VOLUME/LOW INTENSITY	REDUCED VOLUME/ MODERATE INTENSITY	LOW VOLUME/HIGH INTENSITY
DURATION	2–6 WEEKS	2–4 WEEKS	1–2 WEEKS
FATIGUE/RECOVERY	SUFFICIENT RECOVERY TIME PROVIDED TO ENSURE ADAPTATION OF PHYSIOLOGICAL MECHANISMS	FATIGUE ACCUMULATES AS INTENSITY INCREASES	FULL RECOVERY; ATHLETE IS WELL RESTED

Phase #1: Accumulation

This first phase is sometimes referred to as the base phase because its main goal is to build a solid foundation of both strength and endurance, building up the athlete's level of homeostasis to enable higher levels of stress to be applied in subsequent blocks. In other words, it is general fitness. Unique to this phase is the long duration of its training residuals. This is due to the training parameters that are specifically targeted during this block—aerobic capacity and maximal strength. While an athlete needs to have some neurological adaptations to see an improvement in both endurance and strength, the main adaptations that take place are physiological. By that I mean they cause physical alterations within the athlete's body—muscle tissue is built through protein synthesis, glycogen stores are increased, and mitochondria are created within muscle fibers to facilitate ATP production and glycogen use.

As a result, this phase is the longest of the three and has the longest lasting residuals. Just as it takes a long time for the athlete's body to build the infrastructure that must come with improved aerobic capacity and strength, it also takes longer for those structures to break down. An athlete will usually spend four to six weeks building this base but will have a residual of nearly 35 days (five weeks) before having to return to it without fear of losing performance. Figure 2.13 gives a visual explanation of this concept:

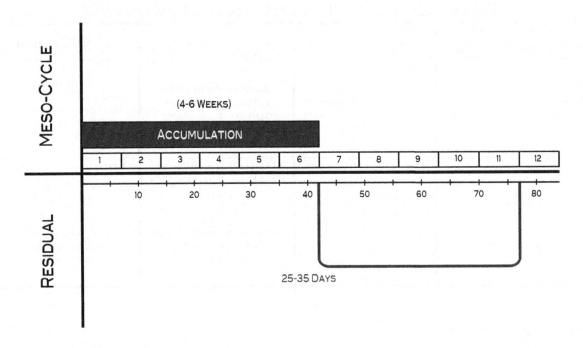

Figure 2.13: The top half of the figure displays the mesocycle. The accumulation phase is shown in the box, lasting for to six weeks. This allows for the full development of physiological mechanisms needed. The subsequent residual effect can be seen by the line on the bottom half of the figure shown in days. For example, the athlete would not have to retrain accumulation parameters until the eleventh week of the training cycle.

Phase #2: Transmutation

The emphasis of the second phase is to take the strength gained during the first phase and teach the athlete to use it in a fast, powerful manner. To accomplish this, less emphasis is placed on stressing the physiological processes of the athlete. Instead, the focus is placed on developing the nervous system and specific motor abilities. During this phase, the speed of the bar begins to become very important, as the goal should always be a high velocity of movement. Because this phase places a higher emphasis on the nervous system, its residual is much shorter than the accumulation phase with residuals lasting only two to three weeks. Figure 2.14 gives a visual explanation of this concept.

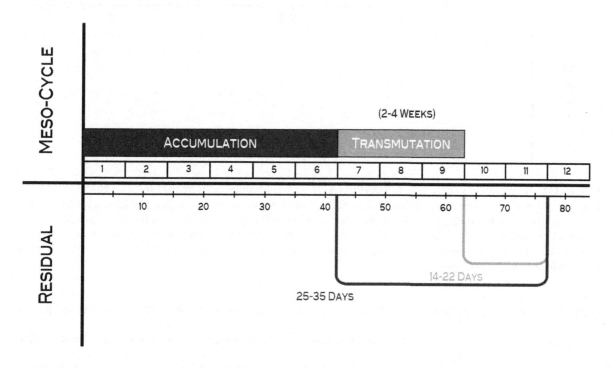

Figure 2.14: The transmutation phase follows the accumulation phase and lasts two to four weeks (dark gray box), focusing on improving the neurological mechanisms of the athlete. Because these adaptations are primarily neurological, the residual effect is substantially shorter than those from the accumulation phase, lasting only 14 to 22 days. This is shown by the dark gray line inlaid over the black line in the bottom of the figure.

Phase #3: Realization

Also known as the peaking phase, its sole purpose is to prepare the athlete for competition. It is during this phase that the performance parameters, improved during the two previous phases, and their residuals are trained to be used by the athlete in an as explosive, powerful manner as possible. Residuals for this last phase are the shortest due to an ever increasing amount of stress placed specifically on the nervous system and thus must be trained as closely to the competitive event as possible. Figure 2.15 gives you a visual explanation of this concept.

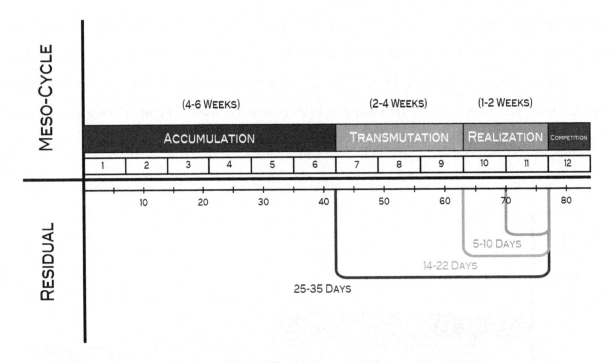

Figure 2.15: The realization phase is very stressful on the athlete because its training is focused on mimicking the rigors of competition. As a result, it is the shortest phase, lasting only one to two weeks. The high level of performance reached during this time also means that it has a small residual training effect, only five to ten days. The proper utilization of RTEs allows the athlete to peak all the performance abilities that are pertinent in optimal performance at once. This is shown in the figure where all the residual lines come together at the same point—week twelve right before competition.

When you understand how the blocks come together in sequence to peak an athlete for competition, you can begin to see how this integrated approach can allow for multiple peaks to be obtained within one training season. For example, in figure 2.16 you can see how a strength coach working with a football team might periodize his annual training cycle using a block system approach.

I can already hear the question being asked, "What if the training cycle lasts longer than the residual training effects allow?" That is a great question! Once the human body has adapted to a stressor, it is much quicker to readapt a second time. In a sense, every time a stress is seen by the body for the first time, it has to come up with a way to adapt to defend against that stress. Once it comes up with a plan that works and the body adapts, it catalogs and stores the process by which it accomplished that feat for future reference. When the stressor is encountered a second time, the body simply references the stored blueprints and carries out the instructions, quickly readapting to the stressor.

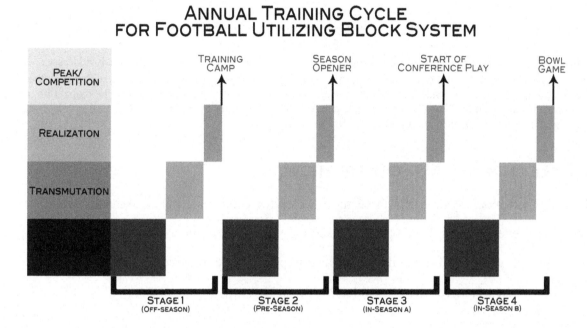

Figure 2.16: In the figure above, there are four "peaks" during a competitive season (shown at the top of the figure). In each case, the athlete's training is periodized to take him through each phase—accumulation (black box), transmutation (dark gray), and realization (light gray). This ensures that each parameter is maintained through the season, optimizing performance to the highest levels. This approach will minimize, if not eliminate, any decrease in performance (strength, power, speed) for an athlete over the period of a long season.

As long as the parameter is retrained within its residual time frame, you only need to superimpose one week of previously applied means to ensure that the adaptation gained when training the parameter is retained. For example, let's say that you have a macrocycle that lasts sixteen weeks. That's four weeks longer than what a normal cycle could support through normal training residuals to ensure that the positive adaptations seen in each parameter are retained all the way through to competition. The graph below depicts how by revisiting previous parameters, a coach can retain performance adaptations from each block.

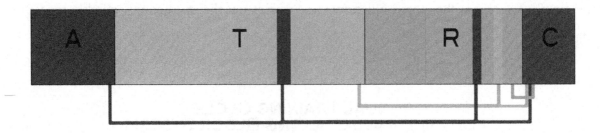

Figure 2.17: The strategic placement of training weeks, in which the athlete returns to previously addressed parameters, can extend their RTE longer than normal. Placing a week of accumulation training within both the transmutation and realization phases as well as an extra week of transmutation training within the realization phase allows for the extension of RTEs. This allows a coach with longer training macrocycles, those lasting longer than twelve weeks, to still peak all of an athlete's abilities for competition.

MY BLOCKS: AN OVERVIEW

My undulated block system has three mesocycles that comprise my off-season training cycle. Using high levels of undulated stress focused on a minimal number of training parameters, this system has proven itself time and again to create powerful, explosive athletes within the limited time frames that we, as coaches, must deal with.

TABLE 2.7: BLOCK SYSTEM OUTLINE				
PHASE (MESOCYCLE)	MY PHASE	BLOCKS	BLOCK CLASSIFICATION	DURATION (WEEKS)
ACCUMULATION	ABOVE 80%	3	STRENGTH 1) ECCENTRIC 2) ISOMETRIC 3) CONCENTRIC	2–3 EACH
TRANSMUTATION	80–55%	1	SPEED-STRENGTH	3–4
REALIZATION	BELOW 55%	1	HIGH VELOCITY PEAKING METHOD	3–5

2.3: COMPARISON TO LINEAR PERIODIZATION

There is always more than one way to skin a cat. My athletic undulating model is not the only method strength coaches could employ to train their athletes. However, with some self-admitted bias, I believe all other training models are inferior. One such approach that is often a popular choice by coaches is the classic linear periodization model. The granddaddy of them all, it is often referred to as the "western method" of training. Classic linear periodization was first implemented in—where else?—the Soviet Union. The first published reference I could find came from a book entitled *Olympic Sport,* written by a Russian named Sergei Kotov in 1917. The book outlined three stages of training—the general, preparatory, and specific stages. In many ways, this was a very crude, early version of what would later evolve into the western linear periodization method.

Your first clue to the inferiority of this method for training athletes should be that the Soviets got rid of it to adopt the Bulgarian undulating model in the 1970s. Furthermore, the western linear periodization model was the method by which the United States trained its athletes leading up to the 1984 Summer Olympics, the year that the Soviets would have taken forty-six gold medals from the US if they hadn't boycotted the games, holding their own Friendship Games in Moscow later that year.

The classic linear periodization model has been modified and altered somewhat since its humble beginnings in Kotov's book almost a century ago. It now consists of four periods, lasting four to six weeks per period:

1) **Preparation period:** This phase is intended to condition the athlete as well as build muscle mass. This phase is characterized by high volume and low intensity with loads generally between 50–70 percent and a rep range of ten to twenty.

2) **First transition period:** This is comprised of two separate sections. First, the strength phase, which is pretty self-explanatory, increases the athlete's strength. Loads are usually

between 70–85 percent of the 1RM with a rep range of four to six. The second part is known as the power phase. This phase is designed to increase the overall power of the athlete. Loads increase to 85–95 percent with a rep range that drops slightly to three to five.

3) **Competition period:** The final phase is designed to "peak" all the abilities that have been developed in earlier phases, specifically strength and power. Loads used here are generally 93 percent and higher. Athletes perform one to three repetitions with long periods of rest between sets (three to seven minutes) to ensure full recovery between sets.

4) **Active rest:** Normal strength training is replaced by general athletic activity. Athletes are encouraged to play organized sports (basketball, ultimate Frisbee, soccer) to allow the body to recover from the high stress of both the peak phase and the competition period.

The basic concept of linear periodization is to decrease the total volume of work while increasing the intensity as the athlete approaches the competitive period (figure 2.18).[10] The ultimate goal is to supercompensate the athletes, peaking them right before competition. While the model looks great on paper, it is fundamentally flawed when applied to sport.

One of the biggest problems with this model, when looked at through an athletic coach's lens, is that it focuses solely on concentric muscle actions. Every phase of the linear

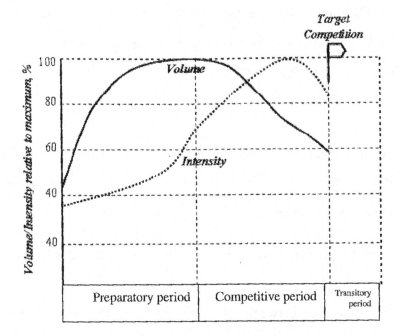

Figure 2.18 - Classic Linear Periodization

[10] Issurin V (2001) *Block Periodization: Breakthrough in Sport Training*. New York, NY: Ultimate Athlete Concepts.

periodization model is geared toward lifting as much weight as the athlete can concentrically handle given the percentage ranges for the given rep range. As you learned in section two, that is only working one-third of the athlete's necessary muscular and neural structures required for top end sport performance. It neglects the eccentric and isometric phases of dynamic movement as well as a host of other neurological processes.

Another drawback of the linear model is the athlete's inability to retain the residual training effects from one phase to the next. They simply can't maintain proficiency in the qualities developed as they move to subsequent phases. For instance, the strength developed in phase two will be lost by the time the athlete returns to the next hypertrophy phase ten to twelve weeks later. Even within the same macrocycle, the hypertrophy gained by athletes at the onset of the cycle will likely be lost or at the very least diminished to a high degree by the time they reach the power phase eight weeks later.

The last stumbling block that the linear model puts in front of a strength coach that I will address here is its focus on peaking the athlete only once per macrocycle. The classic linear periodization is aimed at giving the athlete one supercompensation prior to competition or the start of the season. Using an undulating model, as I do, you actually peak your athletes more often with smaller, weekly supercompensations. I don't know of any college sport that only has one game a year. Football, basketball, hockey, track, volleyball, softball, baseball—they all have long, grueling competitive seasons consisting of multiple games. It's physiologically impossible to peak athletes at the onset of a season and expect them to maintain those residuals throughout.

As a result, a strength coach must continue to train the athlete on the linear model through the season in an effort to maintain any positive training effects from the off-season work. This brings up a host of new issues. For example, an in-season hypertrophy phase for basketball players on the linear model could make them very sore and energy deprived, as this type of workout is usually associated with higher volume (four to five sets of ten to twenty reps) that will deplete muscle glycogen stores. This, in turn, will reduce the athlete's ability to perform at a high level in practice or a game later that day/week.

The undulated application of stress within a block periodization model is the strength coach's best option for in-season and out-of-season training. It gives the ability to modify methods and loading parameters on a weekly, even daily, basis to ensure the athlete is both neurally and muscularly primed to perform at optimal levels. In essence, it allows the coach unparalleled options to modify the stress levels being administered to the athletes. When you look at the two methods side by side (figure 2.8)[11] and compare them based on the factors that were found in successful programs throughout history, the answer is clear. The undulating block model enables an athlete to be stressed at a high level consistently with a high level of variability and volume, allowing for weekly supercompensations through progressive overtraining. Which model would you use to train your athletes?

TABLE 2.8: TRAINING SYSTEM COMPARISON

CHARACTERISTICS OF TRAINING SYSTEM	LINEAR/MIXED SYSTEM	UNDULATED BLOCK SYSTEM
LOADING PRINCIPLES	COMPLEX USE OF DIFFERING LOADS DIRECTED AT MANY PERFORMANCE ABILITIES (PARAMETERS).	HIGHLY CONCENTRATED LOADS DIRECTED AT SPECIFIC PERFORMANCE ABILITIES (PARAMETERS).
SCIENTIFIC JUSTIFICATION	CUMULATIVE TRAINING EFFECT.	CUMULATIVE, RESIDUAL, AND BIOLOGICAL EFFECTS.
SEQUENCING OF TRAINING TO DEVELOP PARAMETERS	SIMULTANEOUS	CONSECUTIVE
COMPETITIONS	CORRESPONDS TO COMPETITIVE PERIOD.	OCCURS AT THE END OF EACH STAGE.
PHYSIOLOGICAL MECHANISM	ADAPTATION TO CONCURRENT TRAINING STIMULI AFFECTING MANY DIFFERENT TARGETS.	SUPERIMPOSITION OF RESIDUAL TRAINING EFFECTS INDUCED BY HIGHLY CONCENTRATED TRAINING STIMULI.

---

[11] Adapted from Issurin, V. (2001). "Block Periodization: Breakthrough in Sport Training." New York, NY: Ultimate Athlete Concepts.

2.4: SUMMARY AND REVIEW

One of the most interesting things about learning, I believe, is that it takes place in nearly the same way that athletes improve their performance. It is through the proper application of stress that an athlete is built. In much the same way, I feel coaches acquire applicable knowledge. I say applicable because it is one thing to know something and quite another to know how to apply it. Everyone who smokes knows that they should quit, yet millions of people still smoke.

In that sense, the first part of this book was all about stress and the need to apply it to an athlete. A strength coach is literally a stress manager, having to know when to add stress and when to take it away, often with only the smallest changes making large differences in the performance of their athletes. If we think of the first section as laying the foundation of knowledge about the importance of stressing the athlete, section two was the "why" and built the first couple floors, gaining knowledge and experience about its application.

I understand that up to this point I have not explicitly showed you exactly how to apply stress through an undulating block system, but I feel it is important that you understand the background and the basic foundational principals of the system with which you, as a coach, must apply stress to your athletes. Subsequent sections of this book will lay out *exactly* how you can use an undulated block model to stress your athletes and improve their performance—just flip through the next couple of hundred pages to see all the tables, charts, and programs laid out. But by learning this material up front, by stressing your brain a little, you have adapted a basic understanding of stress, undulation, and the block system of training that will enable you to fully grasp the programming that follows—its purpose, application, and results in sport performance.

SECTION 3

THE TRIPHASIC NATURE OF ATHLETIC MOVEMENT

3.1: THE IMPORTANCE OF TRIPHASIC TRAINING

The revelation that led to the creation of the triphasic undulating block system and ultimately this book occurred in the fall of 2003. I'm very fortunate to work at a university with an engineering department willing to loan out its $20,000 force plate to a bunch of meatheads over in the athletic building. A huge thanks must go out to that entire department as well as the wealthy guy who donated the money for it. Now, I'm not any smarter than the next guy. I don't claim to be a genius, but I've been blessed with two gifts—logical reasoning and critical thinking. These gifts have allowed me to make certain connections and realizations with training that have enabled me to come up with a training model that generates incredible results for athletes of all sports.

At the time, I had two track and field athletes—throwers—who had me perplexed. One of these athletes (let's call him Ben) was a potential world-class thrower. He could throw the shot over 65 feet. The other athlete, Tommy, was an average D-1 thrower. He had trouble breaking 55 feet. Aside from the large throwing discrepancy, the loads they used in the weight room were basically the same. Nothing jumped out that you could point a finger at and say, "Ah ha, that's why Ben is so good!" or "That must be why Tommy is struggling." I couldn't figure out what the limiting factor was that caused a difference of over ten feet between their top throws. I knew it had to have something to do with their rate of force development (RFD), but I wanted to understand specifically how it applied to their throws. More importantly, I wanted to understand, physiologically, what made the difference between world class and average.

To find some answers, I decided to test their bench press using the force plate. I chose this exercise for two reasons.

1) Specificity: The bench press has direct carryover and transferability to the throwing motion.

2) At the time, both athletes had the same bench press max—415 pounds. Because they both had the same max, it eliminated one of the variables that contributes to RFD—max strength. The other variable is time (which we will talk about in short order).

Wanting to see how Ben and Tommy produced force explosively, I used the band method on the bench press so that I could see acceleration throughout the entire range of motion on the lifts. Without the extra band tension at the top of the movement, both athletes would have had to decelerate the bar halfway through the concentric phase or the bar would fly out of their hands. This early deceleration would skew the results. The band tension ensured that both of them, Ben and Tommy, would drive the bar as hard as they could, generating a high rate of force through the entire range of motion. For those of you not familiar with the banded bench method, the hyperlink gives you a visual of the exercise — Bench press band method

The bar was loaded with 205 pounds (50 percent of their 1RM) and 90 pounds of band tension (20 percent of their 1RM). At the top of the press, each athlete would be moving 70 percent of their 1RM. Both athletes were instructed to bring the bar down hard and fast, stopping it at their chest, and reaccelerating the bar upward as fast as they could. It should be noted that neither athlete bounced the bar off his chest. (I will talk about the importance of this detail in a moment.)

Figure 3.1 shows the results recorded by the force plate. The x-axis (horizontal axis) depicts time in hundredths of a second. The y-axis (vertical axis) represents power in watts. In essence, the graph is showing how much force each athlete absorbed and displaced in a given amount of time. Ben's repetition is shown by the black line while Tommy's is shown by the gray line. The actual repetitions are taking place during the "V" shaped segment of the lines in the middle of the graph. The descending line of the "V" is the eccentric or yielding phase of the bench press. The bottom, or point, of the "V" is the isometric or static phase, and the line ascending from the bottom of the "V" is the concentric or overcoming phase.

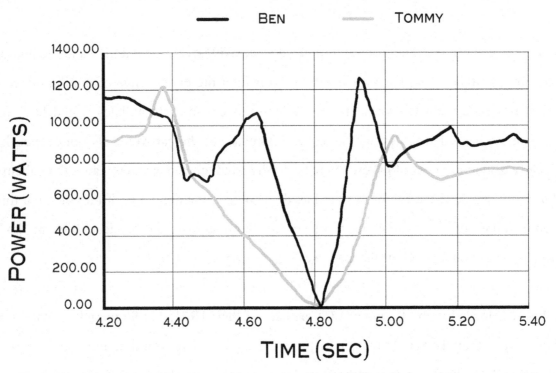

Figure 3.1: Graph comparing the ability of Ben and Tommy to absorb and displace force during a maximal dynamic contraction. Notice the athlete that can absorb eccentric force more quickly has a higher power output in the resulting concentric phase.

As soon as I saw the graphical printout for the first time, I realized what separated Ben and Tommy. While both athletes could produce the same amount of maximal force in the bench press (each with a 415-pounds 1RM), Ben could absorb more force eccentrically at a higher velocity. This is where it was essential to make sure that neither athlete bounced the bar off his chest. If they had, they would have eliminated their stretch reflex and lost power in reaccelerating the bar. Instead, the absorbed energy went directly from the bar into their arms, shoulders, and chest, maximizing both the stretch reflex and the stretch shortening cycle (SSC) before being recoiled back into the bar and reaccelerated upward (I'll speak more about the stretch reflex and SSC later.) The graph (figure 3.1) shows that Ben was able to load up his muscles with more energy to use concentrically, enabling him to accelerate the bar faster than Tommy did, producing more power. Applying this same idea to throwing, Ben could store more energy in his muscles during the stretch of his windup, thus applying more force to the shot before it left his hand than Tommy could. When Ben's shot left his hand, it was powered by a jet engine. When Tommy's shot left his hand, it was powered by a propeller.

You have just learned the key to improving sport performance in every athlete. It isn't about who is the strongest, although many coaches incorrectly believe this to be the case. The key to improved sport performance is producing more force in less time. This results when an athlete can absorb more force eccentrically, allowing him, in turn, to apply higher levels of force concentrically in less time. In other words, the athlete who has the narrowest "V" wins every time. Looking back

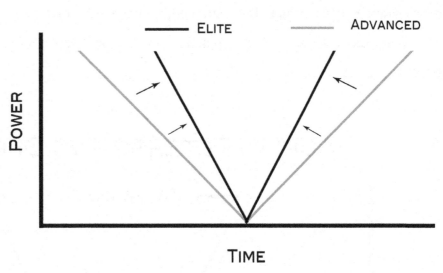

Figure 3.2: Graph showing the tri-phasic "V" of an elite athlete (black line) verses an advanced athlete (gray line). This holds true for any maximal effort, dynamic contraction.

at Ben and Tommy's graph, it becomes very clear—sport performance is about which athlete can absorb more force, enabling the athlete to produce more power. It's all about the "V" baby!!

Have you ever noticed that Adrian Peterson breaks a lot of arm tackles? The reason isn't because his legs are huge or because he keeps pumping his knees. Granted, those are contributing factors, but there are many average runners whose legs are just as huge and who pump just as hard. The reason Peterson is able to break so many tackles is because he gets defenders out of position to make a solid tackle in the first place. How does he do that? He has superior triphasic muscle action. When Adrian Peterson goes to make a cut, so does the defender. However, Peterson can decelerate his body more quickly by absorbing more kinetic energy eccentrically in a shorter amount of time, come to an isometric stop, and then explode concentrically in a new direction. The defender meanwhile takes a few hundredths of a second longer to completely decelerate his body. He can't absorb eccentric force at the same rate as Peterson, so he takes longer to decelerate. He has to spread the force out over a longer period of time to reduce the net effect on this muscles. This results in a longer deceleration period as well as less force absorbed into the stretch shortening cycle to be used during the concentric contraction. When the defender does finally make his cut and tries to make the tackle, Peterson is already out of his break and reaccelerating. It's too late. The extra couple hundredths of a second it takes the defender to decelerate has cost him. His only option is to dive at Peterson's legs and try to make an arm tackle.

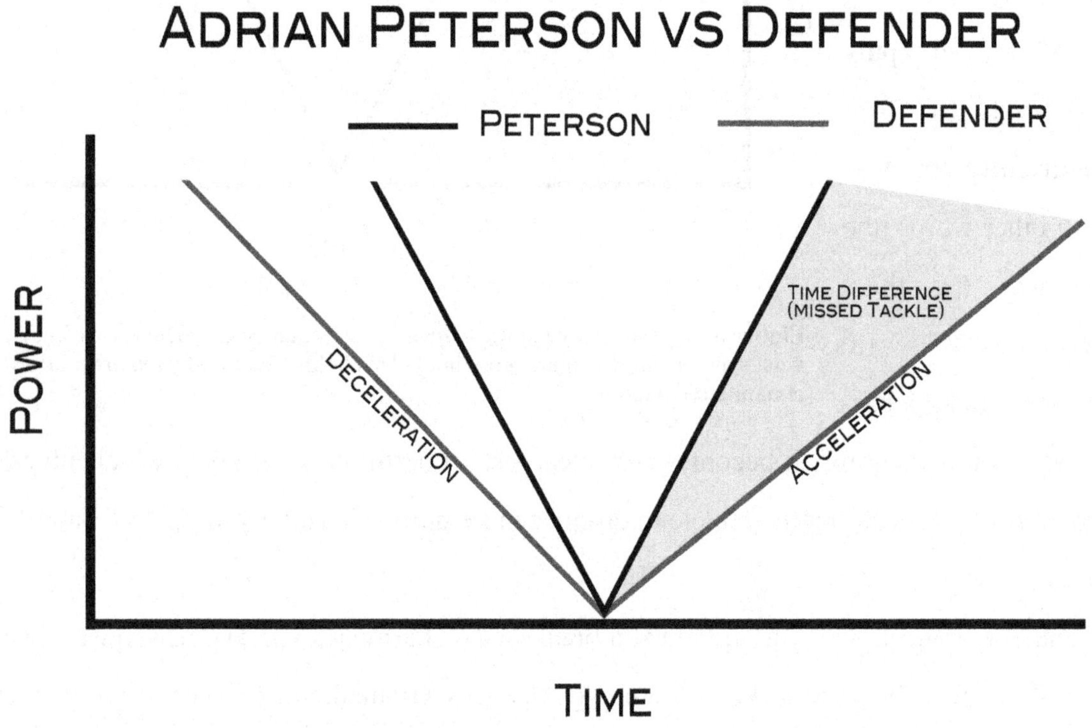

ADRIAN PETERSON VS DEFENDER

Figure 3.3: Graph depicting the difference in rate of force production and power output of Adrian Peterson and a defender. The shaded area shows the increased time it takes the defender to accelerate compared to Peterson.

Many traditional training methods teach athletes how to expel energy; little time and effort is spent teaching them to absorb it. That is the entire point of the triphasic method—learning how to eccentrically and isometrically absorb energy before applying it in explosive dynamic movements. It is important to note that triphasic training and the "V" are improving and referring to maximal dynamic movements only. During a maximal effort dynamic contraction, you will never see the eccentric portion of the "V" at a shallower angle than the concentric portion. The body can't generate more force than it can absorb maximally. If an athlete deliberately slows the rate of the eccentric contraction such as during a slow tempo squat, it's possible for the eccentric rate of force absorption to be less than the resulting force output. However, in anaerobic sports, an athlete never deliberately gives less than 100 percent effort in competitive movements.

As a strength and conditioning coach, you must remember that athletes aren't powerlifters. They must be strong but only to the extent that can benefit them in their sport. Every dynamic human movement has a time frame, a limited amount of time in which an athlete has to produce as much force as possible. Ben was a world class thrower because he could generate more explosive strength (defined as maximal force in minimal time) in the time frame it took to throw a shot. Here are some examples of dynamic movements and their allotted time for force development:

TABLE 3.1: TIME TO MAXIMAL FORCE DEVELOPMENT	
DYNAMIC ACTIONS	TIME (SECONDS)
SPRINTING	0.08–0.12
JUMPING	0.17–0.18
SHOT PUT	0.15–0.18
POWERLIFTING	0.8–4.0

Looking at table 3.1, it's clear that an athlete doesn't have much time to produce force. Numerous studies have been done showing that the average person takes 0.3 to 0.4 seconds to generate maximal muscular force and sometimes longer—up to 0.7 seconds.[12] Usually these studies are performed by hooking subjects up to an electrocardiogram (EKG) and having them perform a

---

[12] Khamoui A, Brown L, Nguyen D, Uribe B (2011) Relationship between force-time and velocity-time characteristics of dynamic and isometric muscle actions. *Journal of Strength & Conditioning Research* 25(1):198–204.

maximal isometric contraction. Then researchers look to see how long it takes the muscle to reach its peak force level. With almost all athletic, dynamic movements taking less than 0.2 seconds to complete, athletes will never develop their full force potential during competition. The only sport that does this is powerlifting, where athletes have upwards of three or four seconds to develop all the power they can muster. As a result, it is imperative that you train your athletes for force development, not just maximal strength!

Figure 3.4 shows how large the gap actually is between maximal strength and dynamic strength.[13] The line represents the force development curve of an athlete with the actual rate of development represented by the slope of the line. The dashed line to the right depicts the time it takes the athlete to develop 100 percent of his maximal muscular force (Fm). The dashed line to the left shows how much force the athlete could produce given a time constraint. In this case, the athlete produced 50 percent of his Fm in 0.14 seconds.

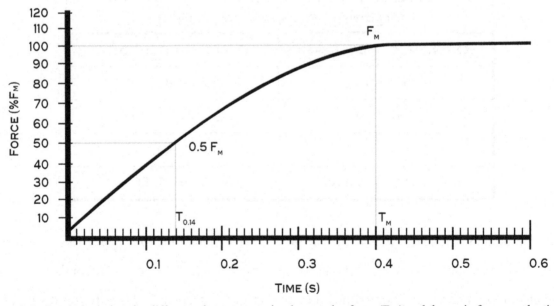

Figure 3.4: Graph depicting the difference between maximal muscular force (Fm) and dynamic force production. It takes roughly 0.4 seconds to develop Fm, yet most sports only allow 0.14 seconds or less to develop dynamic force.

---

[13] Zatsiorsky VM, Kraemer WJ (2006) *Science and Practice of Strength Training*. Champaign, IL: Human Kinetics.

The goal of all athletes should be to increase the slope of the line, in essence shifting the force line to the left and enabling them to produce a higher percentage of their maximal muscular force (Fm) in the period of time allotted for their sport. In other words, the goal is to shrink the time difference between their maximal strength and dynamic strength. For further reading on the subject, I highly recommend the book *Science and Practice of Strength Training* by Vladimir Zatsiorsky and his explanation of the explosive strength deficit.

Let's go back and look at what Ben and Tommy's graphs would look like. First, let's look at Tommy's. Looking back at our "time to maximal force development table" we see that a thrower has about 0.15 to 0.18 seconds to develop force before the shot leaves his hand. We'll give Tommy the benefit of the doubt and give him the full 0.18 seconds. In the graph below, you will see a line extending upward from the x-axis at 0.18 and running into the force development curve at a point that correlates on the y-axis to 61 percent. This means that within the time constraint of throwing a shot, 0.18 seconds, Tommy only has enough time to develop 61 percent of his maximal force behind the shot to propel it.

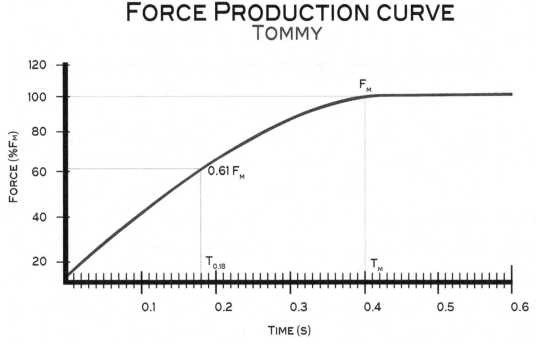

FORCE PRODUCTION CURVE
TOMMY

Figure 3.5: Graph depicting the theoretical force production curve for Tommy. Notice that in 0.18 seconds, Tommy only produces 61 percent of his Fm.

Now let's take a look at what Ben's graph would look like next to Tommy's. Below you see the same basic graph with a line extending up from 0.18 seconds on the x-axis. However, the difference is that Ben's force production line is shifted to the left; its slope has increased. The line intersects the force development curve at a point associated on the y-axis with 78 percent. This means that Ben, again with the same time constraints as Tommy, could develop 78 percent of his total force behind the shot before it left his hand—a difference of nearly 20 percent!

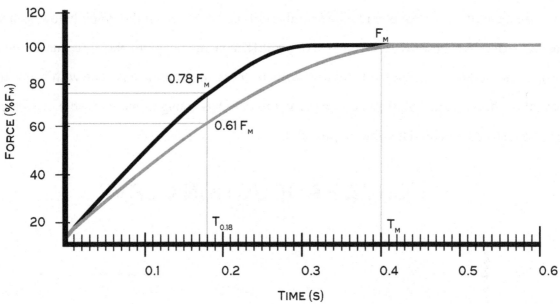

Figure 3.6: Graph comparing the force production curves of Ben and Tommy. Ben's curve (black line) is shifted up and to the left of Tommy's (gray line). This shift shows that in the same amount of time (0.18 seconds), Ben can produce 17 percent more of his F*m* than Tommy.

The concept of needing to increase an athlete's RFD is nothing new. I wish I could take credit for it, believe me. But the concept is one that the Russians have known about for decades, researching RFD and training methods since the early 1960s. They came up with a great training method to try and enhance it. *Accommodated resistance*, which is the use of chains, bands, or weight releasers to modify a load to match an athlete's RFD curve, was created to try to maximize an athlete's explosive contraction. The use of these implements allowed the athlete to push all the way through his entire range of motion without having to decelerate the bar at the end, allowing for pure explosive concentric contractions. This concept was identified by Fred Hatfield and termed compensatory acceleration.

The shortcoming of these methods is that they focused solely on the development of explosive strength by emphasizing the concentric phase of dynamic movement. My epiphany—my 'light bulb going off' moment in 2003—was when I first looked at that printout and realized that we (and by "we" I mean strength and conditioning coaches) were approaching the development of force from the wrong angle. The key to improved force production, and thus sport performance, doesn't lie in the concentric phase. In order to develop explosive strength and do so in a manner that is transferable to sport, you must train the eccentric and isometric phases of dynamic movements at a level equal to that of the concentric phase.

I have used the force plate with hundreds of athletes and on dozens of different dynamic movements—everything from plyometric jumps to squats to presses. In every instance, the results come back the same. The better athletes, defined as being those with higher rates of force production, are the ones who can absorb more kinetic energy eccentrically. The steeper the left line of the "V" going in, the steeper the right side of the "V" going out (assuming a maximal dynamic movement).

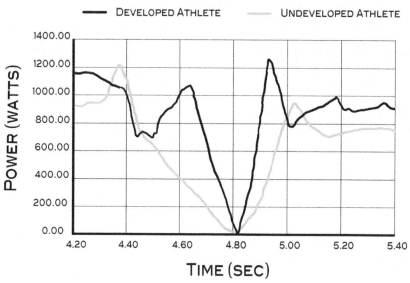

Figure 3.7: Tri-phasic "V" depicting a developed and undeveloped athlete.

Look at the original printout again in Figure 3.7 (and get used to it because you're going to see it about a dozen more times in this book). This is the key, folks. It's the Holy Grail of improved sport performance. Don't think of this graph as depicting two separate athletes anymore. Imagine the graph as depicting the same athlete at different times during his development. The red line is the athlete when he first walks through your doors. The blue line is where the athlete will be by the time he walks out two, three, or four years later. The lines are the same athlete, but one shows the results of an athlete developed using the triphasic undulating system of training while the other is in the early stages of development. Your new goal as a strength and conditioning coach is to narrow that "V" as much as possible.

3.2: ECCENTRIC PHASE

Once I realized the importance of the eccentric phase and the role it plays in dynamic movement, I had to answer two more questions—why is it so important and how do I train my athletes to improve it? First, let's address the "why."

An eccentric action can be defined as one in which the proximal and distal attachments (closest to and furthest away from the center of the body) of the muscle move in opposite directions from each other. In other literature, this is often referred to as the lengthening (or yielding) phase as the muscle is stretched due to the force of an imposed load. Now, make sure you read this next sentence very carefully. ***Every dynamic movement begins with an eccentric muscle action.*** I'll write it again. ***Every dynamic movement begins with an eccentric muscle action.*** For example, when an athlete jumps, his hips perform a slight dip, eccentrically lengthening the quads and glutes before takeoff. Counter movements or pre-loading such as the hip dip in jumping are paramount in force production of an athlete. The eccentric yielding of a muscle puts in motion a series of physiological events that pre-load a muscle, storing kinetic energy to be used in an explosive, concentric dynamic movement.

When athletes train the eccentric phase of a movement, they are actually training two physiological processes that contribute to force development. One of them is the most powerful human reflex in the body—the stretch reflex. The other, whose force producing abilities are dependent upon the stretch reflex, is a close second in terms of force production and is called the stretch shortening cycle (SSC).

STRETCH REFLEX

The net force production of the stretch reflex is comprised of the sum of two proprioceptive nerve signals:

1) **Muscle spindles**, which act as neuromuscular stimulators

2) **Golgi tendon organs (GTO)**, which act as neuromuscular inhibitors

When trained eccentrically, these produce a stretch reflex within the muscle structure that is responsible for explosive, dynamic movement.

The stretch reflex is induced by intramuscular sensory receptors called muscle spindles running parallel to the muscle fibers within a given muscle. The spindles' job is to relay information to the brain via the central nervous system (CNS) about the amount of force acting on a muscle. As the stretch or force on a muscle increases, the muscle spindle will relay information to the brain (afferent neural pathway) telling it how hard it must contract to overcome the force acting on it and return to its original length. The greater the signaling of the muscle spindle, the harder the resulting signal of contraction from the brain (efferent neural pathway). The muscle spindle doesn't know the athlete is trying to lift a weight or make a cut on the field. Its only concern is to stop the eccentric lengthening of the muscle. The primary function of the muscle spindle is to tell the brain how hard it must contract a muscle to overcome a load.

While muscle spindles signal how hard to contract, Golgi tendon organs (GTO) tell the brain when to relax. GTO are found within the tendons attaching muscle to bone. Unlike the muscle spindles, which measure changes in length, the GTO measure changes in the force being placed on a muscle. Inhibitory mechanisms, such as the GTO, are necessary to prevent the muscles from exerting more force than the connective tissues can tolerate. This is referred to as autogenic inhibition. For all intents and purposes, the GTO act like the body's emergency cutoff switch. If the force or stretch being placed on a muscle reaches a point where continued muscular tension will result in serious structural damage (muscle or tendon tearing), the GTO signal an inhibitory muscle reflex (figure 9). The ensuing decrease in muscle tension is intended to prevent serious injury to the muscle structure.

However, we know that this system can be overridden and allow a person or athlete to produce levels of force that are much higher than his normal maximums. An example of a seemingly superhuman feat of strength would be a mother lifting a burning car off her four-year-old daughter. When these people are examined after exceeding their usual maximum strength, there is often significant damage to the musculoskeletal structures, suggesting that the autogenic inhibitory mechanism was deactivated. Numerous studies have also shown that dynamic and ballistic stretching protocols known to help inhibit the GTO response lead to improved force production during both maximal strength and explosive strength testing.[14] While it would not be good to completely shut off this safety measure, training has been shown to reduce the GTO inhibitory impulse, allowing muscles to reach greater levels of force production.

At first glance, the GTO look like good guys. They are looking out for you; they've got your back. They would never let anything bad happen to you. Of course, the problem is that this isn't true. In reality, the GTO act as an overprotective mother. Most people's GTO appear to come pre-set with a "kill switch" set nearly 40 percent below what the structure can actually handle before serious damage occurs.[15] Ultimately, untrained GTO are terrible for the development of explosive power, because they limit an athlete's potential to absorb high levels of force.

When you train the eccentric phase of dynamic movement, you are training these proprioceptive structures of the muscle, the muscle spindles and GTO. In order to maximize an athlete's force producing ability, a coach must use methods in training that will decrease the inhibitory effect of the GTO while maximizing the excitatory response of the muscle spindle. During the eccentric phase of a squat, a stretch is applied to the quadriceps, hamstrings, and glutes that produces via the stretch reflex a muscular contraction. At the same time, the GTO from each of those muscles interpret the force acting on them and cause an inhibitory reflex. If an athlete isn't used to handling high levels of eccentric force, the resulting concentric muscle action will be weakened.

The goal of the eccentric phase is to improve the neuromuscular synchronization of the afferent/efferent neural pathway between the muscle spindle, CNS, and muscle while desensitizing the GTO, allowing the athlete to absorb higher levels of force without triggering an inhibitory GTO reflex. The athlete who can eccentrically absorb more kinetic energy will be able to produce

---

[14] Jaggers J, Swank A, Frost K, Lee C (2008) The acute effects of dynamic and ballistic stretching on vertical jump height, force, and power. *Journal of Strength & Conditioning Research* 22(6):1844–49.

[15] Nelson A, Guillory I, Cornwell A, Kokken J (2001) Inhibition of maximal voluntary isokinetic torque production following stretching is velocity-specific. *Journal of Strength & Conditioning Research* 15(2):241–46.

more concentric force and take advantage of the second physiologic muscle action—the stretch shortening cycle.

STRETCH SHORTENING CYCLE

The SSC, as it relates to the eccentric phase, is responsible for the absorption of kinetic energy within the muscle and tendon. Elasticity means that a structure is able to resume its normal shape (length) after being distorted (lengthened). When a muscle and its attaching tendon are stretched, the elastic energy is stored within these two structures to be used later during the concentric phase. Think of it as stretching a rubber band or loading a spring. The more energy an athlete can absorb, the more energy he can apply dynamically.

The amount of energy that can be absorbed and used by the SSC is largely dictated by the combined effect of the stretch and GTO reflex. Other contributing factors are motor unit recruitment and rate coding, which will be addressed later. However, the percentage that each contributes to total force production is heavily debated among physiologists. Physiologists do agree, however, that the intensity of the eccentric contraction dictates the signal from the muscle spindle and how hard a muscle contracts. Simultaneously, the GTO signal the brain to relax the muscle to avoid injury. The sum difference of those two signals is the remaining energy (force) that is absorbed into the muscle/tendon to be used in the concentric phase. You can think of this as a formula:

STRETCH REFLEX − GOLGI TENDON ORGAN REFLEX = FORCE PRODUCTION

The amount of force an athlete can eccentrically load into a muscle/tendon is directly proportional to the amount of force he can apply. This is a principal law of physics known as *the law of conservation of energy*, and no, we aren't going to go into a physics dissertation. Just trust me.

Let's go back to the "V" so you can see exactly what I'm talking about. When you look at the graph below, you begin to see that there is a correlation between the eccentric and concentric phases. The steeper the eccentric line is coming into the bottom of the "V," the steeper the concentric line is leaving the bottom of the "V." The greater the velocity of stretching during the eccentric contraction, the greater the storage of elastic energy. This goes back to what we went over with the stretch reflex, GTO reflex, and the SSC. The athlete who can handle higher levels of force through an increased stretch reflex and inhibited GTO reflex will be able to apply more force concentrically due to higher levels of absorbed kinetic energy applied through the SSC.

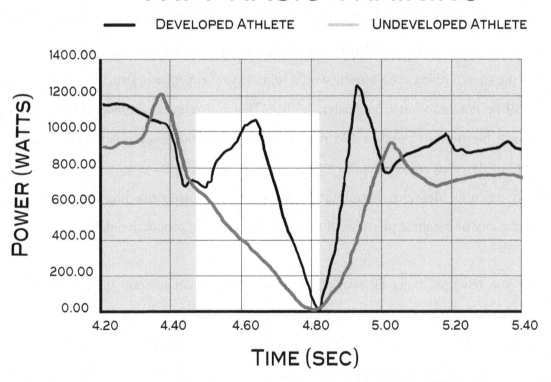

Figure 3.10: Graph showing the importance of a well trained stretch reflex and inhibited GTO. The developed athlete (black line) can absorb/withstand higher levels of eccentric force than the underdeveloped athlete (gray line). This leads higher rates of force production and higher power outputs during the concentric phase.

I promise you that you'll never see an athlete whose "V" comes in with a gradually descending line (figure 3.10, gray line) and leaves with a steeply ascending line (figure 3.10, black line) in a maximal effort dynamic movement. That's because it's impossible according to Newton's second law of motion:

The acceleration of an object as produced by a net force is directly proportional to the magnitude of the net force, in the same direction as the net force, and inversely proportional to the mass of the object.

- SIR ISAAC NEWTON

In layman's terms, that means the force applied by an athlete is directly proportional to the energy he first absorbs. For every athlete I checked, if the eccentric line was shallow, meaning the line had a more gradual downward slope (remember slope is rise/run so that means the athlete is absorbing less force over a given amount of time), the concentric line was also shallow, meaning it had a more gradual upward slope.

I should interject that there are limits to this law. It doesn't apply with certain external variables such as high loads. If an athlete dropped fast with a 100 percent max squat, it would be impossible for them to absorb all that force eccentrically. As a result, their GTO reflex would outweigh the stretch reflex. The muscle would relax to prevent serious structural damage, and the athlete will be crawling out from under the bar. This is irrelevant anyway because an athlete doesn't have the time to produce 100 percent of his maximal force potential within the time constraints of dynamic movement. Remember, these laws and the examples I have referenced only apply when an athlete is performing a dynamic action with maximal intent. Submaximal effort during any of the three phases will result in altered force production patterns.

Now that you have an understanding of "why" it is important to train the eccentric phase of dynamic muscle action, let's get to the "how." The next part of this section will show that you can maximize the power of the stretch reflex, reduce the inhibition of the GTO reflex, and turn your athletes into SSC powerhouses.

HOW TO APPLY ECCENTRIC MEANS

The most effective means in applying stress to the athlete to improve the eccentric qualities outlined above is to have them perform large, compound movements with an accentuated (slow) eccentric phase. The extended time under eccentric tension allows both the muscle spindle and GTO to adapt and "feel" higher levels of stress than would be present during normal, dynamic lifting. This stress response will potentiate the muscle spindle and inhibit the GTO, leading to an improved SSC and increased force production.

As a coach, you must remember that eccentric specific work is extremely taxing on an athlete's nervous system. Studies have found that eccentric training recruits fewer total motor units compared to concentric training.[16] This, in turn, increases the amount of stress placed on each of the recruited motor units, which can lead to fatigue. In addition, some research has shown that eccentric training seems to preferentially recruit Type II, high threshold/fast twitch motor units, motor units that are imperative in the development of anaerobic power.[17] Due to the volatility of these means, a coach must understand their capabilities and know when to use them to maximize adaptation.

Because eccentric training places large amounts of stress on the athlete, eccentric specific work should only be performed with large, compound exercises at the beginning of a workout. As an athlete progresses, becomes more advanced, and adapts to higher levels of stress, eccentric means can be introduced throughout the workout. The remainder of the workout should consist of exercises that work the specific parameter being trained within the athlete's current block with loads that fit within the undulation for that day.

For example, an athlete who is on a strength block with an undulated load goal of 80 percent will perform heavy, slow eccentric back squats at the onset of the workout with a load that equals 80 percent of his 1RM (for sets and reps, see table). Once complete, the athlete will proceed through the rest of the workout using exercises with loads of 80 percent (in keeping with the undulated model). These exercises are to be performed with a dynamic focus, moving the load as fast as possible.

---

[16] Owings T, Grabiner M (2002) Motor control of the vastus medialis oblique and vastus lateralis muscles is disrupted during eccentric contractions in subjects with patellofemoral pain. *The American Journal of Sports Medicine* 30(4).

[17] Howell et al. (1995).

Table 3.2 shows the rep ranges and sets that constitute the eccentric loading variables. In addition, the loading variables are allocated by color, showing the parameters for each mesocycle:

LOAD	TOTAL TIME OF ECCENTRIC (SECONDS)	REP RANGE	SETS	MESOCYCLE
TABLE 3.2: ECCENTRIC LOADING PARAMETERS AND THEIR RESPECTIVE MESOCYCLE				
85%	5-6 (ASSISTED)	1-2	1-2	ABOVE 80%
80%	5-6 (ASSISTED)	2-3	2-3	
75%	6-8	3-4	3-4	80-55%
70%	6-8	4-5	4-5	
65%	6-8	5-6	5-6	
60%	6-8	5-6	5-6	
55% AND BELOW	ECCENTRICS NOT IMPLEMENTED WITH THESE LOADS			BELOW 55%

To maximize the eccentric adaptation and ensure the safety of the athlete, there are a couple rules I follow. Based on what I've seen over the past twenty years, following these rules yield the best results for my athletes when performing eccentric focused work:

1. Due to the intense stress placed on the athlete by eccentric training, its application should be limited to large, compound exercises.

When an athlete is first exposed to eccentric training, their physiological system will likely only be able to handle one compound exercise per workout (as always, certain "genetically gifted athletes" are the exception to this rule). This exercise should be placed early in the workout while the nervous system is fresh, allowing for maximal focus on the parameter being trained. As athletes progress, that is to say as their training age increases (two to four years of experience), a coach is able to introduce additional eccentric training throughout the workout. This is possible because the athlete has adapted and is able to handle higher levels of stress without excessive fatigue. For example, a more advanced athlete can start a workout with heavy eccentric back squats and then add <u>eccentric Romanian deadlifts</u> and <u>single leg eccentric dumbbell squat</u>.

2. Never perform slow eccentrics with loads greater than 85 percent of an athlete's 1RM.

This rule is based on my own risk/reward analysis. To me, the risk is far too great to have an athlete with a weight close to, at, or above his 1RM load his body for an extended period of time. I've seen torn pecs and quads, blown backs, and screwed up shoulders. At the end of the day, you can get the same physiological adaptation using lighter loads for longer times with half the risk.

3. Always spot the athlete when performing slow eccentrics.

This is a widely practiced rule when an athlete is trying to lift heavy loads, but some coaches may not see the need when using lighter, submaximal loads. You must remember that when performing eccentrically focused training, you're maximally taxing the eccentric minded nervous system and the physiological structures it supports, even with submaximal loads. As you can see in Table 3.2, as the load decreases, the time of the eccentric increases. The resulting increase in time under tension means an athlete's muscular system could give out at any point during the lift, so proper spotting is crucial.

4. Always finish an eccentric focused lift with an explosive, concentric movement.

As a coach, the most important aspect of performance that you're constantly trying to improve within the athlete is his nervous system. Every jump, cut, and throw an athlete makes begins with an eccentric lengthening of the muscle and ends with an explosive concentric contraction. The neurological pathways that signal these contractions are entirely different and independent of one another. Each time the athlete's nervous system transitions from the eccentric to the concentric phase, it has to change its firing pattern to initiate the next part of the movement. The signal has to jump switchboards, if you will. It is imperative to an athlete's success that this process is as fluid and seamless as possible. The bar will not necessarily move fast, especially using heavy eccentric loads, but the intent to accelerate the bar, changing over from an eccentric to a concentric signaling pattern, must be trained every time an athlete performs a repetition.

In sections four, five, and six of this book, I'll show you how to take these eccentric means and rules of application to build programs for your athletes that effectively maximize the kinetic energy absorption capabilities of their stretch reflex while optimizing the explosiveness of their SSC. For now, simply understand which types of exercises should be used as well as the loads and repetition ranges associated with each. Table 3.3 outlines some, but not all, possible eccentric focused exercises.

TABLE 3.3: EXAMPLE EXERCISES WITH ECCENTRIC MEANS	
EXERCISE	**COACHING POINTS**
BACK SQUAT - ECCENTRIC	1. Set up with the bar on the back of the shoulders. 2. Keeping the chest up and the back flat, sit back as if to a chair. 3. Descend into the bottom of the squat in the prescribed time. 4. Once the time has been reached, explosively fire up back to the start.
FRONT SQUAT - ECCENTRIC	1. Set up with the bar on the front of the shoulders. 2. Keeping the chest and elbows up and the back flat, sit back as if to a chair. 3. Descend into the bottom of the squat in the prescribed time. 4. Once the time has been reached, explosively fire up back to the start.
RDL - ECCENTRIC	1. Grab the bar just outside of the thighs with the feet shoulder width apart. 2. Keeping the back flat and the chest up, bend the knees slightly. 3. Allow the bar to slide down the thighs for the prescribed time. 4. Once the time has been reached, explosively fire up back to the start.
BENCH PRESS - ECCENTRIC	1. While laying on your back, grab the bar one thumb length away from the knurling. 2. Unrack the bar, keep the shoulders pulled back, and pull the bar into the chest. 3. Lower the bar in the prescribed time until it touches the chest. 4. Once the time has been reached, explosively fire up back to the start.
DB SHOULDER PRESS - ECCENTRIC	1. Begin standing with a dumbbell in each hand, palms facing each other. 2. Press the dumbbells up explosively to begin the exercise. 3. Lower the dumbbells back to the shoulders in the prescribed time. 4. Once the time has been reached, explosively fire up back to the start.
CAMBERED BAR SQUAT - ECCENTRIC	1. Using a cambered bar, set up just as you would for the back squat. 2. Keeping the chest up and the back flat, sit back as if to a chair. 3. Descend into the bottom of the squat in the prescribed time. 4. Once the time has been reached, explosively fire up back to the start.
CLOSE GRIP BENCH - ECCENTRIC	1. While laying on your back, grab the bar with the pointer on the edge of the knurling. 2. Unrack the bar, keep the shoulders pulled back, and pull the bar into the chest. 3. Lower the bar in the prescribed time until it touches the chest. 4. Once the time has been reached, explosively fire up back to the start.

3.3: ISOMETRIC PHASE

Understanding the eccentric phase is only one-third of the battle. Knowing how an athlete can increase power output through improved eccentric muscle action is useless unless that athlete has a way to harness that power to use concentrically. The isometric phase poses a unique challenge in that it is both the hardest of the three phases to explain and the most important to understand. It is difficult to describe due to its duration; it is practically instantaneous with a nearly indistinguishable beginning and end. Yet, it is imperative to understand its impact on force development.

Essentially, the isometric phase is the energy transfer station of all muscular actions, turning absorbed eccentric energy into explosive, concentric actions. Once again, I had to answer two questions—why is the isometric phase so important as it relates to dynamic athletic movement and how do I train my athletes to improve it? First, let's answer the "why" question.

The term itself, isometric, is a combination of the Greek roots "iso," which means "same," and "metric," which means distance—same distance. An isometric action can be defined as one in which the proximal and distal attachments of a muscle don't move in relation to each other; muscle length remains constant. It occurs when the force being exerted by a muscle equals the force being imposed on it by a load. Now, part of that definition—muscle length remains constant—isn't entirely accurate. It would be more precise to define an isometric action by saying that it's the joint angle, not the muscle, that remains constant. During an isometric phase of dynamic movement, a muscle moves quite a bit, albeit very minutely. Remember, we are talking about an isometric *contraction*. I often find people getting confused during this phase because they fail to think of an isometric action as a contraction. They envision an isometric action as a hold or a state of non-movement. They probably get that from all those iso-squat holds their high school football coach had them do with a 45-pound plate over their heads as punishment for starting a food fight in the cafeteria. No? Didn't happen to you? Never mind then.

When you begin to think of the isometric phase as a contraction, you realize that it is trainable—just like every other muscle action. Similar to the eccentric phase, the isometric phase has two neurological processes that need to be trained to maximize the force transfer from the eccentric to concentric contractions. When muscles need to increase their level of force production, as in the instance of decelerating and stopping an eccentric contraction, they have two options:

1) **Motor unit recruitment:** Increase the number of muscles fibers that fire.

2) **Rate coding:** Increase the rate at which each of these fibers fire, which increases muscular tension.

I firmly believe that the neural pathways stimulating each of the phases are independent of one another. The neuron pathway in charge of signaling an isometric contraction is different than the one stimulating the eccentric, and that pathway is different from the concentric signaling pathway. At the very least, the signaling frequencies or rates are substantially different enough that the body must learn how to maximize the effectiveness of each phase independent of the others. Training just the eccentric or isometric phase doesn't make a more dynamic, explosive athlete. All three phases must be trained to maximize their unified effect. A study by Gordon and colleagues (1998) found that there isn't any significant enhancement of maximal concentric force when training with only accentuated eccentric resistance.[18] That piece of information is vastly important to strength and conditioning coaches, as it shows that each phase of the system must be trained independently of the others to improve the net effect—dynamic force production. By increasing the amount of motor unit recruitment as well as the rate coding of an athlete's isometric phase, we enable that athlete to produce more force in less time.

MOTOR UNIT RECRUITMENT

Motor unit recruitment is dictated by the size principal—a recruitment pattern based on the size of the motor neuron and the number of fibers it innervates. Think of the motor neurons arranged from smallest to largest like you see in Figure 3.11. In addition to being allocated by size, research has conclusively shown that the larger motor neurons innervate primarily Type II or fast

---

[18] Godard M, Wygand J, Carpinelli R, Catalano S, Otto R (1998) Effects of accentuated eccentric resistance training on concentric knee extensor strength. *Journal of Strength and Conditioning Research* 12(1).

twitch muscle fibers. As the force imposed on a muscle increases, additional larger motor neurons are recruited.

MOTOR UNIT(MU) RECRUITMENT

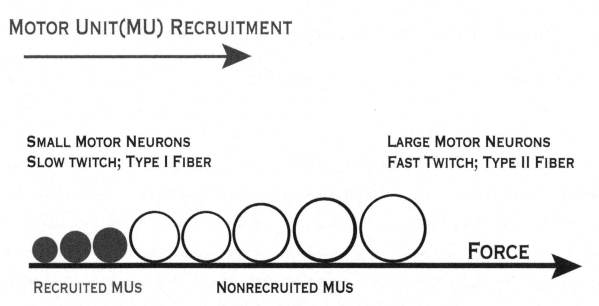

Figure 3.11: Size principle of motor neuron recruitment. The motor neurons are arranged according to their size. The small motor neurons innervate slow twitch fibers while large motor neurons innervate fast twitch fibers. When the muscle force increases, the motor neurons are activated (recruited) according to size from small to large. In this figure, the required force is slow and only small motor neurons are recruited. When the force builds up, the number of active motor units increases and the fast motor units are recruited. Adapted from Brooks, Fahey, & Baldwin (2005).

As an example, think of motor unit recruitment as one of those games you would play at the state fair or Six Flags, the one where you walk up and give a guy five bucks to swing a sledgehammer as hard as you can and hit a base that shoots a small weight up a pole, trying to ding the bell at the top to win a stuffed toy. This game usually has a set of lights that runs up the pole from the base to the bell. When you hit the base, the lights turn on in order from the base up to the highest point that the weight reaches before gravity wins out and it falls back down to earth. The harder you hit the base, the more lights turn on as you produce more force to propel the weight upward.

The same basic thing occurs during the isometric phase of dynamic movement. The more force that is applied eccentrically (the sledgehammer), the higher the resulting level of motor unit recruitment must occur (more lights turn on) to decelerate and stop the load. The only difference between an athlete's nervous system and the lights on the pole is that the athlete must be trained to respond instantly to increased levels of force. By improving the isometric strength of athletes through muscle recruitment, you are enabling them to ping a higher light on the pole, activating larger, higher end, fast twitch motor units. This enables more force to be absorbed into the stretch reflex and SSC, the result of which will be a higher level and rate of force development.

RATE CODING

As a general rule, the firing rate or discharge frequency of a motor neuron can vary widely. Rate coding is the primary responder when a muscle needs to build intramuscular tension quickly to overcome an imposed load. To do this, the nervous system is taught to increase the frequency of signaling discharge of a motor unit's alpha motor neuron. Going back to Physiology 101 for a second, recall that the signal strength of a motor neuron never changes. If the nervous system needs to increase the force of a contraction, it increases the frequency of the signal, causing numerous contractions to happen in quick succession. Each signal is called a twitch. All these smaller twitches or mini-contractions build on one another until the muscle reaches a state of tetanus—the muscle's absolute peak force.

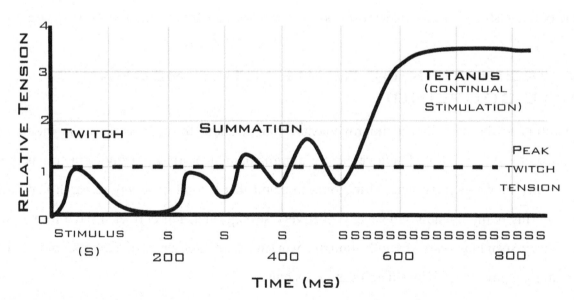

Figure 3.12: Example of rate coding in a muscle. One twitch (or signal) from the nervous system doesn't produce much tension (force). If twitches follow in quick succession, however, as seen in the middle of the figure, tension (force) begins to build. Maximal tension or tetanus occurs when numerous twitches occur in quick succession (far right of figure). Adapted from Brooks, Fahey, & Baldwin (2005).

Looking at Figure 3.12, you can see that one single twitch (the far left of the figure) has little effect on increasing total muscular tension (force). However, if three or more twitches are signaled from the alpha motor neuron, innervating the muscle in quick succession (as shown in the middle of the figure), the tension from the twitches is the sum total of the twitches, raising the total level of tension (force) within the muscle. If dozens of twitches are signaled instantly by a well-trained alpha motor neuron, as seen in the right portion of the graph, the muscle reaches a state of tetanus or maximal force production.

It is important to understand that rate coding is a response variable. By that I mean that the muscle must be taught to respond to a certain situation through training. As it pertains specifically to the isometric phase, an athlete's nervous system must respond to high levels of eccentric force instantly. By increasing the rate coding of its isometric motor neuron pathway, the muscle builds tensions quickly, bringing the load to a halt. Remember, the eccentric action is controlled by a separate neural pathway independent of the isometric action. When an athlete performs an isometric contraction to stop the force imposed by a load, he is in essence flipping a switch to a different power grid. There isn't any time to wait for that system to boot up. It has to come online instantly or the athlete loses potential energy transfer from the eccentric phase.

COORDINATION OF CONTRACTILE MECHANISM (RATE COUPLING)

In addition to the neurological improvements brought about through increases in motor unit recruitment and rate coding, I believe there is a third component trained using isometric methods that further shows its importance. I'm going to admit that I don't have any research that backs this up. This is my opinion. However, I feel very strongly that I'm correct. I have formed this opinion by spending years strength training, working with thousands of athletes, and reading more muscle physiology books than I care to recount.

I think we can agree, especially when it comes down to the processes of the human body, that athletes are only as strong as their weakest link. In affirming that, I believe that the actual physiological process of muscle contraction itself is the third, trainable component of an isometric contraction. This training applies to all three phases of dynamic movement. However, I think it has special importance with the isometric phase, so I will outline it here.

Go perform an isometric squat. Squat down to parallel and hold it from sixty seconds to two minutes. At some point in that time frame, your legs are going to start to shake uncontrollably. That, ladies and gentlemen, is the myosin cross-bridge coupling system becoming more and more inefficient as some part of the contractile mechanism begins to fatigue and fail. You can't tell me that this isn't a trainable muscle quality. Improving this mechanism is essential to the development of a strong, instantaneous isometric contraction, the result of which is increased RFD.

Just a moment ago, I talked about rate coding and the importance that high signaling frequency plays in muscle twitch (contraction) summation. Every time a muscle contracts, it performs hundreds, if not thousands, of smaller, mini-contractions that all add up to one big contraction. Now, I won't turn this into a physiology book. Nonetheless, I think a quick review of the contractile mechanism, specifically as it relates to isometric contraction, is warranted to better understand the big picture: the training of the isometric phase.

You can break every muscle twitch (remember that the sum of which is your total force during a contraction) down into ten individual steps, each with a process essential to muscle contraction.

MUSCLE FIBER TWITCH (CONTRACTION):

1) Muscle contraction initiated by signal from alpha motor neuron

2) Action potential signals release of acetylcholine (Ach), opening sodium ion gates into cell membrane

3) Acetylcholine (Ach) binds to receptors on motor end plates, releasing sodium ($Na+$), which enters the cell, depolarizing muscle fiber

4) Depolarization travels down the T-tubules of the muscle fiber, releasing stored calcium ions ($Ca2+$) into the sarcoplasm from the sarcoplasmic reticulum

5) $Ca2+$ binds with troponin along the actin (thin) filament, moving the attached tropomyosin band and exposing active binding sites

6) Myosin globular heads from the myosin (thick) filament bind to the exposed active sites on the actin filament.

7) The myosin head tilts, locking the actin filament in place and shortening (or preventing further lengthening) of the muscle

8) Myosin head detaches from actin filament when adenosine triphosphate (ATP) binds to the globular head

9) ATP is split by ATPase into adenosine diphosphate (ADP) and phosphate (P), releasing energy

10) Energy release recocks the globular head of the myosin filament, priming it for another contraction

Each of those ten steps takes place every single time an alpha motor neuron shoots a signal down its axon to thousands of myosin cross-bridge sites—every single time! If that doesn't already seem like a lot to do for one muscle twitch, understand that all ten steps must take place in less than one hundredth of a second or 0.01 seconds during the isometric phase of dynamic movement. That is ridiculous, and yet your body does it on a daily basis over and over again. The timing and efficiency that must take place is unfathomable. Of course, if you had more time, the above example would be much easier. But sport isn't about "more time," remember? Sport is about who can produce more force in *less* time.

Understand that when I talk about an isometric contraction, I am referring to it in terms of dynamic movements. Actual maximal isometric force takes 0.3 to 0.7 seconds to accumulate in a muscle, depending on which study you look at. This level of maximal force is irrelevant to the athlete. The only thing that matters is the amount of isometric force that can be produced between the eccentric and concentric phases of maximal dynamic movement.

Based on this understand of a muscle contraction, some questions that need to be asked are, what happens if the rate of muscle twitches can't keep up with the signaling frequency? What happens if one of the ten steps in a muscle contraction lags behind the rest? Where is the weak link? What is the limiting factor? It is imperative that every step of a muscular contraction operates as a well-oiled machine, occurring exactly on cue so that it doesn't impede the next step. This is important for all muscular contractions—eccentric, isometric, and concentric—but it is especially imperative for the isometric phase.

During the isometric contraction of a maximal dynamic movement, high rates of intramuscular tension must be attained instantly. The myosin heads in the contractile mechanism have less than 0.01 second to attach to the actin filament, stopping the eccentric lengthening of the muscle. A mechanism that is trained to grab and stop 5000 N is capable of transferring more energy to the subsequent concentric contraction than a mechanism that can only stop 1000 N. Athletes are only as strong as their weakest link. Having an underperforming isometric contraction results in less force available for absorption and a subsequent decrease in force output.

Take a basketball player for example. The player has 0.01 seconds to produce an isometric force great enough to completely stop the energy of the eccentric contraction, loading his quadriceps before reaccelerating concentrically and jumping for a rebound. The athlete who can jump higher and quicker will get the ball. For the sake of this example, let's assume that the athlete has 1000 myosin cross-bridge sites that can attach during an isometric contraction. This best case scenario assumes three things:

1) The athlete recruits the largest, most explosive motor units (*motor unit recruitment).*

2) The athlete's nervous system is efficient enough to signal each of those motor neurons, innervating the entire quadriceps (*rate coding).*

3) The athlete's contractile process is trained well enough to perform all 10,000 steps (ten steps per twitch times 1000 myosin cross-bridges) in 0.01 seconds, maximizing the total force potential *(rate coupling).*

If any of the above three components of isometric strength are undertrained or lagging behind the others, the athlete won't be able to perform at an optimum level. Some research has shown that muscles look to increase force through the improved recruitment of more motor units.[19] Other

---

[19] Deschenes M (1998) Short review: rate coding motor unit recruitment patterns. *Journal of Strength and Conditioning Research* 3(2):34–39.

studies have found that the main mechanism in isometric force production is rate coding.[20] My point is that failure to train any of these components will result in the diminished rate of force production for the athlete.

It is imperative that the athlete can forcibly bring the eccentric load to a halt instantly. Research has shown that improved neuromuscular action, through improved recruitment, coding, and coupling by means of isometric training, leads to improved RFD.[21] The athlete who can stop the eccentric stretch of a muscle the quickest is going to benefit with an improved stretch reflex as well as have more energy absorbed into the musculoskeletal structure to be used in the SSC. To maximize this conduit of energy transfer, an athlete needs a fast developing, transitioning, isometric contraction. Any delay between eccentric and concentric phases will result in lost energy from the SSC, as this energy store begins to dissipate as heat the instant it is absorbed.

When you look at Figure 3.13, this becomes very apparent. At some point on the graph, both lines have a transition point—a point where the line changes from a negative, eccentric slope to a positive, concentric one. That point, that exact instant, is where the isometric contraction takes place. As I said before, the difficulty in understanding the isometric phase is that you can't really see it. You have a good idea of "about" where it is, but it is impossible to pinpoint. It is not like the eccentric phase where there is an entire line you can see and follow. Yet this single point is hugely important, as it acts as the springboard that launches the force from the stretch reflex, the SSC, into the concentric contraction. The harder the stop, the better the total force recoil from the stretch reflex and SSC and therefore a more explosive dynamic action. If you were to bounce a basketball, would it bounce higher off concrete or sand? The concrete is solid, allowing nearly full transfer of the kinetic energy of downward motion of the basketball to be transferred back into an upward movement. The sand on the other hand acts as a decelerator, dispersing the eccentric energy into the granules and limiting the kinetic recoil.

---

[20] Behm D (1995) Neuromuscular implications and applications to resistance training. *Journal of Strength and Conditioning Research* 9(4):264–74.

[21] Burgess K, Connick M, Grahm-Smith P, Pearson S (2007) Plyometric vs. isometric training influences on tendon properties and muscle output. Neuromuscular implications and applications to resistance training. *Journal of Strength and Conditioning Research* 21(3):986–89.

TRI-PHASIC TRAINING

—— DEVELOPED ATHLETE   ········· UNDEVELOPED ATHLETE

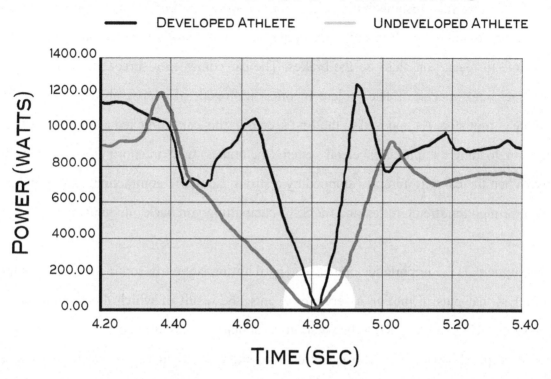

Figure 3.13: Example highlighting different isometric contractions and their resulting concentric rate of force development (RFD). In looking at the white section of the graph, notice the developed athlete (black line) has a much better defined point at the bottom of the "V." This point is his isometric contraction. Compare that to the much wider, almost rounded point for the isometric contraction of the underdeveloped athlete (gray line). The narrower the angle of the "V," the steeper the successive concentric contraction (increased RFD).

To better understand the importance of a strong, immediate isometric contraction and the role it plays in force production, I want you to think of it in terms of hitting the brakes in your car. In the first scenario, you're out driving and you can see the stoplight up ahead of you turn red. You take your foot off the gas and start to apply slow, even pressure to the brake, bringing the car to a nice, slow stop over a distance of let's say two hundred feet (I'm assuming that you're a responsible driver). You barely feel any recoil at all when the car ceases all forward motion and stops. This is because there was little to no energy built up in the brakes of the car. Think of braking over the two hundred feet as a long, slow, eccentric contraction. Little to no energy is built up in either the stretch reflex or the SSC. When the car finally stops, performing an isometric contraction, there is only a small amount of energy for it to recoil in the opposite direction (according to Newton's Laws). As a result, you, the driver, barely feel the car rock back.

Now, in a second scenario, let's say you are on a country road driving up the cabin for the weekend. You are still a responsible driver, going the speed limit of 55 mph when all of a sudden Bambi's crazy twin brother, Bernard, jumps out on to the road only fifty feet in front you. Barely having time to react, you slam on the brakes. The car comes to a screeching halt and you get thrown back into your seat. The violent recoil is the result of energy absorbed by the brakes during the abrupt stop. As opposed to the first scenario, this car mimicked a strong, fast eccentric contraction, loading the musculoskeletal system (the brakes) with an enormous amount of kinetic energy. When the car was abruptly stopped by a strong isometric contraction, all the energy was expelled through the stretch reflex and the SSC, catapulting you back into your seat.

That, right there, is the importance of a strong, hard hitting isometric contraction. It plays the role of a catalyst that puts in motion a series of events, the result of which dictates the difference between high RFD and low RFD, between great athlete and good athlete. Looking back at the isometric graph (Figure 3.13), you can see the relation between the eccentric and concentric lines. This relation exists due to the strength and efficiency of the isometric phase. If an athlete has poor isometric strength, it forces a slower rate of energy absorption. It is impossible for an underdeveloped athlete to absorb energy, eccentrically, at the same rate as a well developed one. The underdeveloped athlete's isometric components aren't efficient enough to transfer that much power to the concentric phase; it overloads the circuit. As a result, the underdeveloped athlete must absorb energy at a slower rate, resulting in a reduced stretch reflex and less power to transfer through the SSC to concentric movement.

Specific attention to isometric training will result in improved force and power outputs for an athlete. Improving the qualities of the nervous system in this regard allows for high amounts of energy to be absorbed through the efficient sequencing and work of recruitment, coding, and coupling rates—diverting maximal energy from the eccentric directly to the concentric with little to no loss of energy. This enables an athlete to maximize the power of both the stretch reflex as well as the SSC. Add these to a strong, concentric contraction, which we will learn about in the next section, and it gives the athlete the appearance that he is jumping off a trampoline instead of a sand pit.

HOW TO APPLY ISOMETRIC MEANS

High load isometrics should be performed at the onset of an athlete's workout. These can be viewed as facilitating a potentiation effect for the remainder of the workout, as the high level of intramuscular tension that takes place during isometric work activates a greater number of high threshold motor units. In essence, it "turns them on" for the rest of the workout.

Isometric contractions aren't as neurally taxing as eccentric focused training. This is mainly due to the reduced time under tension (TUT) of the muscle. As a result, lightened load isometrics can, and should, be used throughout the entire workout to further improve an athlete's force absorption qualities. Understand that when I say "lightened," I mean assistance lifts; exercises that use lighter loads compared to large compound movements. For example, a dumbbell lunge uses lighter relative loads than a back squat. If an athlete is presently performing a strength block at 85 percent, the dumbbell lunge should be performed with a weight that is 85 percent of his 1RM in that exercise. This load, however, would be much lighter, overall, than the athlete's load when performing a isometric back squat. Often implemented with assistance exercises such as lunges or close grip pressing, lightened load isometric work helps to further build the adaptive qualities needed within an athlete's physiological system to absorb ever higher levels of force. There are two possible ways to apply isometric means to training:

1) **Resisted load isometrics** consist of performing a dynamic movement with an isometric pause at its midpoint (between the eccentric and concentric phase) or resisting a load at a specific position and not allowing the joint angle to change. These exercises are performed through their entire range of motion with an eccentric, isometric, and concentric phase. However, the isometric phase is accentuated. Resisted load isometrics are usually performed by large, compound exercises with medium to high loads on the bar.

The position of the isometric or specific joint angle is dictated by the demands of an athlete's sport to ensure transferability. Isometric strength only transfers five to ten degrees from where the parameter is trained. That means if your athlete only squats down to 45 degrees but he makes his cuts or jumps on the field from 65 degrees (a difference of 20 degrees), the isometric parameter he trained so hard to improve won't transfer. He won't be able to absorb high levels of force at that angle. Find what joint angle(s) your athletes explode from in their sport and make sure that they're trained properly in the weight room.

Table 3.4 shows the rep ranges and sets that constitute the resisted isometric loading variables. In addition, the loading variables are allocated by color, showing the parameters for each mesocycle:

TABLE 3.4: RESISTED ISOMETRIC LOADING PARAMETERS AND THEIR RESPECTIVE MESOCYCLE

LOAD	TOTAL TIME OF ISOMETRIC (SECONDS)	REP RANGE	SETS	MESOCYCLE
85%	3–4 (ASSISTED; HELP UP)	1–2	4–5	ABOVE 80%
80%	3–4 (ASSISTED; HELP UP)	2–3	4–5	
75%	4–5	3–4	3–4	
70%	4–5	4–5	3–4	55–80%
65%	4–5	5–6	3–4	
60%	4–5	5–6	3–4	
55% AND BELOW	ISOMETRICS NOT IMPLEMENTED WITH THESE LOADS DURING THIS TRAINING CYCLE			BELOW 55%

2) **Push/pull isometrics,** like the name implies, push or pull against immovable resistance. Similar to resisted load isometrics, the joint angle of the athlete won't move. However, in this case, the athlete starts at the specific joint angle being trained. This isn't a dynamic movement. The only contraction that takes place is an isometric contraction. These exercises are usually

performed in a rack or up against a wall with the bar being pushed or pulled against pins. These aren't differentiated between heavy or lightened load isometrics. They should be performed at the end of a workout because they are the equivalent of doing maximal effort work and are extremely taxing on an athlete's nervous system. If performed at the onset of a training day, it is unlikely that the athlete's nervous system would be able to perform quality work afterward.

Table 3.5 shows the rep ranges and sets that constitute the push/pull isometric loading variables. In addition, the loading variables are allocated by color, showing the parameters for each mesocycle:

LOAD	TOTAL TIME OF ISOMETRIC (SECONDS)	REP RANGE	SETS	MESOCYCLE
85%	5–6	1	3–5	ABOVE 80%
80%	5–6	1	4–5	
75%	6–8	1	3–4	55–80%
70%	6–8	1	3–4	
65%	6–8	1	3–4	
60%	6–8	1	3–4	
55% AND BELOW	ISOMETRICS NOT IMPLEMENTED WITH THESE LOADS DURING THIS TRAINING CYCLE			BELOW 55%

TABLE 3.5: PUSH/PULL ISOMETRIC PARAMETERS AND THEIR RESPECTIVE MESOCYCLE

To maximize the isometric adaptation and ensure the safety of the athlete, there are a couple rules I follow based on what I've seen over the past twenty years that yield the best results for my athletes when performing isometric focused work:

1) Hit the ground like a brick.

The main goal of performing isometric work is to teach the athlete's physiological structure (muscular, connective, and skeletal) to absorb energy instantly. When performing a resisted load isometric, the athlete must perform the eccentric portion quickly, pulling the bar down before trying to instantly stop its momentum. Oftentimes, an athlete will lower the bar quickly during the first eighty-five degrees of the eccentric range of motion (ROM) and then decelerate it slowly over the remaining fifteen degrees before actually reaching the isometric. This drastically reduces the force needed to be absorbed to stop the eccentric motion of the bar while also reducing the training effect of the repetition. They *must* hit the isometric like a brick hitting a pavement floor—no give whatsoever! It can't decelerate over ten to twenty degrees. It must stop within only two, one, or none!

TABLE 3.6: ISOMETRIC COMPARISON		
ISOMETRIC BACK SQUAT	OBSERVATIONS	LINK
INCORRECT FORM (POOR ISOMETRIC ACTION)	1) SLOW ECCENTRIC 2) SLOW DECELERATION OF THE BAR 3) REDUCED ISOMETRIC STRESS	BAD ISOMETRIC
CORRECT FORM (OPTIMAL ISOMETRIC ACTION)	1) FAST MOVING ECCENTRIC 2) INSTANT DECELERATION OF THE BAR 3) HIGH ISOMETRIC STRESS	GOOD ISOMETRIC

2) Squeeze it!

I've found that the best coaching cue is to tell athletes to squeeze their muscles as they hit the isometric contraction. I find that it helps them visualize the physiological action taking place and increases the speed of the firing rate, helping build intramuscular force more quickly. To help new athletes learn and understand this concept, have them get into their isometric position without any load placed on them. For example, if you're teaching the back squat, have the athletes squat down to where they will be performing the isometric contraction during their sets. Once they have squatted down, tell them to squeeze their legs and glutes as hard as they can for several seconds. Once they understand what the isometric contraction should feel like, they can begin their work sets.

3) Always spot the athlete when performing loaded isometric work.

As I pointed out in the previous eccentric section, this is a widely practiced rule when an athlete is trying to lift heavy loads, but some coaches may not see the need when using lighter, submaximal loads. You must remember that when performing isometrically focused training, the athletes are deliberately trying to create as much force as possible to stress the absorption qualities of their system. With every rep, they're pushing the limits of the isometric nervous system and accompanying physiologic structures. It is not uncommon to see athletes hit their isometric contraction like a brick and then be unable to lift the load concentrically without the assistance of a spotter. When pushing the limits of the human body, diligent spotting is always essential.

4) Always finish an isometric focused lift with an explosive, concentric movement.

Every movement an athlete makes in competition is triphasic—eccentric, isometric, and concentric. The neurological pathways that signal these contractions are entirely different and independent of one another. Each time the athlete's nervous system transitions from the isometric to the concentric phase, it has to change its firing pattern to initiate the next part of the movement. The signal has to jump switchboards if you will. It is imperative to an athlete's success that this process is as fluid and seamless as possible. If there is any lag time between these signals, energy absorbed during the eccentric phase will be lost as heat to the environment, decreasing the contribution of the stretch reflex and SSC to power development. The intent to accelerate the bar, building intramuscular force quickly and recruiting intermuscular recruitment neurally, must be trained every time an athlete performs a repetition.

TABLE 3.7: EXAMPLE EXERCISES WITH HIGH LOAD RESISTED ISOMETRIC MEANS
(MAIN COMPOUND, PERFORM AT ONSET OF WORKOUT)

EXERCISE	COACHING POINTS
BACK SQUAT - ISOMETRIC	1. Set up with the bar on the back of the shoulders, keeping the chest up and the back flat. 2. Sit back and descend into the bottom of the squat rapidly. 3. Once in the bottom, become a statue and pause for the prescribed time. 4. Once the time has been reached, explosively fire up back to the start.
FRONT SQUAT - ISOMETRIC	1. Set up with the bar on the front of the shoulders, keeping the chest up and the back flat. 2. Sit back and descend into the bottom of the squat rapidly. 3. Once in the bottom, become a statue and pause for the prescribed time. 4. Once the time has been reached, explosively fire up back to the start.
RDL - ISOMETRIC	1. Grab the bar just outside of the thighs with the feet shoulder width apart. 2. Keeping the back flat and the chest up, lower the bar rapidly along the thighs. 3. Once the bar passes the knees, become a statue and pause for the prescribed time. 4. Once the time has been reached, explosively fire up back to the start.
BENCH PRESS - ISOMETRIC	1. While laying on your back, grab the bar one thumb length away from the knurling. 2. Unrack the bar and pull it rapidly toward the chest. 3. Right before the bar hits the chest, stop it completely and pause. 4. Once the time has been reached, explosively fire up back to the start.

TABLE 3.8: EXAMPLE EXERCISES WITH LIGHTENED LOAD RESISTED ISOMETRIC MEANS
(ASSISTANCE, PERFORMED THROUGHOUT WORKOUT)

EXERCISE	COACHING POINTS
DB WALKING LUNGE- ISOMETRIC	1. Holding a pair of dumbbells, take a moderate step forward. 2. Keeping the chest up and the back flat, descend into the bottom of the lunge. 3. Lower yourself until the back knee is just above the ground and pause. 4. Once the time has been reached, explosively fire through and step forward.
INCLINE DB BENCH	1. Holding a dumbbell in each hand, set up on an inclined bench. 2. Beginning the dumbbells near the shoulders, pause for the prescribed time. 3. Be sure to keep the chest up, the lower back arched, and the eyes toward the ceiling. 4. Once the time has been reached, explosively fire up and back to the start.
DB RDL	1. Holding a pair of dumbbells, begin with the arms just along the thighs. 2. Keep the chest up, the back flat, and the knees slightly bent. 3. Lower the dumbbells along the thighs rapidly until just below the knees and pause. 4. Once the time has been reached, explosively fire up and back to the start.
DB ROW - ISOMETRIC	1. Hold one dumbbell in the hand and use the other to stabilize the body on a bench. 2. Keeping the back flat, pull the dumbbell rapidly into the ribs. 3. Allow the dumbbell to return slightly toward the ground and pause. 4. Once the time has been reached, explosively fire up and back to the start.
BENCH PRESS REACTIVE DROP PAUSE TOSS	1. While laying on your back, grab the bar one thumb length away from the knurling. 2. With a spotter, rapidly drop the bar until it is just about to hit the chest. 3. Pause with the bar right above the chest. 4. Once the time has been reached, explosively throw the bar as high as possible.

TABLE 3.9: EXAMPLE EXERCISES WITH PUSH/PULL ISOMETRIC MEANS	
EXERCISE	COACHING POINTS
ISOMETRIC CHEST HOLD	1. Set up on the three boxes, placing the hands on the edge of the first two. 2. Keeping the abs and back tight, pull into position and pause. 3. While in the bottom, keep the body perfectly still. 4. Once the time has been reached, explosively press yourself up.
BENCH PRESS RACK - ISOMETRIC	1. While laying on your back, grab the bar one thumb length from the knurling. 2. Using a spotter, press the bar into a fixed support in the weakest position. 3. Press as hard as possible for the prescribed time. 4. Once the time has been reached, rack the bar.
HIP FLEXOR ISO PRONE	1. Set up with one foot on a bench and the hands on the ground in the plank position. 2. Keep the foot not on the bench straight. 3. Keep the body in a straight line and be absolutely still. 4. Once the time has been reached, switch legs and repeat.
SINGLE LEG ISO DEADLIFT	1. Set up with a bar under a fixed support and a bench behind. 2. One foot should be elevated to the rear with the other in front of the bar. 3. Grab the bar and pull into the fixed support at the weakest position. 4. Once the time has been reached, switch legs and repeat.
ISOMETRIC BALL GROIN SQUEEZE	1. Using a Swiss ball, place the knees just outside of the edge. 2. In an athletic stance, squeeze the ball using the groin muscles. 3. Squeeze the ball for the prescribed time. 4. Once the time has been reached, rest and repeat for desired sets.
HEX BAR ISO DEADLIFT	1. Set up using a hex bar under a fixed support. 2. Keep the feet shoulder width apart, the back flat, and the chest up. 3. Pull the bar as hard as possible into the fixed support. 4. Once the time has been reached, rest and repeat for desired sets.

3.4: CONCENTRIC PHASE

The concentric portion of the triphasic model is the sexy phase of dynamic muscle action. It's the rock star, the front man that gets all the attention. You never walk into a gym and ask someone, "How much can you eccentrically lower to your chest?" No! Hell no! You walk up and ask, "How much do you bench?" The implication is that you're asking how much weight he can concentrically lift by pushing it off his chest. The concentric portion is the measuring stick used to evaluate all athletic performance. How much can an athlete lift? How far can he jump? How fast can she run? These are all performance measures based on force output measured in the concentric phase. Specifically as it relates to dynamic movement, the concentric phase is the measure of an athlete's rate of force development (RFD).

By definition, the concentric phase is an action in which the proximal and distal attachments of a muscle move toward one another. It refers to a muscle producing enough force to overcome a load, shortening the length of the muscle. This explanation has also lead to the concentric phase being referred to the "overcoming phase" in some literature.

In any dynamic movement, the RFD of the concentric contraction is aided by the combined force of the stretch reflex and SSC. Remember that the amount of potential energy stored within the musculoskeletal structure is dependent on the preceding eccentric and isometric contractions. When we understand how the concentric phase works in conjunction with these phases, we see why the concentric phase is imperative for maximizing explosive strength, RFD, and ultimately, performance. Would Nolan Ryan have been as intimidating without his fastball? Would Muhammad Ali have been as great if he couldn't throw a punch? Would Walter Payton have been as sweet if he couldn't cut? The answer to all these examples is an emphatic "No!" An athlete who can quickly build and absorb energy is nothing if that energy can't be used concentrically to rapidly produce force.

Up to this point, I have singled out individual muscles to explain the neural and physiological mechanisms of dynamic movements, explaining why they are important and how they must be trained. Now, in talking about the concentric phase, we must think in terms of whole neuromuscular systems. The true importance of training the concentric phase is the synchronization of the entire triphasic muscle action—maximizing the energy transfer from the preceding eccentric and isometric phases into a unified, explosive, dynamic movement. For the purpose of simplicity, we are going to package all these mechanisms into one of two categories —intramuscular and intermuscular coordination.

1) Intramuscular coordination (*within the fibers of the same muscle group*)

    I. Motor unit recruitment: The maximum number of motor units are recruited.

    II. Rate coding: The discharge frequency of motor neurons is at the highest possible level.

    III. Rate coupling: The myosin heads attach, pull, and detach.

This list should look very familiar. It is the same list used explaining the importance of developing intramuscular tension during the isometric phase. For all intents and purposes, it is exactly the same, the only difference being that, once again, it is a different neural pathway than that of the eccentric and isometric phases. When I say pathway, I don't mean that it's a completely different set of neurons. This is a hotly debated topic in physiology. However, it appears that the differentiation takes place in the motor cortex of the brain.[22] There, different rate coding and frequency patterns, sent through the same neural pathway to the muscle, appear to innervate the same motor units differently, resulting in the differentiation seen in eccentric, isometric, and concentric contractions. For athletes to generate high levels of concentric force, they must train the specific mechanism that signals a highly efficient concentric contraction, specifically the alpha motor neurons and muscle fibers to fire at high levels.

2) Intermuscular coordination (*between different muscle groups*)

    I. Inhibition/disinhibition

    II. Synchronization

Let's take a moment to describe these components more thoroughly.

---

[22] Kidgell D, Pearce A (2011) What has transcranial magnetic stimulation taught us about neural adaptation to strength training? *Journal of Strength and Conditioning Research* 25(11):3208–17.

INHIBITION/DISINHIBITION

In every muscular action, there is an agonist and an antagonist, an inhibitor and a disinhibitor. For our purposes here, all you have to understand is that while the agonist is concentrically contracting to produce force, the antagonist is eccentrically contracting. The purpose of this eccentric contraction is to try to decelerate the speed and force of the concentric contraction to protect the joint and ensure that the antagonist muscle doesn't tear from rapid stretching. Like most defense mechanisms of the body (e.g., GTO), this one is overprotective and must be detrained. Training the concentric phase to perform explosive dynamic movements improves intermuscular coordination, allowing for the inhibition of the antagonist muscle and resulting in maximal RFD. Put another way, by training the concentric phase, the athlete is also training the inhibition of the antagonist. Looking forward, this concept is what I have come to term "antagonistically facilitated specialized methods of training" (AFSM). Because this falls outside the parameters of the triphasic model, I won't take time here to outline it in depth. However, you can find a full explanation of both the physiology and methods in section five.

SYNCHRONIZATION

Clearly there is more to training the concentric phase than just improving the contractile mechanism and subsequent RFD, although that is a very important part. There isn't any question that the athlete who can generate more explosive force in less time has a decisive advantage. This, however, is only advantageous to an athlete if he can unleash that power in a manner that gives him a performance edge, a step up on his opponent. Nolan Ryan could touch 100 mph on the radar gun consistently, but that isn't what made him a Hall of Fame pitcher. Being able to place that 100 mph fastball wherever the catcher put his glove from sixty feet and six inches away is what made him the most feared pitcher of his era.

As a generalization, the concentric phase of dynamic movements is a much more complicated motor task than the eccentric or isometric phases. As explained above, this is due to the fact that dynamic concentric actions require a significant amount of coordination and synchronization between numerous neuromuscular systems to produce a high level of force output. A dynamic concentric contraction is the culmination of every neuromuscular mechanism we have talked about up to this point:

- Golgi tendon organ reflex
- Stretch reflex
- Stretch shortening cycle (SSC)
- Rate coupling
- Motor unit recruitment
- Rate coding
- Reactive ability

As an example, compare the <u>hang clean</u> to a <u>Romainian deadlift and shrug</u>. A novice athlete can quickly learn and perform a proper Romanian deadlift and shrug. For the most part, it is a slow, controlled movement that allows more time for the athlete's neuromuscular system to interpret, process, and execute instructions from his entire neuromusculature of the posterior chain (calves, hamstrings, glutes, and back). On the other hand, teaching the hang clean, though a very similar movement pattern to that of an Romanian deadlift and shrug, can be a long, arduous process. Decreasing the weight and increasing the speed of the exercise, the athlete's neuromuscular system gets overloaded.

The take home point from this example is that just like the eccentric and isometric phases of dynamic movement, the concentric phase is a learned, trainable skill. Not every concentric dynamic action is as hard to learn as the hang clean. I can teach an athlete to concentrically perform a back squat in a few minutes. It's intuitive—once he squats down I simply tell him to stand up. It is a neuromuscular action that he has likely performed hundreds, if not thousands, of times in his life. Every time he has sat down and stood up, he has performed at least a partial rep. But to teach that athlete to fire all his hip extensors, drive his feet through the floor, and activate his high threshold motor units through afferent neural pathways that are likely underdeveloped all while trying to move the bar like it was just shot out of a cannon—that takes time and lots of training.

During the concentric phase, the actual concentric contraction takes place sandwiched between the stretch reflex and SSC. For maximal explosive strength in dynamic movements, all three components must fire in rapid succession—stretch reflex, then concentric contraction, and then SSC. This sequence has been termed *reactive ability,* or the ability to rapidly generate explosive force resulting from a preliminary dynamic stretch followed instantly by a subsequent concentric contraction. An athlete's reactive ability (which is, in essence, their RFD) is determined by the efficiency and speed with which the concentric contraction follows the preliminary force output from the stretch reflex and, in turn, determines the amount of stored kinetic energy used from the SSC to improve overall force output.

Try to think of reactive ability in terms of an athlete performing a back squat with 85 percent of his 1RM. The athlete eccentrically squats the load, dropping quickly to maximize the absorbed potential energy in the muscles and connective tissue, and stopping the load with a strong, instant isometric contraction. This strong isometric acts like a concrete floor, giving the resulting stretch reflex something hard to push off of, signaling the start of the concentric phase by reaccelerating the load in a vertical direction. From this point, there are two scenarios that can play out in the subsequent concentric phase—a well-trained athlete can accelerate the load with a high RFD through the entire range of motion, maximizing energy transfer, or a poorly trained athlete will lose RFD due to lost energy from an uncoordinated concentric mechanism. Let's take a look at what both of these scenarios would look like.

1) Well-trained concentric/high energy transfer/high RFD

In this scenario, the athlete's concentric mechanism quickly builds intramuscular tension greater than that of the load imposed on the muscle structure. The force produced by the concentric contraction is added immediately to the force generated by the stretch reflex, having an additive effect and accelerating the load at a constant high rate. The total force acting on the load is further increased by the energy, now transferred from the connective tissue of the muscle structure through the SSC. Due to the speed with which the stretch reflex and concentric contraction began to move the load, a high percentage of the total stored energy from the SSC is transferred, as little of the energy had time to dissipate from the muscle as heat. For this example, let's say that 95 percent of the SSC energy is transferred. This is represented in Figure 3.14 by the steep sloping, smooth force curve. The first part of the graph shows the isometric tension (force) building within the muscle until it reaches a level of force greater than that being imposed on the muscle, signaling the beginning of the concentric phase as the bar begins to move. The second part of the graph depicts the force produced during the concentric phase, its continued acceleration, and its deceleration as the athlete completes the movement. A well-trained concentric muscle action will show up as a seamless transition between the isometric and concentric point on the graph, keeping a constant slope or rate of acceleration. When you watch this athlete perform the squat, the bar moves fluidly, accelerating through the entire range of motion.

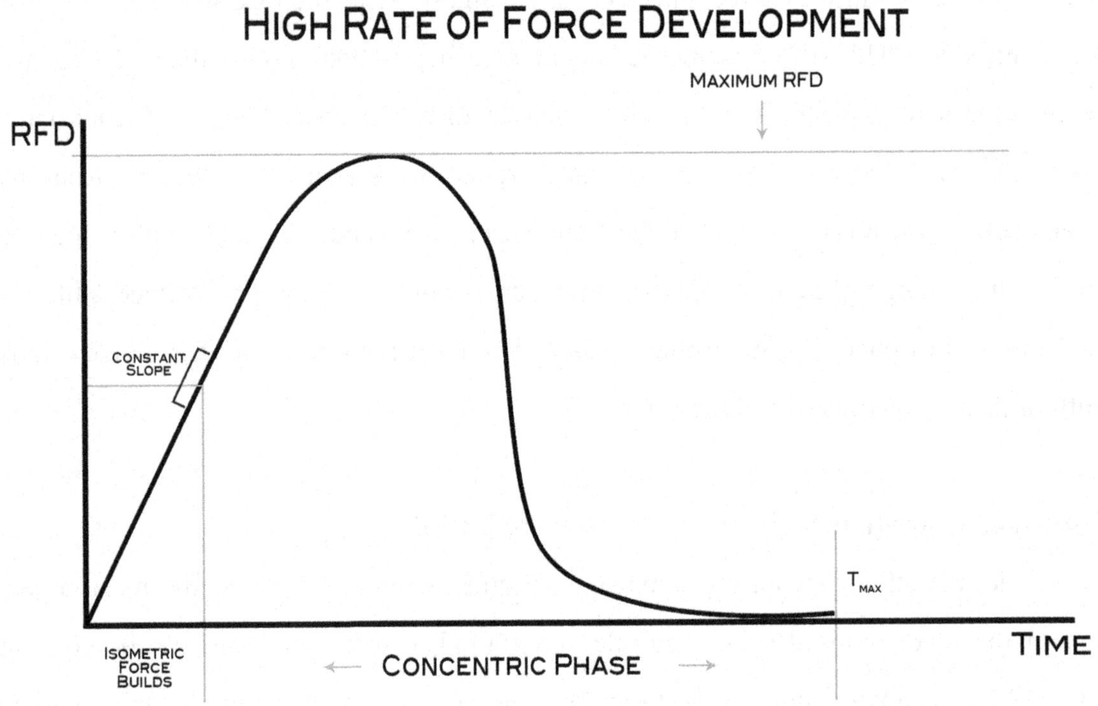

HIGH RATE OF FORCE DEVELOPMENT

Figure 3.14: Graph depicting a fluid transition between the isometric and concentric phases of a dynamic contraction. Adapted from *Supertraining* 6th edition by Y. Verkhoshansky and M. Siff (Ultimate Athlete Concepts, 2009).

2) Poorly trained concentric/low energy transfer/decreased RFD

In this scenario, the athlete's concentric mechanism takes longer to build intramuscular tension to a level greater than that of the load imposed on the muscle structure. Due to this increased lag time, there isn't any additive effect between the stretch reflex and the concentric contraction.

You can see this in Figure 3.15 in the dip in the force production line. This is shown by a change in the slope of the force line at the transition point between the isometric and concentric phases. At this point, the force produced by the stretch reflex has peaked, but the concentric contraction hasn't reached a level of intramuscular force to continue accelerating the load at the same rate. As a result, the rate of the concentric shortening of the muscle slows, effectively negating the contribution of the stretch reflex. This has further negative effects on RFD because the extra time that it takes for the concentric contraction to build sufficient force to move the load allows energy, stored within the connective tissue, to dissipate as heat, resulting in decreased force production from the SSC. In this example, let's say that 60 percent of the SSC energy is transferred. This can be seen in the graph by noticing that the decreased slope of the concentric portion now makes it impossible to reach the same maximum RFD as in the previous graph (Figure 3.14).

When you watch this athlete squat, the bar will slow immediately after coming out of the hole— think of it as a mini-sticking point. The bar will then begin to reaccelerate through the remaining range of motion, never reaching the velocity of the bar squatted by the athlete in the first scenario.

DECREASED RATE OF FORCE DEVELOPMENT

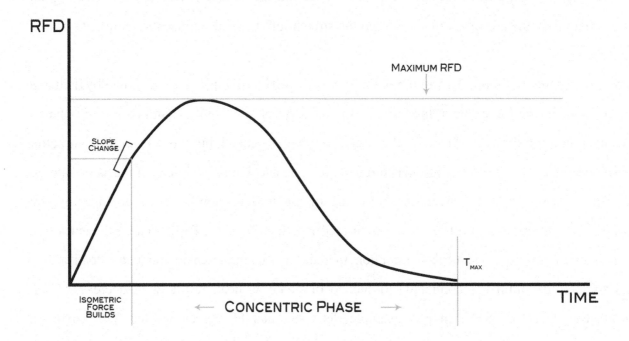

Figure 3.15: Graph depicting a inefficient transition between the isometric and concentric phases of a dynamic contraction. Notice that the slope of the line changes, signaling a decrease in the rate of force developed (RFD) for the remainder of the contraction. This results in lower power output.

A well-trained concentric phase is the organization of chaos into a deliberate, focused application of force. Athletes may be able to absorb great amounts of kinetic energy during the eccentric and isometric phases, but it won't do them any good if they don't have a trained concentric system to release it. In order to reap the benefits of the stretch reflex and the SSC, athletes must train the neurological and physiological systems of the concentric phase to improve the rate of both intramuscular and intermuscular coordination—motor unit recruitment, rate coding, rate coupling, synchronization, inhibition, and disinhibition. In figure 3.16 you will see the RFD lines from figure 3.14 and 3.15 overlaid. Both athletes develop isometric force at the same rate. However, when the isometric phase transfers to the concentric phase, the underdeveloped athlete's RFD drops off considerably (slope of the line decreases). The developed athlete has a better trained concentric muscle action, allowing him to coordinate and use the energy from the stretch reflex and SSC to build force rapidly.

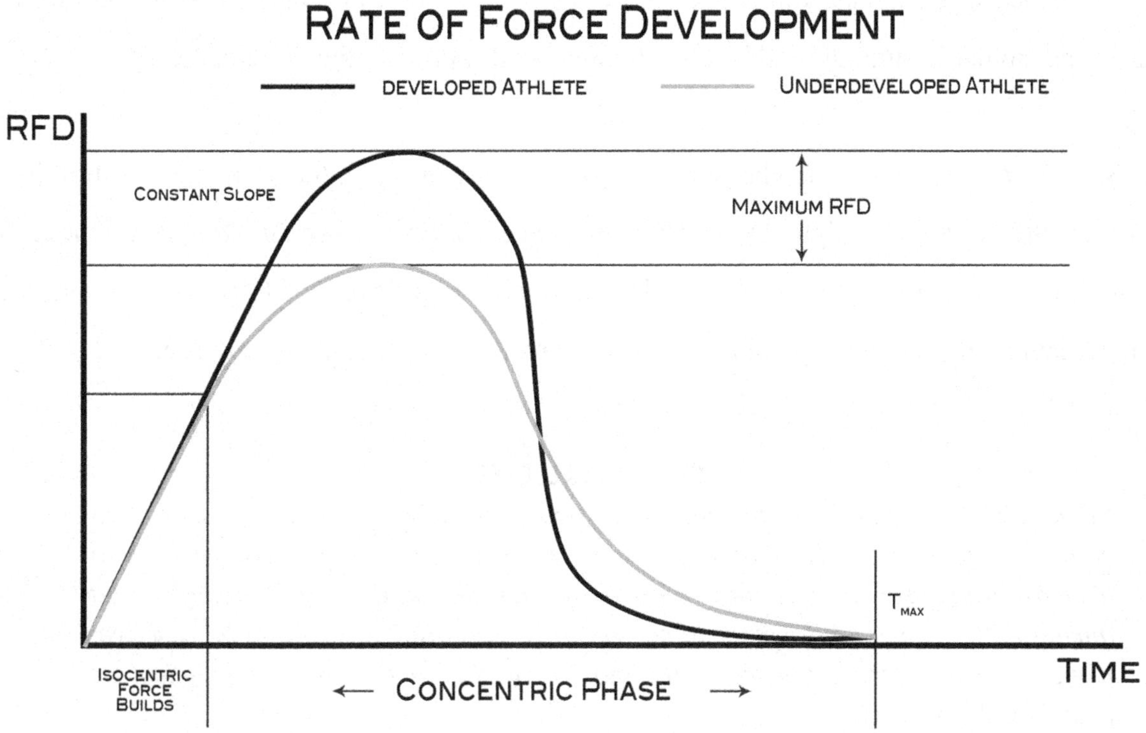

RATE OF FORCE DEVELOPMENT

—— DEVELOPED ATHLETE ⸺⸺ UNDERDEVELOPED ATHLETE

RFD

CONSTANT SLOPE

MAXIMUM RFD

ISOCENTRIC
FORCE
BUILDS

← CONCENTRIC PHASE →

T$_{MAX}$

TIME

Figure 3.16: A side by side comparison showing the resulting disparity in RFD between a developed (fluid transition) and underdeveloped (inefficient transition) athlete.

A coach can't take the concentric phase for granted. While it is always the most coached and most trained aspect of the three triphasic components, it rarely, if ever, is taught and trained in a way that maximizes the use of the kinetic energy absorbed by an athlete. As a result, the concentric phase can often be the most important. Athletes can spend weeks learning how to eccentrically and isometrically absorb energy, but if they fail to teach their body how to unleash that power, it is all for nothing.

HOW TO APPLY CONCENTRIC MEANS

This is fairly straightforward and simple—train fast!! The goal of concentric training is to maximize intermuscular coordination, increase motor unit recruitment, and maximize force production. This is where every rep should start to resemble a red rubber ball slamming off a concrete floor. Concentric means will look very familiar to most strength coaches because they are the predominant form of stress used in training. I should say, however, that it will only look similar on paper, as an athlete training concentrically after first building a solid foundation of eccentric and isometric strength will be able to move loads at much higher velocities.

Table 3.10 is a breakdown of the loading parameters for an athletic model of training. Remember, athletes aren't bodybuilders. The percentages and reps correlate to ensure that each rep is high quality, neurological work aimed at producing high levels of force. In addition, the loading variables are allocated by color, showing the parameters for each mesocycle:

TERMINOLOGY

"Reactive" is defined as the ability to switch instantly from the eccentric to concentric phase of a dynamic movement. The goal of a reactive movement is to lose as little force as possible from the stretch shortening cycle accumulated during the eccentric and isometric phases. When an athlete is told to be reactive, it means that all three phases of the movement should be completed as fast as possible. Be explosive.

TABLE 3.10: CONCENTRIC LOADING PARAMETERS AND THEIR RESPECTIVE MESOCYCLE				
LOAD	TOTAL TIME OF CONCENTRIC	REP RANGE	SETS	MESOCYCLE
97.5%	REACTIVE	1	1-2	ABOVE 80%
95%	REACTIVE	1	2-3	
90%	REACTIVE	1-2	3-4	
85%	REACTIVE	1-2	3-4	
80%	REACTIVE	1-3	4-5	
75%	REACTIVE	1-3	4-5	55-80%
70%	REACTIVE	2-3	4-6	
65%	REACTIVE	3	4-6	
60%	REACTIVE	3	4-6	
55%	REACTIVE	3	4-6	BELOW 55%
50%	REACTIVE	3	4-6	
45%	REACTIVE	3	4-6	
40%	REACTIVE	4	4-6	
35%	REACTIVE	4	4-6	
30%	REACTIVE	4	4-6	

The most important thing to remember when performing dynamic, concentric focused work is to push against the bar as hard as possible, driving the bar all the way through its entire range of motion. Again, the focus should always be on developing a synchronized, powerful concentric contraction.

	TABLE 3.11: EXAMPLE EXERCISES WITH REACTIVE CONCENTRIC MEANS	
EXERCISE	**COACHING POINTS**	
BACK SQUAT - REACTIVE	1. Set up with the bar on the back of the shoulders. 2. Keeping the chest up and the back flat, pull yourself down into the bottom of the squat. 3. Once in the bottom, explosively fire out as fast as possible. 4. Repeat for the desired number of repetitions.	
SINGLE LEG DB FRONT SQUAT - REACTIVE	1. Holding a pair of dumbbells on the shoulders, keep the chest up and the back flat. 2. One leg should be elevated to the rear. 3. Using the front leg, pull rapidly into the bottom of the squat. 4. Once in the bottom, explosively fire out and repeat for the desired repetitions.	
RDL - REACTIVE	1. Grab the bar just outside of the thighs with the feet shoulder width apart. 2. Keeping the chest up and the back flat, lower the bar along the thighs rapidly. 3. Once the bar hits the bottom position, explosively fire up and return to the start. 4. Repeat for the prescribed repetitions.	
BENCH PRESS - REACTIVE	1. While laying on your back, grab the bar one thumb length away from the knurling. 2. Using the upper back, pull the bar rapidly into the chest. 3. Once the bar touches the chest, explosively throw it as hard as possible. 4. Repeat for the prescribed repetitions.	

3.5: SUMMARY AND REVIEW

I often find that strength and conditioning coaches fall into the trap of focusing solely on the concentric phase of dynamic movement. All they are concerned about is the load on the bar and that the load is constantly increasing for each athlete year to year, workout to workout. To some extent, this is understandable because most every performance measure we take of an athlete is concentrically tainted. The deadlift, back squat, and bench press—all are measures of concentric force production at low velocities. At the end of the day, strength coaches have to prove to their employer that their methods are somehow resulting in improved performance of the athletes they work with or they will lose their jobs. It's very simple to show that progression by giving the coach a printout of the athletes' 1RM for the bench press and back squat from the start of the off-season as compared to the end of it. "See, coach, every guy increased his back squat by 30 pounds. I did a great job and your athletes are better." I will admit that they are stronger, but are they "better" athletes? That remains to be seen.

Strength is not what sport is about. Sport is about force production at high velocities and high rates of speed. Sport is about being powerful. Every dynamic movement in sport is a skilled act requiring the coordination of dozens of muscle groups, hundreds of motor neurons, and thousands of muscle fibers. The emphasis placed on concentric loading has limited the potential of many athletes by failing to also address the eccentric and isometric phases.

I am a firm believer that the best way to learn new concepts and ideas is to apply them to real life situations. The material then becomes relatable and real to the learner. To get a better idea of the results you can expect from programming triphasic methods of training into your athletes' workouts, I want to tell you a story about a team of baseball players I worked with back in 2004.

Every fall when the baseball players first get to campus, we put them through testing so that we have baseline numbers to compare to when they're done with winter workouts before the start of the season. One of the tests that I have them run is the pro-agility or pro-shuttle drill. This is a great drill for testing an athlete's lateral power, acceleration, and overall state of their triphasic muscle response. Why? Because the pro-shuttle drill forces an athlete to decelerate (eccentric) at high speeds, stop (isometric), and then reaccelerate (concentric) in the opposite direction. A deficiency in any of the three phases will become instantly apparent both in the time it takes the athlete to complete the drill and in the form exhibited by the athlete during the drill's execution (more on that in a second).

In the drill, the cones are spaced five yards apart. The athlete starts at the center cone (Figure 3.17) facing straight ahead so that one cone is to the athlete's right and the other is to the athlete's left. Once the athlete is set, the clock will start on the athlete's first movement. The athlete will choose which direction he wants to go first and then take off. The athlete will sprint five yards, touch the cone, turn, sprint ten yards back to the furthest cone, touch it, turn, and sprint five yards, finishing at the cone from which he started.

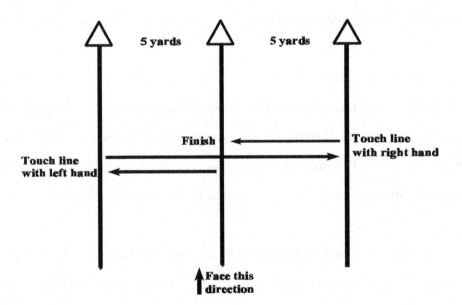

Figure 3.17: Pro-agility drill (20-yard shuttle).

When the baseball team ran the drill that fall...well, let's just say that I was less than impressed. Their times were terrible and their technique was horrendous! As I watched them run through the drill, I realized that they were bending over at the waist to touch each cone instead of sinking their hips at the turns. The key to a good shuttle time is to stay as low as possible and explode with the hips out of each turn. I realized that the guys' hip extensors were so eccentrically and isometrically weak that they couldn't absorb the force going into the turn at full speed. As a result, they had to start decelerating much earlier, using their quads as the eccentric decelerator to decrease the total amount of force they had to isometrically absorb in order to bring themselves to a stop. This forced them to stay high through the entire drill, slowing their times.

From what I saw in testing, I decided to carry out a little experiment with the baseball team. I had yet to implement any of my triphasic methods into their training program, so the group posed a great opportunity for me to test performance improvements resulting from the implementation of triphasic means in training.

To do this, I performed a longitudinal study lasting four weeks and consisting of two groups—standard method (SM) and triphasic method (TM). I randomly split the baseball team into two equal groups. SM worked out in the morning session at 9 a.m. while TM worked out later in the afternoon at 2 p.m. The SM workout program didn't have anything programmed to specifically work eccentric or isometric strength. They performed an off-season program that would look very similar to any done by a Division I baseball program across the country—lots of medicine ball throws, explosive squatting, and proprioceptive work. To try to improve their shuttle times, they also followed a protocol that many baseball strength coaches would employ—they practiced the drill. Every week they ran the drill three times before their normal lift and every time they were coached on form and technique, trying to make them as proficient at the drill as they could possibly be.

Meanwhile, the TM group had triphasic elements added to their normal workouts, specifically drills to emphasize eccentric deceleration and isometric absorption. Using exercises and means that I outlined in the previous section such as slow tempo eccentric squats and single leg isometric deadlifts, I tried to make their hip extensors as strong as possible, eccentrically and isometrically, to be able to absorb force at high velocities going into the turns of the pro-agility drill. In sharp contrast to the SM group, the TM group did not perform any repetitions of the pro-agility drill nor were they coached on technique.

Both groups went through the above protocol for four weeks. At the conclusion, I ran them through the test a second time. Remember:

Standard method (SM): Normal lifting, no eccentric training, practiced drill three times a week

Triphasic method (TM): Eccentric/isometric training, no practice with drill

TABLE 3.12: PRO-SHUTTLE RESULTS			
GROUP	PRE-TEST TIMES	POST-TEST TIMES	DIFFERENCE
STANDARD METHOD	4.8 SEC	4.7 SEC	-0.1
TRIPHASIC METHOD	4.8 SEC	4.4 SEC	-0.3

I don't think I can give you a better example that shows the importance of triphasic training with your athletes. During this experiment, the athletes who trained with the triphasic method improved their time by eight percent compared to a two percent improvement for those who used a traditional training program—a fourfold difference! Instead of focusing on trying to improve dynamic performance through concentric only methods, you need to use a program that physiologically improves the weak links in dynamic human movement. In this case, you need to specifically train the eccentric and isometric portions of the triphasic muscle action. The hyperlinks in table 3.13 show the drastic difference triphasic strength can make in an athletes performance performance.

TABLE 3.13: PRO-SHUTTLE COMPARISON		
INCORRECT FORM (POOR TRIPHASIC ACTION)	1) HIGH HIPS 2) REACHING FOR CONE 3) SLOW TURNS	1. BAD PRO-SHUTTLE 2. BAD PRO-SHUTTLE END VIEW
CORRECT FORM (OPTIMAL TRIPHASIC ACTION)	1) LOW TO THE GROUND 2) HIPS SINK TO CONE 3) EXPLODE OUT OF TURN	1. GOOD PRO-SHUTTLE 2. GOOD PRO-SHUTTLE END VIEW

The question I get asked most often when I talk to people about stress and triphasic training is the "how" question. How do I implement these within my own system? People see the importance of stress. They see the need of applying specific stress to each phase of dynamic movement. They understand the means that can be used to apply it, but they don't have a firm grasp on how to implement it within their own training programs. After reading the first two sections, you, too, should have a good understanding of stress, triphasic training, and the role they play in developing your athletes. Right now, however, these concepts are very fluid. They aren't singularly focused or contained within the confines of an organized system.

In the next section, I will show you how to take these fluid concepts and solidify them by using two different periodization models—a weekly undulating model and a monthly block system. Together, these methods form a framework within which you will be able to manipulate and implement the stress placed on your athletes. So take a deep breath and bear with me. What now seems to be a complicated, insurmountable mountain of information will be by the end of this book a logical and intuitive reference that you will be able to use time and again in helping your athletes reach their athletic potential.

Below are hyperlinks to a video series where I elaborate and explain further the triphasic training principles, methods, and periodization schedule outlined in this section. The videos will serve as a great review, as well as give some additional insights into how to apply triphasic principles with your current programs.

TRIPHASIC TRAINING METHODS: PART I

TRIPHASIC TRAINING METHODS: PART II

TRIPHASIC TRAINING METHODS: PART III

SECTION 4

HIGH FORCE AT LOW VELOCITY
(Above 80 Percent)

4.1: TRAINING ABOVE 80 PERCENT

The first question to address in this section is, "Why use loads above 80 percent of a one rep max for strength? Why not loads above 85 or 90 percent?" In the 1980s, a man by the name of Dr. Fredrick Hatfield (also known by his alias, Dr. Squat) did a study. For those of you wondering about the nickname, the man stood five feet, six inches high, weighed 260 pounds, and had a personal best squat of 1014 pounds (figure 1).[23] No, that isn't a typo. It's supposed to be a four-digit number. He clearly earned the nickname. What his study found was that an athlete's highest power output occurred when using loads equal to 78 percent of his one rep max (1RM).[24] (For those of you familiar with the hyperbolic curve and the force velocity relationship, bear with me. The physiological explanation for this will be explained in the following section where moderate loads of 55–80 percent better explain optimal power outputs in athletes.)

Fred Hatfield Squatting 1014

Image 4.1- Dr. Hatfield

This finding—that power peaks at 78 percent—seemed to hold true regardless of the exercise performed (squat, bench press, shoulder press, barbell curl, etc.). All athletes who Dr. Hatfield worked with attained their highest power levels for a given exercise at 78 percent. He concluded that when an athlete reaches this percentage (78 percent), the neurological system is stimulated at its highest level.

---

[23] Image 4.1: Used with permission from Fred Hatfield (www.Drsquat.com).

[24] Hatfield F (1989) *Power: A scientific approach.* New York: McGraw-Hill Publishing.

Two things happen at this point:

1. The recruitment of the motor units is optimized as a result of high levels of tension within the muscle due to the combined high velocity of movement and heavy loading.

2. Synchronization (inter/intramuscular coordination) of the motor units becomes unified in order to produce an efficient, powerful movement while accelerating the load through its entire range of motion.

Ideally, the most adaptation/stimulation would take place at 78 percent of a 1RM where the optimal power is generated.

In reading Dr. Hatfield's study, I realized that it showed how the nervous system was organized. If the nervous system produced maximum power output at 78 percent, then loads above it would be producing forces at *lower average velocities* and loads below it would be producing forces at *higher average velocities*. Power consists of two variables—force (strength) and velocity (speed). Power is defined as the ability to produce force in a specified period of time. It can be expressed by the equation:

$$\text{POWER} = \text{FORCE} \times \text{VELOCITY}$$

While the power equation doesn't explicitly state time as a variable, it is assumed because time is a factor in both acceleration and velocity. Now, I'm not about to turn this into a physics lecture, but bear with me for the next three sentences.

1) **Force** is measured as the load (mass) of an object multiplied by how fast that load is accelerated.

2) **Acceleration** is the change in the speed of an object divided by the time it takes that change to take place (ΔVelocity/ΔTime, where the symbol "Δ" means change).

3) **Velocity** denotes the speed of an object as it moves over a specified distance, dividing the distance an object travels by the total time it takes to cover that distance (ΔDistance/ΔTime).

When you combine these concepts, you come up with a series of equations that quantify **power** (the amount of force generated in a specified time frame). The equations are written as follows:

$$\text{FORCE} = \text{MASS} \times \text{ACCELERATION}$$

$$\text{VELOCITY} = \Delta\text{DISTANCE} / \Delta\text{TIME}$$

$$\text{POWER} = \text{FORCE} \times \text{VELOCITY}$$

$$\text{POWER} = (\text{MASS} \times \text{ACCELERATION}) \times (\Delta\text{DISTANCE} / \Delta\text{TIME})$$

Please understand that this is a very simple explanation of a very complicated set of variables. If athletes worked out in outer space, it would be much simpler to calculate these measures. Here on earth where you have to account for things like gravity, it gets a little tricky. The only goal of this little physics lesson is to show that the most important component of **p**ower, in relation to sports performance, is **t**ime. This "limitation" on performance must be understood by a trainer or coach in order to produce training programs that garner results. As you have hopefully learned by now, the athlete who wins in sport is the one who can produce more power in less time. The basic principle of power is this—to increase power, one must either increase the load of the object to be moved (force) or increase the velocity (decrease the time) at which that object is moved.

Now that I have rambled about power development for the last two pages, I have to throw you a curve ball and tell you that the goal of this phase of training is *not* power but strength. There is an old saying that goes, "Never put the carriage before the horse." That is, don't get ahead of yourself or you will go nowhere. The same thing applies to power development. Yes, you want the car (athlete) to go fast, but first you have to build the V-10 turbo engine to drop under the hood.

Strength consists of only one variable—force, which is the ability to generate maximum force against an object or load independent of time or velocity. Increasing strength lays a foundation that will eventually lead to increased power in subsequent training phases.

To understand how increased maximal strength leads to increased power development, we must take a closer look at the hyperbolic curve. A hyperbola is a curved line that is open, continuing to infinity without closing in on itself. A hyperbolic curve describes a *parametric relationship*. A parametric relationship is defined as two dependent variables (in this case, force and velocity) that share an inverse relationship. That is as one variable increases, the other decreases. As you can see in this graph (figure 4.1), as force increases, velocity decreases. For example, one throws a shot put more slowly than a baseball.

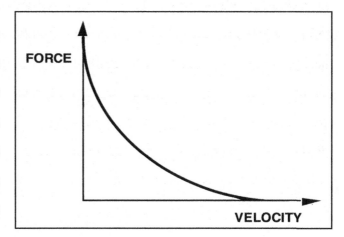

- Figure 4.1

The hyperbolic curve shows four separate values that are important for performance. Through the work of Vladimir Zatsiorsky and William Kramer, these values have come to be known as maximum maximorum force (F*mm*), maximal force (F*m*), maximum maximorum velocity (V*mm*), and maximum velocity (V*m*).[25] F*m* and V*m* are points anywhere along the hyperbolic curve. For example, an athlete who performs a back squat with a load of 60, 70, or 80 percent (F*m*) will have a corresponding velocity value (V*m*) along the hyperbolic line (figure 4.2). I should point out that all F*m* and V*m* values assume that the movement is performed with maximal intent. Performing a bench press with less than maximal effort in any of the three phases of movement (eccentric, isometric, and concentric) will not correspond to the curve. This

25 Zatsiorsky VM, Kraemer WJ (2006) *Science and Practice of Strength Training*. Human Kinetics.

relationship is always parametric. An athlete will not be able to move a load of 85 percent (F*m*) with a greater velocity (faster) than a load of 65 percent (F*m*).

The other two points, *maximum maximorum* force (F*mm)* and *maximum maximorum* velocity (V*mm)*, are considered peaks that correspond to the highest possible force and velocity outputs, respectively, attainable by an athlete. They are represented by the points on the curve that intersect the y-axis (F*mm*) and x-axis (V*mm*) (figure 4.2). These values act as anchor points that define the maximal power outputs associated with any force (F*m*) and velocity (V*m*) value along the hyperbolic line. They are normally viewed as hypothetical, only attainable under specific conditions such as measuring force during a maximal isometric contraction (F*mm*) or the leg speed during a downhill sprint (V*mm*). However, F*mm* is usually associated with an athlete's 1RM, so it is accurate to say that lifting a load of 70 percent of a 1RM is the same as saying the athlete lifted 70 percent of his F*mm*.

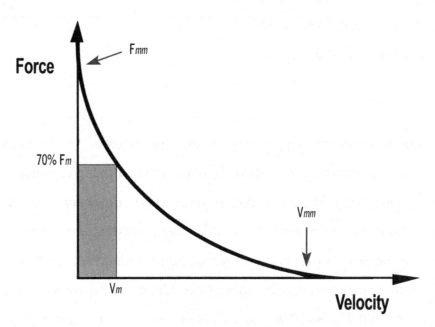

Figure 4.2: (a) The horizontal line extending form the y-axis to the hyperbolic curve shows a force (F*m*) of 70 percent of a 1RM and its associated velocity (V*m*). The shaded area in the box represents the total power developed at that F*m* value. (b) The arrows point to the maximum maximorum values for both force (F*mm*) and velocity (V*mm*).

The most important thing about these two points, F*mm* and V*mm*, is that scientists have found them to have a *nonparametric* relationship when compared to F*m* and V*m*. A nonparametric relationship is the exact opposite of parametric one. As one variable increases, so does the other; their relationship is positive. Unlike F*m* and V*m* whose values are defined by the hyperbolic line, F*mm* and V*mm* can shift, changing the x- and y-intercept and altering the power values attainable at different loads and velocities.

Research has shown time and again that athletes with greater F*mm* have a higher associated V*m*, meaning they can produce more power across the entire hyperbolic curve. Increased strength (F*mm*) causes the hyperbolic curve to shift up and to the right, improving the athletes' ability to handle high forces at increased velocities (figure 4.3). Because the line shows the point of intersection of force and velocity, the area under the line represents the product of the two—total power. Athletes with a higher F*mm* (1RM) back squat have higher vertical jumps than other athletes with the same body mass.[26] One of the best correlates of knowing the throwing distance of a shot putter is to know how much he can bench press.[27] The higher the bench max, the further the throw. Stronger athletes run faster, jump higher, and cut quicker.

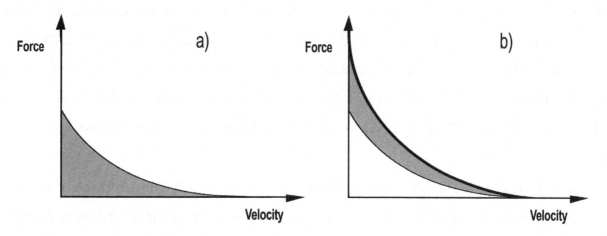

Figure 4.3: (a) Graph represents a typical hyperbolic curve of an athlete. The shaded area underneath the line represents the potential power development at any given point along the line. (b) The light line represents the original hyperbolic curve in the graph (a). The thick, dark line represents the shift associated with strength training, moving the line up and to the right. The shaded area represents increased potential power output along the entire curve.

---

[26] Yamauchi J, Ishii N (2007) "Relations between force velocity characteristics of the knee-hip extension movement and vertical jump performance." *Journal of Strength and Conditioning Research* 21(3).

[27] Patrick TJ, Bellar D, Judge LW, Craig B (2011) "Correlation of height and preseason bench press 1rm to shot put and weight throw performance during the competitive season." *Journal of Strength and Conditioning Research* 25(1).

By increasing the athletes F_{mm} and training them to handle heavy loads and high levels of force, you are training multiple physiological parameters that will pay dividends in subsequent training blocks. The goal of this mesocycle is to increase an athlete's general strength, specifically by training and strengthening the neural and physiological mechanisms of each of the three phases of dynamic movement. I say "general strength" because the means used within the mesocycle aren't aimed at improving specific parameters that will directly transfer to the arena of competition. This phase of training instead focuses on forming a foundation of general strength, high rates of force development, and intermuscular and intramuscular coordination for the athlete. Remembering Dr. Hatfield showed that loads above 78 percent produced forces at lower average velocities, it only makes sense that the focus of loads above 80 percent should be on a performance parameter that doesn't rely on high velocities. The development of general strength and increased F_{mm} will allow for the high transferability of performance parameters in subsequent training blocks as the athlete looks to peak before competition. (This is known as specificity and will be explained in length in section six.)

It should be mentioned that greater F_{mm} only leads to significant increases in power development when the loads used are moderate to heavy—movements and loads associated with sport (things like body weight jumps, squats, presses, throws, sprints, etc.). The correlation between F_{mm} and V_m is much lower if the required F_m is very light (the classic example is playing table tennis or ping pong). In these cases, F_{mm} doesn't increase performance.

Throughout this book, I've talked about the nervous system and the important role it plays in developing athletes. I would adamantly argue that the nervous system is far and away the most important component of athleticism, greater than any other structural or physiological component. In the last section, we looked at the negative effects that mixed training programs have on performance, the result of confusing different neural pathways and signaling rates of the nervous system. Using the block system of training does a great job of limiting that "noise." However, I've found that by using loads that correlate within the specific ranges of Dr. Hatfield's findings (above 80 percent, 55–80 percent, and below 55 percent), further specification enables the nervous system to receive a clear signal and promote greater adaptation within the parameter being trained. I decided to compartmentalize my training mesocycles to simulate the properties exhibited by the nervous system and maximize adaptation in my athletes.

4.2: LOADING PARAMETERS

For the sake of simplicity, all the explanations regarding the application of training means and parameters within my triphasic undulated block system will be explained using a three-day model. At the end of this section, there will be four-day, five-day, six-day, and two-day in-season models. Each is completely built out so that you can take it and immediately implement it with your athletes. The principles and foundations of each program are identical, so understanding a three-day model (Monday, Wednesday, Friday) will teach you all you need to know when reviewing and building similar models of differing training week lengths.

When training with loads above 80 percent, greater emphasis is placed on the force variable (**F**) of the power equation. Using loads at 80–85 percent of one's 1RM, the power output remains high because, as stated previously, the percentages are within Dr. Hatfield's *training zone*. However, as the weights get closer to the 1RM, the speed of the bar starts to decrease. Remember, when training outside the power zone (above 85 percent), the velocity of the movement is compromised. To ensure that the quality of work remains high when using loads above 85 percent, sets should be limited to one repetition (as seen in our loading variables table). This ensures that velocity remains as high as possible for a given load. Performing additional repetitions with these loads drastically compromises power production, as it decreases the velocity of the movement and limits the transferable adaptation of the nervous system. While training with loads above 85 percent is paramount to building strength and ultimately power, these loads must be limited in their application to single repetition sets with the athlete moving the load at the highest velocity possible, exploding through the movement.

When training athletes at intensities of 80–87 percent, the bar velocity typically decreases after the first work set (more specifically after the third repetition of the first work set). Through my own experiences with using the force plate to analyze the force development characteristics of my athletes, I noticed a pattern with their power development. Within these percentages, 80–87 percent, the force plate showed that the power output dropped dramatically after the third repetition in the athlete's first work set. Not only did the power output drop, but it remained low for all of the athlete's subsequent work sets, causing the latter sets to lose velocity and, therefore, power. With this perspective, a coach must look at each individual rep with the intent of keeping the power output of each repetition as high as possible. When the velocity decreases, the quality of work and power decreases, causing the purpose of your training to suffer. When using heavy loads, velocity is the pivotal factor for high power output.

When training for strength and power, your goal must be the highest quality—not quantity—of work possible. Realizing that the power suffers after the third repetition, the only sensible answer is to end the set and save energy for a high quality second set. If athletes perform five repetitions with an 80 percent load, their fourth and fifth repetitions do nothing to effectively train their nervous system. In addition, those last two repetitions push the nervous system to a mild state of fatigue that inhibits it from performing repetitions in subsequent sets with the same power outputs seen in the first three repetitions of the first set.

TABLE 4.1: EXAMPLE QUALITY REPS OVER QUANTITY							
PARAMETERS:	SET 1	SET 2	SET 3	SET 4	SET 5	TOTAL REPS	NUMBER OF QUALITY REPS
3x5 AT 80%	5 REPS	5 REPS	5 REPS			15	4–5
5x3 AT 80%	3 REPS	3 REPS	3 REPS	3 REPS	3 REPS	15	13–14

A sensible suggestion would be to limit work sets at 80 percent to three repetitions. This keeps the power output of the work sets high for the duration of three to five work sets. The alternative is to lose power output after the first work set and never again reach that power level for the duration of that workout. Performing five sets of three repetitions at 80 percent gives the athlete twelve quality high end nervous system stimulating repetitions (table 4.1). Performing three sets of five repetitions gives an athlete three quality repetitions and twelve pointless repetitions. What rep scheme would you use? These concepts can be applied to all percentages. The heavier weights make it easier to notice a difference in the speed of the bar (power output). Table 4.2 shows the loading (sets/reps/percentages) for the high force at high velocity mesocycle:

TABLE 4.2

7 1-RM	MAXIMUM REPS POSSIBLE	MONDAY LOADING (MEDIUM INTENSITY)			WEDNESDAY LOADING (HIGH INTENSITY)			FRIDAY LOADING (HIGH VOLUME)		
		HIGH QUALITY REPS (STRENGTH)	SETS (OFF-SEASON)	SETS (IN-SEASON)	HIGH QUALITY REPS (STRENGTH)	SETS (OFF-SEASON)	SETS (IN-SEASON)	HIGH QUALITY REPS (VOLUME)	SETS (OFF-SEASON)	SETS (IN-SEASON)
97.5%	1 - 2				1	1 - 2	1 - 2			
95 %	2				1	2 - 3	1 - 2			
92.5%	2 - 3				1	3 - 4	1 - 2			
90%	3 - 4				1	3 - 4	2 - 3			
87.50%	4	1	3 - 4	2 - 3						
85%	4 - 5	1 - 2	4 - 5	2 - 3						
82.5%	5	1 - 2	4 - 5	2 - 3						
80%	5 - 6							3 - 4	4 - 5	IN-SEASON VOLUME COMES FROM PRACTICE
77.5%	6 - 7							3 - 4	4 - 5	
75%	7 - 8							4 - 5	4 - 5	

This table displays my three-day loading variables of the above 80 percent undulated mesocycle. The column on the far left displays the percentage load of the athlete's 1RM with the maximal number of repetitions possible listed in the column to the right. The reps and sets within each training day indicate the number of both that can be performed while maintaining the quality of work at a high level for the athlete. A couple things to notice—the rep ranges stay the same regardless of whether the athlete is in in-season or off-season training and the number of sets used for in-season training are fewer than off-season training. This is due to the high work demands and the added stress of practice and games during the season. Also, look at Friday, Sets (in-season). During the season, all the volume work comes from practice and games. Don't train volume in-season! You'll overtrain your athletes.

The graph below depicts my above 80 percent three-day undulated model. This is what I also refer to as my *high force at low velocity phase.*[28]

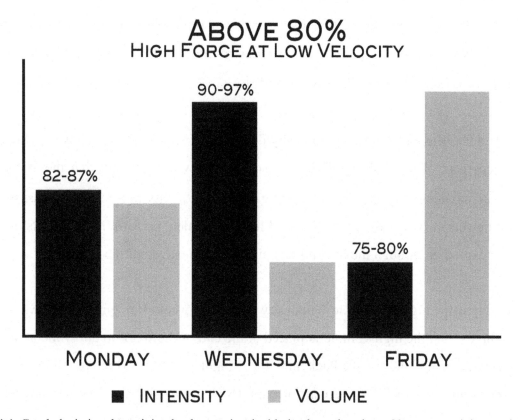

Figure 4.4: Graph depicting the training loads associated with the three-day above 80 percent training model.

The medium intensity, heavy load day is Monday. Typically, I associate this with loads of 82–87 percent of an athlete's 1RM—a weight that an athlete could lift maximally for four or five repetitions. For example, if an athlete has a 1RM of 400 pounds, he will be able to lift 340 pounds for four reps (400 X 0.80 = 340). Now, this doesn't mean that I have him perform sets of four reps at 340 pounds. If the athlete did that, he would only get one quality set. As I just explained, the successive sets would be worthless because the athlete's neuromuscular system would be shot, unable to produce force and power at the same level of the initial set. Performing a true maximal effort lift, regardless of the number of reps, will completely exhaust the muscle and its energy substrates, inhibiting its ability to perform at the high levels required in training. So what do I do? Well, this is the heavy loading phase, so I don't want to decrease the load. I

---

[28] Term coined by Mark Stevenson, a biomedical engineering student at the University of Minnesota.

want to stress the athlete's system as much as possible. Instead, I modify the rep scheme of the sets. Rather than performing sets of four, the athlete will perform singles or doubles. For higher levels of stress levied against the athlete, I often have them perform cluster sets of two or three reps with ten to twenty seconds of recovery between reps (clustering is explained in detail below). In this way, I'm allowing the athlete to perform more quality reps at a higher percentage of his 1RM, ultimately inducing a higher level of stress.

Wednesday is the heavy loading, high intensity day of the week. As shown above, it is correlated with 90–97 percent of the athlete's 1RM. I associate this with a weight that the athlete could perform for a maximum of two or three reps. Again, I want quality reps at these loads, so instead of performing sets of two or three repetitions, I have the athlete perform multiple sets of singles, focusing on exploding through the bar and reaching the highest velocity possible.

Finally, Friday is the high volume, low intensity day of the week. Remember what we discussed in section three—that the high volume is placed at the end of the week to allow the athletes time to fully recover before they walk back into the weight room on Monday. Here the athletes perform sets with loads of 75–80 percent of their 1RM. I typically associate 80 percent with a 6RM. Instead of performing sets of six, however, I will have the athlete perform sets of three to four. Again, I can't stress enough the importance of quality reps over quantity even on a volume day. Any training performed with a suboptimal focus—that is to say with a low rate of force development and diminished velocities—will send mixed neural signaling patterns and inhibit the athlete's adaptability to other training stressors within the block.

Flip back a few pages and take a second look at the loading variables table. Any area in the chart that is shaded means it's a load that you would *not* use in a given training day. You should also notice that while sets used for in-season and off-season training differ, the reps within those sets don't. One final note to point out about the chart is in the sets (in-season) column for Friday. Notice that the volume work in-season takes place during the athlete's practice. This is a huge mistake that many coaches make. They continue to train with high volume during the season for fear of losing some aspect of performance. Instead of maintaining these parameters, however, many coaches overtrain their athletes in-season and end up decreasing their athletes' performance. In-season practices and games are grueling and take their toll on the athlete. Eliminate the volume work in the weight room, continue to train for strength and power, and I promise that your athletes will maintain their gains throughout the year.

4.3: ABOVE 80 TRAINING BLOCKS

Now that you understand the loading scheme and undulation used within the above 80 percent training week, let's take a look at the individual blocks within the mesocycle. There are three blocks total, each lasting two to three weeks and each focusing on one specific aspect of triphasic training. The length of each block can be adjusted to fit different training schedules or to allow an athlete more time to adapt to a certain triphasic parameter. For example, if you have seven weeks to train the above 80 percent mesocycle, you can allocate two weeks for block one (eccentric focus), three weeks for block two (isometric focus), and two weeks for block three (concentric focus). You can adjust the training block lengths as you see fit based on your observations on the adaptive state of your athletes. The chart below shows which aspect of the triphasic muscle action is targeted for a given block as well as the loading variables used on each day in the training week. In this specific case, it shows the blocks being separated into three equal lengths of two weeks each.

TABLE 4.3: TRIPHASIC LOADING VARIABLES (ABOVE 80 PERCENT)					
BLOCK	DAY	LOAD	TIME	REPS	SETS
BLOCK 1 (ECCENTRIC) WEEKS 1–2	MONDAY (MEDIUM INTENSITY)	82–87%	5–6 SECONDS	1–3	2–4
	WEDNESDAY (HIGH INTENSITY)	ECCENTRIC MEANS NOT APPLIED			
	FRIDAY (HIGH VOLUME)	75–80%	6–7 SECONDS	2–4	2–4
BLOCK 2 (ISOMETRIC) WEEKS 3–4	MONDAY (MEDIUM INTENSITY)	82–87%	2–3 SECONDS	1–3	4–5
	WEDNESDAY (HIGH INTENSITY)	ISOMETRIC MEANS NOT APPLIED			
	FRIDAY (HIGH VOLUME)	75–80%	3–4 SECONDS	3–4	4–5

BLOCK	**DAY**	**LOAD**	**TIME**	**REPS**	**SETS**
BLOCK 3 (CONCENTRIC) WEEKS 5–6	MONDAY (MEDIUM INTENSITY)	82–87%	REACTIVE	2–3	3–4
	WEDNESDAY (HIGH INTENSITY)	90–97%	REACTIVE	1	1–4
	FRIDAY (HIGH VOLUME)	75–80%	REACTIVE	3–4	3–5

TABLE 4.3: TRIPHASIC LOADING VARIABLES (ABOVE 80 PERCENT)

One thing to notice and understand in the table above is that both eccentric and isometric means aren't used on Wednesday, the high intensity day of the training week. This is because the stress imposed on the athlete with heavy loading is sufficient on its own without the addition of an accentuated eccentric or isometric means to cause significant adaptation. In addition, I have found that using eccentric and isometric means with heavy, high intensity loads can be somewhat dangerous. With a heavy load, the athlete should be thinking solely about driving the bar as hard and as forcefully as possible. The addition of other mental processes, such as trying to descend slowly or hold a certain joint angle with a near max load, inhibit an athlete's ability to produce force and can at times lead to injury. As a result, within my model, Wednesday is always a reactive day.

✓ Coach's Corner

Throughout the remainder of the book, you will find article inserts called "Coach's Corner" that aim to give concise advice, tips, and tricks to help train and improve athletic performance.

Each of the four numbers associated with an exercise (as seen in the example above) indicate how long in seconds the specific "phase" (**eccentric, isometric, concentric,** and **pause time between reps**) should be performed. For example, a squat may have the following tempo: **3:1:0:0**. The first number (**3**) represents the eccentric phase of the movement; in this case, it would last three seconds. The number (**1**) represents the isometric phase; here, it would be held in the bottom position for one second. The number (**0**) represents the concentric phase. A zero always means that that segment should be performed with a reactive emphasis (as fast as possible). Finally, the number (**0**) represents the amount of rest between reps, which would be zero seconds here. If you would like the athlete to isometrically hold the bottom position of the squat, for example, you would change the middle number so that the tempo reads **3:5:0:0** to indicate that you want a five-second pause at the bottom of the squat.

Table 4.4 gives an example of a six-week back squat progression that an athlete could use during the above 80 percent mesocycle to increase his leg strength and rate of force development:

TABLE 4.4: TRIPHASIC BLOCK PROGRESSION OF THE BACK SQUAT			
TRAINING WEEK	MONDAY LOADING	WEDNESDAY LOADING	FRIDAY LOADING
WEEKS 1–2 (ECCENTRIC)	BACK SQUAT TEMPO - 6:0:0:0 AT 82.5–87.5% LOAD	BACK SQUAT TEMPO - 0:0:0:0 AT 92–97.5% LOAD	BACK SQUAT TEMPO - 5:0:0:0 AT 75–80% LOAD
WEEKS 3–4 (ISOMETRIC)	BACK SQUAT TEMPO - 0:3:0:0 AT 82.5–87.5% LOAD	BACK SQUAT TEMPO - 0:0:0:0 AT 92–97.5% LOAD	BACK SQUAT TEMPO - 0:3:0:0 AT 75–80% LOAD
WEEKS 5–6 (CONCENTRIC)	BACK SQUAT TEMPO - 0:0:0:0 AT 82.5–87.5% LOAD	BACK SQUAT TEMPO - 0:0:0:0 AT 92–97.5% LOAD	BACK SQUAT TEMPO - 0:0:0:0 AT 75–80% LOAD

Taking into account the range of loading variables that can be used within each training day of the undulated week, coaches can develop progressive loading schemes to constantly spur gains week after week for their athletes. Below is a table outlining the typical progression that I have found to work the best with my athletes. This progression can be repeated every block to correlate with an athlete's new 1RM as he progresses through the high force at high velocity mesocycle.

TABLE 4.5: PROGRESSIVE LOADING SCHEME			
WEEK	MONDAY LOADING (MEDIUM INTENSITY)	WEDNESDAY LOADING (HIGH INTENSITY)	FRIDAY LOADING (LOW INTENSITY)
1	82.5% 1–2 REPS, 4–5 SETS	87.5% 1 REP, 3–4 SETS	75% 4–5 REPS, 4–5 SETS
2	85% 1–2 REPS, 4–5 SETS	90% 1 REP, 3–4 SETS	77.5% 3–5 REPS, 4–5 SETS
3	87.5% 1–2 REPS, 4–5 SETS	92.5% 1 REP, 3–4 SETS	80% 3–4 REPS, 4–5 SETS

4.4: HOW TO READ THE WORKOUT SHEET

Before we dive into the actual programs, I need to take a few moments to explain how to read my workout sheets. At first, they may look a little intimidating or confusing, but once you understand the basic structure and flow of the sheets, you will find that they are very effective at conveying an enormous amount of information to the athlete.

To get an idea of what a workout sheet looks like, below is an example of a training week for block one, week one in the three-day model. Each training day will contain six to eight training boxes. A training "box" is a layout format I came up with that allows for assistance and pre-habilitation exercises to be programmed during the rest periods of larger, compound movements. Right now, this won't mean anything to you. If anything, it will likely confuse you. Bear with me. I just want you to get a visual of what the whole sheet looks like before we dissect it into its parts. Following the workout sheet, you will find a step by step breakdown of the key components and aspects needed to read, understand, and apply it:

Figure 4.5: Example training program.

What follows is a descriptive breakdown of how to read the workout sheets. For the sake of consistency, all the workout sheets are made using an imaginary athlete who has a 1RM of 500 pounds in the back squat, 300 pounds in the bench press, 300 pounds in the clean, and 200 pounds in the snatch. Using these four lifts, a coach can calculate an athlete's estimated 1RM for his assistance exercises by taking the numbers and putting them into the *max and reps calculator* (xlathlete.com). If you wish to know the loads used for a given exercise, simply divide the prescribed load by the athlete's 1RM to get his working percentage. For example, if an athlete's prescribed load in the bench press is 215–230 pounds, you would divide 215/300 and 230/300. This gives you 72 to 77, so the athlete is to perform sets at 72–77 percent of his 1RM.

1) The first column shows the athlete's 1RM in the programmed exercise, that is to say his 100 percent effort for that given lift. In this case, the athlete has a bench press max of 300 pounds.

- Figure 4.6

100%	Monday	22-Jun-10			
		REPS	LOAD	SETS	NOTES
300	BENCH PRESS	6	225 - 240	4	0:2:0:0
	Pair w/				
	Med Ball Chest Pass	4		4	
	Pair w/rest 30				
	Infraspinatus	10		4	

2) The second column tells the athlete the day of the training week and the exercises to be performed. In this case, the athlete is lifting on Monday, performing the bench press, medicine ball chest pass, and infraspinatus.

- Figure 4.7

100%	Monday	22-Jun-10			
		REPS	LOAD	SETS	NOTES
300	BENCH PRESS	6	225 - 240	4	0:2:0:0
	Pair w/				
	Med Ball Chest Pass	4		4	
	Pair w/rest 30				
	Infraspinatus	10		4	

3) The reps column specifies how many repetitions should be completed per workout set. In this case, the athlete is performing sets of six repetitions in the bench press, sets of four repetitions in the medicine ball chest pass, and sets of ten repetitions for the infraspinatus.

- Figure 4.8

100%	Monday	22-Jun-10			
		REPS	LOAD	SETS	NOTES
300	BENCH PRESS	6	225 - 240	4	0:2:0:0
	Pair w/				
	Med Ball Chest Pass	4		4	
	Pair w/rest 30				
	Infraspinatus	10		4	

4) The load column specifies the weight to be used while completing the exercise. As mentioned earlier, simply divide these numbers by the athlete's 1RM (found in column one) to find the percentages used for the lift. *Hint: You should already know these, with relative accuracy, from reading the book if you know which mesocycle and block you are in.*

- Figure 4.9

100%	Monday		22-Jun-10		
		REPS	LOAD	SETS	NOTES
300	BENCH PRESS	6	225 - 240	4	0:2:0:0
	Pair w/				
	Med Ball Chest Pass	4		4	
	Pair w/rest 30				
	Infraspinatus	10		4	

5) The sets column indicates how many groups of repetitions the athlete will perform with that particular exercise. For example, the athlete will complete four sets of the bench press, each set consisting of six repetitions.

- Figure 4.10

100%	Monday		22-Jun-10		
		REPS	LOAD	SETS	NOTES
300	BENCH PRESS	6	225 - 240	4	0:2:0:0
	Pair w/				
	Med Ball Chest Pass	4		4	
	Pair w/rest 30				
	Infraspinatus	10		4	

6) The notes column is where you will find extra information needed to perform the exercise. Some examples of notes include tempos (6:2:0:0), alternating (one arm/leg at a time), or bands/chains (applied method). There will also be rest intervals

- Figure 4.11

100%	Monday		22-Jun-10		
		REPS	LOAD	SETS	NOTES
300	BENCH PRESS	6	225 - 240	4	0:2:0:0
	Pair w/				
	Med Ball Chest Pass	4		4	
	Pair w/rest 30				
	Infraspinatus	10		4	

labeled in this column. In this case, the bench press has a tempo of 0:2:0:0, meaning the athlete should pause for two seconds during the isometric phase of the movement. All other phases should be reactive.

7) The "pair w/" and "pair w/rest" notations in column two tell an athlete the sequence and rest intervals that should be applied to the exercises in a given box. For example, in the box below, the athlete would complete one set of bench presses for six

- Figure 4.12

100%	Monday		22-Jun-10		
		REPS	LOAD	SETS	NOTES
300	BENCH PRESS	6	225 - 240	4	0:2:0:0
	Pair w/				
	Med Ball Chest Pass	4		4	
	Pair w/rest 30				
	Infraspinatus	10		4	

repetitions and then immediately follow the set with four medicine ball chest passes. This is signified by the "pair w/" between the two exercises. After completion of the medicine ball chest pass, the athlete would rest for thirty seconds and then complete a set of ten repetitions of the infraspinatus. This is signified by the "pair w/rest 30." After completing one set of all three exercises, the athlete would return to the top of the box and complete another set of each exercise. This process is repeated until the athlete completes all the prescribed sets listed in the box.

There are also times when the sheet will say "rest 25-BB." This means the athlete is supposed to rest for twenty-five seconds while focusing on belly breathing (BB) to drop the heart rate and recover before proceeding to the next exercise in the block. The "rest 25-BB" implies "pair w/."

8) Without the "pair w/" between exercises, the athlete completes all sets listed for a single exercise before moving on to the next exercises. For example, in the box below, the athlete would complete three sets of five repetitions in the bench press with a load of 240–250 pounds. Once all the sets are completed, the

100%	Monday		24-Jun-10			
			REPS	LOAD	SETS	NOTES
300	BENCH PRESS		5	240 - 250	3	
60	Arnold Press		8	40 - 45	3	
150	Tri Push Down		10	100 - 105	3	

- Figure 4.13

athlete moves on to complete the Arnold press, performing three sets of eight repetitions.

Now that you have a general overview of the mesocycle—its blocks, loading variables, and triphasic progression—as well as an understanding of how to read the workout sheets, it's time to take an in-depth look at each training day to gain an intricate look at the finer details and concepts that must be incorporated to gain maximal improvement of your athletes. To accomplish this, we will examine each training day in depth, looking at the means, loading variables, and triphasic focus of each block. Remember, each of the three blocks within the mesocycle are very similar. The parameter for each is the same—increase the athlete's level of general strength. The means used to accomplish this change from block to block, however, with each block focusing on a different aspect of triphasic muscle action.

4.5: SPECIALIZED METHODS OF APPLYING TRAINING MEANS

Just as the parameters of each mesocycle are specialized, it only makes sense that the methods used to develop them should be specifically molded as well and developed to produce the best results. It would be foolish to take a method that is great at developing speed endurance and expect it to have the same effect on raw strength. It won't. Over the years, I have found or developed several specialized methods of training that have, time and again, proven themselves to be the most effective means at developing the athlete's nervous system within the training loads (power producing range) of a specific parameter. It is important that the use of various lifting methods is applied to ensure continuous adaptation of the athlete through the varied application of stress. The ability of these methods to promote positive adaptation through increased rate of force development (RFD) and power development is unparalleled. For this specific mesocycle, the above 80 percent phase, there are three methods in particular that develop strength and reactive ability under high load/high intensity means better than any other. They are the *French contrast, clustering,* and *oscillatory* methods of training, and they accomplish these things in two ways:

1) Potentiating the nervous system through the alternated sequencing of loaded, un-loaded, and accelerated exercises.

2) Keeping the quality of each repetition high, ensuring that the nervous system is engaged at a high level, and improving intramuscular coordination.

Potentiation is the increase in efficiency or speed of nerve impulse signaling rate along a neural pathway. Often referred to as post-activation potentiation (PAP), it is the enhanced contractile ability of a muscle to generate force with moderate to light loads after performing an exercise consisting of maximal or near maximal loads. The heavy loaded exercise increases the recruitment of high threshold motor units, improves intermuscular and intramuscular coordination, and decreases pre-synaptic inhibition. The combination of these three actions allows for greater force production and power output of the subsequent exercise. In layman's terms, the nervous system goes into overdrive thinking that it's going to lift a heavy load, resulting in an explosive lift of a lighter load—it is potentiated.

For example, imagine that you're loading boxes of bricks into your car. You have loaded several boxes when you go to pick up another box that is mislabeled. Instead of bricks, it's loaded with pillows. You grab the box and nearly fall over backward as it comes flying off the floor. Your perceived force needed to lift the box was much greater than the force actually needed to lift it— you were potentiated from lifting the heavier boxes first. This positive effect of potentiated training has been estimated to increase maximal power output by 18 percent as compared to work conducted without performing any type of priming exercise.[29] That is to say, an athlete with a vertical jump of twenty inches could jump an additional two to three inches if his nervous system was potentiated prior to the jump.

These specialized methods should be applied at the beginning of the workout when the nervous system is fresh. After the specialized method is used, the nervous system will be slightly fatigued. In this state, supplemental and pre-habilitation exercises can be applied to finish the workout.

FRENCH CONTRAST

The French contrast method was originally developed by the French track and field coach, Gilles Cometti (I will let your imagination decide how the method got its name). In reviewing his French contrast method, I began to realize that it was a combination of various exercises and methods placed together. The best way to describe this particular method is to say that it's a combination of complex and contrast training methods. I should take a moment here to clear up some of the misconceptions regarding the application of these two methods before I explain their combined effect in the French contrast. Many coaches I talk to understand the basic concepts of these methods, but their use and sequencing of the exercises and means used is often misplaced.

---

[29] Verkhoshansky Y, Verkhoshansky N (2011) *Special Strength Training Manual For Coaches*. Verkhoshansky SSTM.

When applying the complex method, an athlete would perform a heavy compound exercise (typically using loads greater than 80 percent of a 1RM) followed by a plyometric jump exercise that mimics the same motor pattern. For example, an athlete would perform a single repetition at 90 percent followed by three box jumps. Typically, this method is performed for three to six sets with rest intervals of five to thirty seconds between the compound and plyometric movements with two to four minutes between complexes.

On the other hand, contrast training is defined as performing a maximal or near maximal lift (80–97 percent) followed by a drop set performed at 50–70 percent of the 1RM. Rest intervals here are usually a little longer compared to complex training, taking two to three minutes between each exercise and another two to three minutes between each contrast set. Completing down sets between the top and bottom percentage results in optimal velocity achievement while maintaining a high power output. In both cases, complex and contrast training are meant to take advantage of the PAP effect, teaching the athlete's neuromuscular structure to produce force at exceedingly high rates.

At its simplest level, the French contrast method is the combination of the complex and contrast methods outlined above. It consists of four exercises—a heavy compound exercise (80–90 percent 1RM), a plyometric jump, a drop set or weighted jump (30 percent 1RM), and a plyometric or accelerated plyometric. While on the surface this may appear to simply be the joining of complex and contrast methods, the physiological and neural adaptation it stimulates makes it a far superior method for training sport performance, especially those that require high rates of force production.

Compared to complex or contrast training, the French contrast method applies a much larger amount of stress (one of the five factors of success), the result of which garners some very specific results—explosive strength and speed endurance. The key difference between the French contrast method and complex or contrast training is its utilization of a number of methods for explosive development of the athlete. The French contrast method, using a four-exercise protocol, pushes the physiological response of the athlete further, forcing the utilization of alactic or anaerobic work capacity to increase. Simply put, the French contrast method makes the athlete powerful for longer periods of time, stimulating greater adaptation within the parameter.

Specifically as I use it, the French contrast method is applied during my above 80 percent mesocycle to emphasize the triphasic loading scheme. As seen below (figure 5), the athlete will first perform a heavy back squat using a triphasic tempo (in this case, an isometric hold for three seconds). Immediately after the squat, the athlete will perform a hurdle hop. Many types of plyometric jumps can be used, but keep in mind you want to use the ones that best mimic the athlete's sport. This plyometric will often be your key guideline in observing the joint stiffness qualities of the athlete change over a six- to nine-week mesocycle. Again, you're using a heavy squat or other compound movement to excite the nervous system before performing the plyometric. This facilitated response or potentiation of the nervous system enables an elevated level of force production to be created when performing an explosive plyometric.

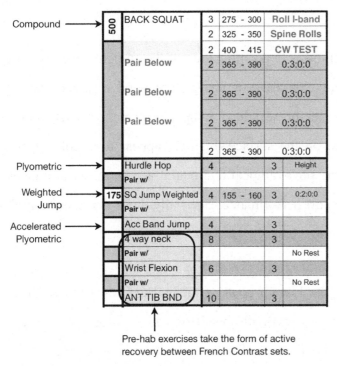

Compound →

500	BACK SQUAT	3	275 - 300	Roll I-band	
		2	325 - 350	Spine Rolls	
		2	400 - 415	CW TEST	
	Pair Below	2	365 - 390	0:3:0:0	
	Pair Below	2	365 - 390	0:3:0:0	
	Pair Below	2	365 - 390	0:3:0:0	
		2	365 - 390	0:3:0:0	

Plyometric →

Hurdle Hop	4		3	Height
Pair w/				
175 SQ Jump Weighted	4	155 - 160	3	0:2:0:0
Pair w/				
Acc Band Jump	4		3	
4 way neck	8		3	
Pair w/				No Rest
Wrist Flexion	6		3	
Pair w/				No Rest
ANT TIB BND	10		3	

Weighted Jump →

Accelerated Plyometric →

Pre-hab exercises take the form of active recovery between French Contrast sets.

- Figure 4.14

Once the plyometric jump is completed, the athlete goes directly to the weighted jump. This is where I believe the athlete switches over from training power development to training explosive work capacity—the ability to produce power in a somewhat fatigued state. Finally, after the weighted jump, the athlete performs a second plyometric jump. Here, I often use an accelerated form of plyometric to keep the velocity of the movement at the highest level possible. This enables the athlete to develop explosive power during a fatigued state. If you don't have the ability to apply accelerated plyometrics, an athlete can perform another plyometric jump, focusing on the top end of the range of motion to keep the motion quick and explosive. For example, have the athlete perform a quarter squat jump rather than a full squat jump. Again, the purpose is to keep the nervous system firing at a high rate during this type of movement and to keep using one exercise to set up the explosiveness of a subsequent exercise.

To maximize the training time of my athletes, I often program to have them perform their pre-habilitation exercises during rest intervals. Due to the extremely taxing nature of the French contrast method, an athlete needs four to five minutes of rest between sets to allow the nervous system to recover and the muscles to replenish energy stores. As seen in the box below, the accelerated band jump is followed by three pre-habilitation exercises—the four-way neck, wrist flexion, and anterior tibial band exercises—before returning to a second set of the French contrast. Inserting pre-habilitation work like this works great because it doesn't physically tax the athlete between sets and shortens the total time required for the workout. The athlete would perform three French contrast sets, starting with the isometric back squat all the way through the anterior tibial band. The fourth set of the back squat would be performed on its own.

The French contrast method is without question the best way to apply stress to the athlete. The gains seen in reactive ability, force production, and raw speed by athletes performing the French contrast method far exceed those of other methods I've tried. The results I've seen through the implementation of this method have been reproduced and extended into multiple arenas of sport —from the world of track and field to ice hockey, basketball, and football. Due to the enormous amount of stress this method of training places on the athlete, I would be very hesitant to use it with young athletes. I define "young" as any athlete who has a training age of less than three years. It is intended for advance high school, collegiate, and advanced elite Olympic athletes.

To the left is another example of how the French contrast method would appear on my workout sheets. Just as in the previous example, after completing his warm-up sets, the athlete would

- Figure 4.15

perform a six-second eccentric sport back squat followed immediately by the hurdle hop, weighted half squat jump, and a 15-yard start, taking fifteen seconds to belly breathe between exercises. After completing a set, the athlete would rest for four minutes before returning to the sport back squat.

Table 4.6 quickly lays out how a coach could alter each exercise in the French contrast method to specialize it for a specific sport, increasing the transferability of gains in the gym to gains on the field. For each sport in the table, two possible substitutions are shown for each exercise.

	TABLE 4.6: APPLYING FRENCH CONTRAST METHOD			
	MEANS FOR GREATEST TRANSFER OF SPORT SPECIFIC ABILITIES			
SPORT	COMPOUND EXERCISE	PLYOMETRIC	WEIGHTED JUMP	PLYOMETRIC
FOOTBALL (LINEMAN)	BACK SQUAT	SPLIT SQUAT ALTERNATING JUMP	BB JUMP SQUAT	ASSISTED BAND SQUAT JUMP
	LEG PRESS	SQUAT DROP JUMP	SAND BAG SQUAT JUMP	ACCELERATED BAND SPLIT SQUAT JUMP
FOOTBALL (SKILL PLAYER)	FRONT SQUAT	HURDLE HOP	BB JUMP SQUAT	ASSISTED BAND SQUAT JUMP
	BACK SQUAT	ALTERNATE LEG BOUNDING	SAND BAG SQUAT JUMP	ACCELERATED BAND SPLIT SQUAT JUMP
HOCKEY	BACK SQUAT	RUSSIAN PLYO BOX	POWER STEP-UP W/ BAG	ASSISTED BAND SQUAT JUMP
	LEG PRESS	SQUAT DROP JUMP	BB JUMP SQUAT	ACCELERATED BAND SPLIT SQUAT JUMP
BASKETBALL	LEG PRESS	HURDLE HOP	SAND BAG SQUAT JUMP	ASSISTED BAND SQUAT JUMP
	HEX BAR DEADLIFT	SPLIT SQUAT ALTERNATING JUMP	SPLIT SQUAT W/ SAND BAG	ACCELERATED BAND SPLIT SQUAT JUMP

CLUSTERING

Using cluster sets in training is an excellent way to stress an athlete, especially during phases of considerably intense loading as in this above 80 percent mesocycle. A cluster set allows for more repetitions to be made at a weight than an athlete would normally be able to lift two or more times in succession without sacrificing velocity and force development. This type of set requires a short amount of rest to be taken between repetitions in order to restore or partially restore the short-term energy systems used to produce bursts of highly intense movement. The use of maximum or near maximum loads stress the systems responsible for neuromuscular coordination in which the recruitment of faster and larger motor units is increased. Rate coding also increases, and the synchronization of motor unit activity becomes optimal for maximum force output. It is therefore beneficial for athletes looking to improve their overall strength levels to train with weights at or near their maximum. However, it can be difficult to perform several repetitions with this type of load in succession, which is where the use of cluster sets becomes warranted.

By including ten to twenty seconds of rest between repetitions, each one is accomplished with maximum or near maximum velocity and force, resulting in maximal power output. This ensures that the athlete is performing more maximum or near maximum efforts per workout, which may ultimately allow for a greater improvement to take place. The bar should be returned to the floor or rack when resting.

The more work (or repetitions) that an athlete can perform with these intense loads, the better his force producing capabilities may become. Even with as little as fifteen seconds of recovery, an individual can perform at near maximum force production capacity. A cluster set allows the athlete to perform greater amounts of work and be exposed to higher levels of stress while not experiencing the fatigue and lowered force output normally associated with traditional sets. This ensures the neurological effect remains high throughout every rep and successive sets.
This is a method that can be applied to both lower and upper body exercises.

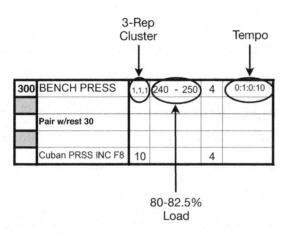

-**Figure 4.16**

In figure 4.7, an athlete would perform three cluster repetitions per set with a load of 240–250 pounds using a tempo with a one-second isometric pause and ten seconds rest between repetitions. In this box, the athlete would follow the bench press set by resting for thirty seconds before performing a set of ten Cuban presses. The athlete would repeat this cycle for four sets before moving on to the next box.

OSCILLATORY METHOD

The oscillatory method was created from an idea I had several years ago to try and reconcile Sherrington's law of reciprocal inhibition with training to maximize performance. His law states that in order for the agonist to contract, the antagonist must relax.[30] Decades ago, Dr. Matveyev (a Russian scientist) found through his research that the difference between elite athletes and great athletes wasn't the speed at which they could contract their agonist muscle as one would intuitively think. The difference lied instead with the athlete's ability to relax the antagonist. The athlete who could do this more quickly was always the superior athlete.[31]

During an explosive contraction in the concentric phase, the antagonist acts as a decelerator, pumping the breaks if you will so that an athlete doesn't tear a limb off his body. When a pitcher heaves a 95-mph fastball, his entire posterior shoulder complex acts as a decelerator to slow the internal rotation of the arm as it comes across the pitcher's body. If it weren't for this system, pitchers would literally throw their arms out of their sockets. Agonist inhibition is a good thing. But like other "good things" we've talked about in this book like the Golgi tendon organ, they are a little overprotective. To enhance sport performance, an athlete must train in such a way as to

---

[30] Johnson WR (1960) *Science and Medicine of Exercise and Sports*. New York: Harper & Row Publishers.

[31] Verkhoshansky Y, Siff M (2009) *Supertraining*. Sixth edition. Ultimate Athlete Concepts.

decrease the inhibitory processes of these systems and allow him to reach higher levels of force production in ever decreasing times.

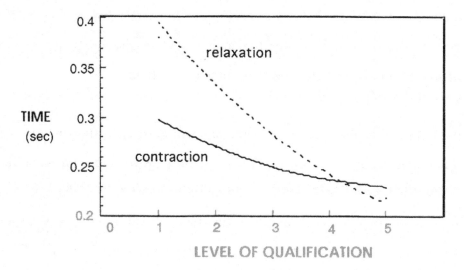

Figure 4.17: Graph showing the relationship between agonist contraction and antagonist relaxation in Soviet athletes. Looking at the contraction line, notice that there is only a 0.05-second difference between level one and level five athletes. Comparatively, there is nearly a 0.20-second difference between the rate of antagonist relaxation. Notice the level five athletes, the best of the best, can relax their antagonist faster than they can contract their agonists.

Figure 4.17 depicts Metveyev's findings. It shows the contraction and relaxation times of increasing levels of qualification as measured by electromyography of top level Russian athletes. *(The Russian's had a classification system to separate their best athletes. As a reference, if the numbers above represented basketball players, a level one classification means that you're a Division I player or an elite player but not the best of the elite. A level five player would represent a Michael Jordan or Lebron James.)* These findings showed that Sherrington's Law was a limiting factor in force production within sport. Athletes with a slower relaxation rate of their antagonist muscle complex slowed the rate of their concentric contraction and limited their force production and, ultimately, their power producing capability.

The best athletes are able to not only contract at high velocities but relax at superior velocities as well. The oscillatory method focuses on limiting the antagonistic inhibition seen in athletes to maximize their ability to generate force in limited amounts of time. Oscillatory movements are performed over a short range of motion either in an advantageous (OC-A) or disadvantageous position (OC-D). Repetitions are short and quick, only traveling over a three- to four-inch range of motion with the athlete consciously pushing and pulling the bar up and down. A great coaching cue that I use is tell the athlete that he is trying to flick the light switch on and off as fast as he can. Every rep is teaching the muscle complex to change from a concentric accelerator to an eccentric decelerator. This increases the speed at which the antagonist muscle learns to relax and improves the rate of relaxation seen in force production.

Oscillatory exercises can be used for two separate applications. First, they can be used as a way to peak an athlete. Using light loads (25–50 percent of a 1RM) and high velocities will help maximize the explosive power of the athlete leading up to competition. This application will be drawn out further in section six. A second way this method can be utilized is to use moderate loads (65–80 percent) at high velocities to increase the force placed on specific parts of the muscle structure. There are several different ways to perform oscillatory exercises. Here, for the above 80 percent blocks, we will look at three different methods of application—OC +1, 2OC +1, and OC-D/OC-A + 1. Remember, OC stands for oscillatory, D for disadvantageous, and A for advantageous. The '+1' at the end is there to remind the athlete that each set should be finished with one complete repetition of the exercise. This serves to teach the nervous system and physiological structure to "finish" through the movement, developing a higher level of force transferability to sport.

TABLE 4.7: OSCILLATORY BENCH PRESS			
OC MEANS:	OC + 1	2OC + 1	OC-D/OC-A + 1
ADVANTAGEOUS	BENCH PRESS OC-A+1	BENCH PRESS 2OC ADVANTAGES	DB BENCH PRESS 2POC
DISADVANTAGEOUS	BENCH PRESS OSCILLATORY	BENCH PRESS 2OC +1	BENCH PRESS 2POC

✓ Coach's Corner

WARM-UP PROTOCOL
By Ben Peterson

Coaches always want to know exactly what weights the athletes are lifting and the progress that they are making. Being able to quantify results with actual data not only motivates the athlete to continue to push himself in the weight room but also validates the methods and practices of the coach. Despite the need and benefits of having up-to-date numbers for an athlete's 1RM, coaches are often hesitant to take the time to perform 1RM testing. Whether it's out of concern for injury to the athlete, interference with the normal lifting schedule, or excessively taxing the nervous system, coaches tend to shy away from max testing other than once per year.

But what if there was a way for coaches to test an athlete's max that could be added safely and effectively to any workout, a test that doesn't tax the athlete's nervous system? This would enable coaches to make adjustments almost instantly to their athletes' workouts, enabling them to maximize gains in a short amount of time. To do this, all the coaches have to do is add one additional set to the end of the warm up at 80 percent of the current 1RM the day they want to test, or adjust, the athlete's max.

A normal and effective warm-up protocol for the bench press may look something like this:

- 1 x 5 reps @ 55% 1RM
- 1 x 3 reps @ 70% 1RM
- 1 x 1 reps @ 80% 1RM

This allows the athlete to quickly stimulate the central nervous system and activate the large, high threshold motor units without stimulating fatigue. Now, let's say that it is the first day of a new microcycle and a coach wants to test his athletes to see if their bench numbers need to be increased for the upcoming phase. To do this, the coach would have an athlete perform one set at 80 percent of his 1RM for three reps. For example:

- 1 x 5 reps @ 55% 1RM
- 1 x 3 reps @ 70% 1RM
- **1 x 3 reps @ 80% 1RM (test set)**

Closely observing the athlete perform the lift by watching the speed of the bar and the level of exertion the athlete exhibits, the coach can estimate how many reps the athlete could have actually performed. If the athlete performed the set with ease, maintaining speed throughout the concentric portion of the lift, the coach may infer that the athlete could have performed five, six, or more repetitions, in which case the athlete's max has increased. If the athlete performs the repetitions but appears to struggle or the bar moves at a slow, steady pace, the athlete's max is likely unchanged and should remain the same.

It should be noted that the athlete doesn't need to perform all three reps in the testing set. As a coach becomes more proficient at observing the athlete, he will be able to estimate the total number of reps that can be performed at a given weight by watching only one or two repetitions. This is beneficial because it diminishes the stress placed on the athlete even further, taking less energy away from his work sets. For example:

- 1 x 5 reps @ 55% 1RM
- 1 x 3 reps @ 70% 1RM
- **1 x 1-3reps @ 80% 1RM (test set)**

After the testing set is completed, the athlete can proceed with the rest of the scheduled workout without any adverse effects to performance. Once the coach estimates the number of repetitions the athlete could have performed, that number can be plugged into the rep max calculator (xlathlete.com) to calculate the athlete's new 1RM.

Being able to watch, evaluate, and change an athlete's max within the outlines of a lifting schedule gives a coach a decisive advantage. It ensures that the athletes are using the correct weights and percentages to maximally tax their system at all times. The biggest factor in dictating progress in the weight room is intensity. If an athlete has adapted to something where the stimulus no longer has a high enough intensity to elicit change, the athlete will plateau. Being able to continually change and accurately measure an athlete's 1RM enables a coach to maintain the right intensity and make gains twelve months a year.

4.6: MONDAY, MEDIUM INTENSITY (SUBMAXIMAL EFFORT)

LOADING

Below is a section from the loading table showing exclusively the loading variables applied on Monday (table 4.8). Just as before, sections that are shaded mean that these are loads that wouldn't be used at this point of the training week.

TABLE 4.8: MONDAY LOADING (MEDIUM INTENSITY)				
% 1RM	MAXIMUM REPS POSSIBLE	HIGH QUALITY REPS (STRENGTH)	SETS (OFF-SEASON)	SETS (IN-SEASON)
97.5%	1–2			
95 %	2			
92.5%	2–3			
90%	3–4			
87.5%	4	1	3–4	2–3
85%	4–5	1–2	4–5	2–3
82.5%	5	1–2	4–5	2–3
80%	5–6			
77.5%	6–7			
75%	7 - 8			

When we take the loading variables from above and apply them to the triphasic methods outlined earlier in this section, the result would be what you see in table 4.9. The loads for all three blocks remain the same. The target parameter for this mesocycle is general strength, so the stimulus (stress) placed on the nervous system must remain within the same range to promote the greatest levels of adaptation. Take care to examine the eccentric block carefully. Because of the excessive amounts of stress that eccentric loading places on both the neurological and physiological systems of the athlete, fewer sets are performed in block one than in either of the succeeding blocks.

TABLE 4.9: MONDAY TRIPHASIC LOADING PARAMETERS					
BLOCK	INTENSITY	LOAD	TEMPO	REPS	SETS
BLOCK 1 (ECCENTRIC)	MEDIUM INTENSITY	82–87%	6:0:0:0	1–3	2–4
BLOCK 2 (ISOMETRIC)		82–87%	0:3:0:0	1–3	3–5
BLOCK 3 (CONCENTRIC)		82–87%	0:0:0:0	2–4	3–4

The tempos and rep ranges outlined above are to be used primarily with the specialized methods of applying training means discussed earlier in this section. When programming for assistance work, don't worry about these tempos, as additional emphasis on eccentric loading will exhaust the neurological system of the athlete. All assistance work should be performed within the loading parameters for that day within the undulated block, in this case 82–87 percent. For examples of assistance work that should be used to optimize performance gains and for suggested rep ranges of these exercises within each block, refer to the programs throughout this section.

SEQUENCING

Keeping the loads in the 82-87 percent range to apply a highly concentrated load stimulus, the sequencing of the triphasic training progression can be accomplished through the use of numerous different means. Table 4.10 is meant to be a guide for choosing an exercise progression for the lower body that best fits your weight room and athletes. It is also meant to give ideas for how to change up the means you use from block to block so that your athletes don't get bored coming in and doing the same thing week in and week out. This is only an example of one compound exercise. Many others can and should be used. For example, from table 10, an athlete could perform a box back squat for the eccentric phase in block one, then perform a box squat with bands for the isometric phase in block two, and finish by performing a conventional back squat for the concentric phase in block three. There isn't any right or wrong progression. Some athletes may adapt to one specific sequence better than others, but that is trial and error. As long as athletes keep the load within the specified range, use proper triphasic tempos, and explode, generating as much force as possible during the concentric phase of each rep, they will see definitive, substantial gains.

TABLE 4.10: MONDAY TRIPHASIC EXERCISE SEQUENCING (BACK SQUAT)		
BLOCK 1 (ECCENTRIC)	BLOCK 2 (ISOMETRIC)	BLOCK 3 (CONCENTRIC)
BACK SQUAT ECCENTRIC TEMPO - 6:0:0:0	BACK SQUAT ISOMETRIC TEMPO - 0:3:0:0	BACK SQUAT CONCENTRIC TEMPO - 0:0:0:0
BOX BACK SQUAT TEMPO - 6:0:0:0	BOX BACK SQUAT TEMPO - 0:3:0:0	BACK SQUAT WITH WEIGHT RELEASERS TEMPO - 0:0:0:0
BACK SQUAT WITH WEIGHT RELEASERS TEMPO - 6:0:0:0	BOX BACK SQUAT BANDS TEMPO - 0:3:0:0	BACK SQUAT WITH BANDS TEMPO - 0:0:0:0
SPORT BACK SQUAT TEMPO - 6:0:0:0	BOX BACK SQUAT WITH CHAINS TEMPO - 0:3:0:0	SPORT BACK SQUAT TEMPO - 0:0:0:0

WORKOUTS

Below, you will find Monday's workout for each block of the three-day, above 80 percent model —the eccentric block, isometric block, and concentric block. The column on the left is the actual workout using our "imaginary" athlete to calculate the loads used on each exercise. The column on the right, labeled "Coaching Points," gives further explanation about exercise sequencing and important coaching queues to use with your athletes. The coaching points are labeled with the respective workout box that they apply to. In addition, every exercise in each workout is hyperlinked. Don't know what an exercise is or exactly how to perform it? No problem. Just click on its blue hyperlink in the "Coaching Points" column for a video tutorial of the exercise. At the end of this section, you will find workouts for each block of a four-day, five-day, six-day, and two-day in-season model.

BLOCK ONE, MONDAY

100%	MONDAY	2-Nov-10			
		REPS	LOAD	SETS	NOTES
500	Sport Back Squat	5,3	250 - 335	1,1	Pw/ Cuban F8
	2-Min Rest/B-Breath				I band Rollers
500	Sport Back Squat	3	390 - 400	1	pw/cuban f8
	2-Min Rest/B-Breath				I band Rollers
500	Sport Back Squat	3	415 - 440	3	6:0:0:0
	Hurdle Hop	5		3	Pull Down
	15 rest- BB				
	1/2 SQ JMP Weighted	4		3	reactive
	15 rest- BB				
	15 Yard Starts	1		3	4:00 Rest
300	BENCH PRESS	5,3	150 - 200	1,1	Ext Shock
	2-Min Rest/B-Breath				
300	Bench Press	3	- 240	1	coach see
	2-Min Rest/B-Breath				Ext Shock
300	BENCH PRESS	4	205 - 210	3	2OC-d+1
	One Leg MB Side Toss	5		3	Pause
	25 rest- BB				
	1 Bent Arm S. L.P Down	6		3	3:0:0:0
	25 rest- BB				
	90 90 Jump Twist	5		3	
500	Glute Bar Lift	8	250 - 300	3	
	25 rest- BB				
	Face Band Pulls	8		3	
	25 rest- BB				
75	1 Arm Lat Pull Supine	10	50 - 55	3	
	GH HYPR	6		3	
	25 rest- BB				
	Iso Ball Grion Sqeeze	10S		3	
	25 rest- BB				
	Round House	8		3	
75	DB Shoulder Press	10	50 - 55	2	oc-D+1
	25 rest- BB				
	Hip FLX BND Pulls	6		2	
	25 rest- BB				
105	Drag Curl	10	70 - 75	2	
45	DB Tri Pro Sup	8	35 - 35	2	
	25 rest- BB				
180	Chin up	6	135 - 145	2	
	25 rest- BB				
	Jobes ECC	6		2	4;0;0;0;

COACHING POINTS AND EXERCISE TUTORIAL

Box 1-2

-The sport back squat is a narrow stance squat used for more specific sports training.

-The first line says that the athlete performs one set of five followed by one set of three reps. Between sets, the athlete performs I-band rollers and Cuban F8. The second line says that the athlete performs another warm-up set of three reps.

-Notice the six-count eccentric on the way down in the work sets of the sports back squat.

-With this particular load and eccentric method, the squat will need to be assisted each rep by the spotter.

-The assistants will take place on the way up but not on the way down.

-The athlete leaves the sport back squat and goes directly to the hurdle hop and half squat jump and then to the 15-yard starts. This is a sample of the French contrast method.

Sport back Squat; Sport Back Squat Eccentric; Hurdle Hop; Half Squat Jump Weighted; 15 yard Starts

Box 3-4

-The bench press block here on the first line has two sets for the warm up. It is paired with the external rotator shock method in the warm up.

-The second line bench press is a three-rep test that we will estimate to either raise or lower the athletes max.

-The work sets on the bench press are two oscillatory movements at the bottom and then one full range of motion at the top. This will be completed for four reps.

-The block after the bench press will be paired with the bench press to provide the athlete with more rest during the pairing of the three exercises below.

Bench Press 2OC; One Leg Med Ball Side Toss; One Arm Side Lat Pull Down; 90 90 Jump Twist

Box 5

Glute Bar Lift; Face Band Pulls; 1 Arm Lat Pull Supine

Box 6

-For the iso ball groin squeeze, take an athletic stance over a Swiss ball and squeeze the knees together into the ball as hard as possible

Glute Ham Hyper; Isometric Ball Groin Squeeze; Round House

Box 7

-The DB shoulder press finishes on a complete rep

DB Shoulder Press; Hip Flex Band Pulls; Drag Curl

Box 8

DB Tri Pro Sup; Chin Up; Jobes ECC

BLOCK TWO, MONDAY

100%	MONDAY	16-Nov-10			
		REPS	LOAD	SETS	NOTES
500	Sport Back Squat	5,3	250 - 335	1,1	Pw/ Cuban F8
	No Rest/B-Breath				I band Rollers
500	Sport Back Squat	3	390 - 400	1	pw/cuban f8
	No Rest/B-Breath				I band Rollers
500	Sport Back Squat	3	390 - 400	3	0:5:0:0
	Hurdle Hop	5		3	Pull Down
	15 rest- BB				
	1/2 SQ JMP Weighted	4		3	reactive
	15 rest- BB				
	15 Yard Starts	T		3	
300	BENCH PRESS	5,3	150 - 200	1,1	Ext Shock
	No Rest/B-Breath				
300	Bench Press	3	- 240	1	coach see
	No Rest/B-Breath				Ext Shock
300	BENCH PRESS	4	205 - 210	3	2OC-d+1
	One Leg MB Side Toss	5		3	
	25 rest- BB				
	1 Bent Arm S. L.P Down	6		3	
	25 rest- BB				
	90 90 Jump Twist	5		3	
500	Glute Bar Lift	8	250 - 300	3	
	25 rest- BB				
	Face Band Pulls	8		3	
	25 rest- BB				
75	1 Arm Lat Pull Supine	10	50 - 55	3	
	GH HYPR	6		3	oc-A
	25 rest- BB				
	Iso Ball Grion Sqeeze	10S		3	
	25 rest- BB				
	Round House	8		3	
75	DB Shoulder Press	10	50 - 55	2	oc-D+1
	25 rest- BB				
	Hip FLX BND Pulls	6		2	
	25 rest- BB				
120	Bar Curl	10	80 - 85	2	
45	DB Tri Pro Sup	8	35 - 35	2	
	25 rest- BB				
180	Chin up	6	135 - 145	2	
	25 rest- BB				
	Jobes ECC	6		2	4;0;0;0;

COACHING POINTS AND EXERCISE TUTORIAL

BOX 1-2
-The sport back squat is a narrow stance squat used for more specific sports training.
-The first line says that the athlete performs one set of five followed by one set of three reps.
-Between sets, the athlete performs I-band rollers and Cuban F8. The second line says that the athlete performs another warm-up set of three reps.
-Notice from the prior block that we went from a six-count eccentric to a five-count isometric. This will also need assistance from the spotter to complete the rep.
-This is still the French contrast protocol, so the three exercises are paired with the sport back squat.
-Fifteen-yard starts are timed and feedback is given to push the athletes harder based upon the results.

Sport back Squat; Sport Back Squat Isometric; Hurdle Hop; Half Squat Jump Weighted; 15 yard Starts

BOX 3-4
Bench Press 2OC; One Leg Med Ball Side Toss; One Arm Side Lat Pull Down; 90 90 Jump Twist

BOX 5
Glute Bar Lift; Face Band Pulls; 1 Arm Lat Pull Supine

BOX 6
-For the iso ball groin squeeze, take an athletic stance over a Swiss ball and squeeze the knees together into the ball as hard as possible
Glute Ham Hyper; Isometric Ball Groin Squeeze; Round House

BOX 7
-The DB shoulder press finishes on a complete rep
DB Shoulder Press; Hip Flex Band Pulls; Bar Curl

BOX 8
DB Tri Pro Sup; Chin Up; Jobes ECC

BLOCK THREE, MONDAY

100%	MONDAY	30-Nov-10			
		REPS	LOAD	SETS	NOTES
500	Sport Back Squat	5,3	250 - 335	1,1	Pw/ Cuban F8
	2-Min Rest/B-Breath				I band Rollers
500	Sport Back Squat	3	390 - 400	1	pw/cuban f8
	2-Min Rest/B-Breath				I band Rollers
500	Sport Back Squat	3	415 - 440	3	0:0:0:0
	Hurdle Hop	5		3	Pull Down
	15 rest- BB				
	1/2 SQ JMP Weighted	4		3	reactive
	15 rest- BB				
	15 Yard Starts	1		3	4:00 Rest
300	BENCH PRESS	5,3	150 - 200	1,1	Ext Shock
	2-Min Rest/B-Breath				
300	Bench Press	3	- 240	1	coach see
	2-Min Rest/B-Breath				Ext Shock
300	BENCH PRESS	4	205 - 210	3	2OC-d+1
	One Leg MB Side Toss	5		3	
	25 rest- BB				
	1 Bent Arm S. L.P Down	6		3	
	25 rest- BB				
	90 90 Jump Twist	5		3	
500	Glute Bar Lift	8	250 - 300	3	
	25 rest- BB				
	Face Band Pulls	8		3	
	25 rest- BB				
75	1 Arm Lat Pull Supine	10	50 - 55	3	
	GH HYPR	6		3	oc-A
	25 rest- BB				
	Iso Ball Grion Sqeeze	10S		3	
	25 rest- BB				
	Round House	8		3	
75	DB Shoulder Press	10	50 - 55	2	oc-D+1
	25 rest- BB				
	Hip FLX BND Pulls	6		2	
	25 rest- BB				
120	Bar Curl	10	80 - 85	2	
45	DB Tri Pro Sup	8	35 - 35	2	
	25 rest- BB				
180	Chin up	6	135 - 145	2	
	25 rest- BB				
	Jobes ECC	6		2	4;0;0;0;

COACHING POINTS AND EXERCISE TUTORIAL

Box 1-2
-Notice how the sets have become more reactive in the sport back squat work sets without any eccentric to isometrics actions. They are still paired with the three exercises following the sport back squat. If put together and trained for the six-week period, you will see great results.
Sport back Squat; Hurdle Hop; Half Squat Jump Weighted; 15 yard Starts

Box 3-4
-You can do the French contrast method with the upper body. However, this particular group of athletes were throwing athletes and it was too much stress for that type of athlete. Sticking with reactive, OC methods improved their throwing distance better than the French contrast methods.
Bench Press 2OC; One Leg Med Ball Side Toss; One Arm Side Lat Pull Down; 90 90 Jump Twist

Box 5
Glute Bar Lift; Face Band Pulls; 1 Arm Lat Pull Supine

Box 6
-The glute ham hyper was done with an advantageous (top half ROM) oscillatory position. This has proven to be somewhat effective for top end speed running, thus I use it during the concentric phase to help with dynamic neuromuscular adaptation.
Glute Ham Hyper; Isometric Ball Groin Squeeze; Round House

Box 7
DB Shoulder Press; Hip Flex Band Pulls; Bar Curl

Box 8
DB Tri Pro Sup; Chin Up; Jobes ECC

**The structure of this program limited the amount of change I allowed from block to block in terms of exercise selection. That is why most of the upper body and assistance exercises remained the same for the entire six-week mesocycle. This particular program was for throwing athletes, and changing too much during a particular transition phase of throwing made them much more sore during the skills acquisition development phase so exercises were kept the same for that reason.

√ Coach's Corner

Peaking with the Sport Back Squat
By: Ben Peterson and Cal Dietz
Edited By: Daniel Raimondi

The main question I usually get asked in regards to the sport back squat is, "When do you incorporate this in a training program?" With the sport back squat, what you want to decide on sooner rather than later is where to place it in your program to yield the best sport's performance results. There are two scenarios that I will paint here as well as my rationale for why we switch from a normal back squat to the sport back squat. Essentially, I've realized more and more that more advanced athletes need less absolute strength and require more sport specificity within their programs. With that in mind, we must realize that many of these are advanced athletes. This could be anyone from an elite high school athlete to a world class runner. Depending on who it is, he may not need to get stronger at that particular time to increase performance in his sport.

Again, starting sooner rather than later on the usage of the sport back squat becomes more important with the advanced athlete. I usually recommend a minimum of four to six weeks to allow the transformation and the true results for the peaking model to take place with the sport back squat in the advanced athlete. This is because the sport back squat is more sports-specific with its narrower stance. It's also more applicable to sport because of the direction in which force will be applied to the ground as opposed to a wider stance squat. Athletes don't need to keep working on hard, straining, maximal effort lifts in very wide stances. We want explosive, reactive athletes who can generate huge forces quickly in the direction where their sport will likely be played (i.e. narrow stance).

Keep in mind also that the sport back squat won't be as deep as a wider stance, deep back squat. Sport back squat depth should be somewhere around hamstring parallel or maybe a little lower, but ultimately this can be adjusted based upon how the particular athlete competes in his sport and at what level he squats down to. For example, a thrower may not squat as deep coming across the ring while performing his throw. A hockey player, on the other hand, may have a lower skating technique and therefore might squat to that particular depth.

Again—and I can't reiterate this enough—this method would be reserved for more advanced athletes. Let me first define 'advanced' as I apply it toward my programming. 'Advanced' essentially is an athlete who has some basic training age (maybe even a high school athlete). For sixteen to twenty weeks of training, use the normal back squat. To get the most out of the sport back squat, place it four to six weeks away from competition in a peaking model. This will yield high results. The second scenario is that you have a young athlete who isn't very strong in your program and you aren't sure when to place the sport back squat to get the best results. There are actually two scenarios with this particular athlete. The first scenario is the athlete will keep getting stronger with your normal wider squat. Three weeks prior to the most important peaking point, transfer him to a sport back squat.

The other scenario that could be used with this young athlete is that you actually switch him six to eight weeks out and still use heavier loads with the sports back squat. This would be for the purpose of getting and keeping the athlete very strong. Three weeks out, lighten the loads of the squat and attempt to move it extremely fast and explosively. Essentially, you want the athlete to be more reactive to transfer that strength into his sporting skill. The loads should be below 55 percent.

Another possibility in peaking with the sport back squat is one you may use with more advanced athletes (elite to high school level athletes who are already strong and have been training for sixteen to twenty weeks). You would actually peak in the sport back squat and switch them over to a lower load sport back squat at six to three weeks out from the most important peaking days. Then from week three to week one, you would reduce the load more and do a sport back squat jump teaching that athlete to apply even more force through the ground. One key technique that a coach must realize is that to transfer this force, you must use the ankle complex very effectively. For this, please refer to my ankle complex article. Another key technique would be to perform the movement utilizing the agonist and antagonist muscles most effectively. The athlete would pull himself into position using the antagonist musculature. Upon contact with the ground, the athlete then redirects the direction upward, attempting to jump as high as possible. This method is what I refer to as the antagonistically facilitated specialized method. Each repetition should be treated on its own so that the quality of the movement remains high. I must thank Dr Michael Yessis for his time and information in regards to using sport back squat methods.

4.7: WEDNESDAY, HIGH INTENSITY (MAXIMAL EFFORT)

LOADING

Wednesday is every strength coach's favorite day or at least my favorite day—the "go big or go home," let's get after it, slap the weight on the bar, high intensity day! Below, again, is a section of the loading table pertaining specifically to the high intensity day within the above 80 percent mesocycle. Just as before, sections that are shaded mean that these are loads that wouldn't be used at this point of the training week.

TABLE 4.11: WEDNESDAY LOADING (HIGH INTENSITY)				
% 1RM	MAXIMUM REPS POSSIBLE	HIGH QUALITY REPS (STRENGTH)	SETS (OFF-SEASON)	SETS (IN-SEASON)
97.5%	1–2	1	1–2	1–2
95 %	2	1	2–3	1–2
92.5%	2–3	1	3–4	1–2
90%	3–4	1	3–4	2–3
87.5%	4			
85%	4–5			
82.5%	5			
80%	5–6			
77.5%	6–7			
75%	7–8			

For the high intensity day, there aren't any triphasic means applied. Every high intensity day is simply that—high loads of 90–97 percent of the athlete's 1RM lifted with a reactive tempo to stimulate neuromuscular recruitment and neural rate coding and improve the organizational sequencing of the athlete. To ensure that the quality of work remains high, efficiently stimulating the nervous system and promoting positive adaptation through explosive force development, only one rep is performed per work set. As we discussed earlier in this section, it is much more advantageous to the athlete to perform seven sets of single repetitions than to perform three sets of three repetitions. In higher reps sets with such high loads, the neuromuscular system will fatigue after the first set to such a degree that the ability to perform high quality work thereafter is impossible.

TABLE 4.12: WEDNESDAY TRIPHASIC LOADING PARAMETERS					
BLOCK	INTENSITY	LOAD	TEMPO	REPS	SETS
BLOCK 1 (ECCENTRIC)	HIGH INTENSITY	90–97%	REACTIVE 0:0:0:0	1	1–4
BLOCK 2 (ISOMETRIC)		90–97%	REACTIVE 0:0:0:0	1	1–4
BLOCK 3 (CONCENTRIC)		90–97%	REACTIVE 0:0:0:0	1	1–4

The tempos and rep ranges outlined in table 4.12 are to be used primarily with the specialized method of applying training means discussed earlier in this section. All assistance work should be performed within the loading parameters for that day within the undulated block, in this case 90–97 percent. An exception to this rule on this (the high intensity day of the week) is to add assistance work in the form of plyometrics. Although they aren't high load means, they exert an enormous amount of force and stress on the athlete. For examples of assistance work that should be used to optimize performance gains and for suggested rep ranges of these exercises within each block, refer to the programs throughout this section.

SEQUENCING

There isn't any sequencing required for the high intensity day of the mesocycle. Walking into the weight room on this day, the goal is simple—move a heavy load as fast as possible. The athlete must be reactive. Remember, the heavy loads alone provide sufficient stimulus to the athlete to promote positive adaptation without the addition of other methods or means.

WORKOUT

Below, you will find Wednesday's workout for each block of the three-day above 80 percent model—the eccentric block, isometric block, and concentric block. Just as before, the column on the left is the actual workout using our "imaginary" athlete to calculate the loads used on each exercise. The column on the right, labeled "Coaching Points," gives further explanation about exercise sequencing and important coaching queues to use with your athletes. At the end of this section, you will find workouts for each block of a four-day, five-day, six-day, and two-day in-season model.

BLOCK ONE, WEDNESDAY

100%	Wednesday	4-Nov-10			
		REPS	LOAD	SETS	NOTES
500	Back Squat	5,3	250 - 335	1,1	
	2-Min Rest/B-Breath				
500	Back Squat	3	■ - 400	1	
	2-Min Rest/B-Breath				
500	Back Squat	3	440 - 465	4	
	Stding SQ Drop Jump	4		3	
	25 rest- BB				
	Delt BO Lat Reb Drop	4		3	
	25 rest- BB				
	Thors Hammer	12		3	
300	BENCH PRESS	5,3	150 - 200	1,1	
	2-Min Rest/B-Breath				
300	Bench Press	3	235 - 240	1	
	2-Min Rest/B-Breath				
300	BENCH PRESS	3	270 - 280	3	miss 2 board
	Med Ball Chest Pass	5		3	
	25 rest- BB				
	1 Arm DB Row	6		3	
	25 rest- BB				
	Pike SWB Abs	5		3	
200	DB Walking Lunge	4		3	Band
	Pair w/				Squeeze
	Laying External Rot	6		3	
	Pair w/				
	1 S.A S. R.G Lat P	10		3	
	GH HYPR	8		3	
	Pair w/				
	Iso Ball Grion Sqeeze	10S		3	
	Pair w/				
	Bam Bam	8		3	
	Inc Delt Lat Reb Drop	6		2	
	25 rest- BB				
	Hip FLXor ISO Pull	6		2	
	25 rest- BB				
75	DB Shoulder Press	10	50 - 55	2	oc-D+1
150	Rev Grip Tri Push	8	115 - 120	2	
	25 rest- BB				
	Bicep shock curls	6		2	
	25 rest- BB				
	Blackburn	6		2	

COACHING POINTS AND EXERCISE TUTORIAL

Box 1-2

-Notice that the back squat is a wider stance back squat used to involve the posterior chain during a max effort squat.

-As in the sports back squat, the key coaching point for this movement is press your feet through the ground.

-Even though we have a wider stance, I don't direct the athletes to drive through the hips.

-These work sets are paired with the three exercises below it. This allows for the athlete to rest and recover between high intensity work sets so that the athlete doesn't stand around for four or five minutes.

Back Squat; Squat Drop Jump; Delt Bent Over Lateral Reactive Drop; Thors Hammer

Box 3-4

-The work sets in the bench press in this particular day are heavy (90–92 percent%).

-If the athlete misses or it is believed that he will miss the next rep of a set, we slide a two-board on to his chest, limiting his range of motion so he can get the rep and finish the set on his own.

-The medicine ball chest pass is always done with one arm. I've found little value in the chest pass because of the lack of stretch reflex and the amount of force generated.

Bench Press; Med Ball Pass; One Arm Dumbbell Row; Pike Swiss Ball Abs

Box 5

-The dumbbell walking lunge is done with a band tied to the athlete's back. The band is pulling backward while the athlete is walking forward to apply force in the same direction as he does when he runs.

-In this particular phase, the athletes are pausing their lunge at the bottom for a couple seconds and trying to squeeze their legs together as like in the running action.

Dumbbell Walking Lunge; External Rotation Prone; Single Arm Supine Rev Grip Lat Pull

Box 6

Glute Ham Hyper; Isometric Ball Groin Squeeze; Bam Bams

Box 7

Incline Delt Drop; Hip Flexor Isometric Pull; DB Shoulder Press

Box 8

Reverse Grip Tricep Push Down Adaptability ; Bicep Curl Shock; Blackburn

BLOCK TWO, WEDNESDAY

100%	Wednesday	18-Nov-10	REPS	LOAD	SETS	NOTES
500	Back Squat		5,3	250 - 335	1,1	
	2-Min Rest/B-Breath					
500	Back Squat		3	■ - 400	1	
	2-Min Rest/B-Breath					
500	Back Squat		3	440 - 465	4	
	Stding SQ Drop Jump		4		3	
	25 rest- BB					
	Delt BO Lat Reb Drop		4		3	
	25 rest- BB					
	Thors Hammer		12		3	
300	BENCH PRESS		5,3	150 - 200	1,1	
	2-Min Rest/B-Breath					
300	Bench Press		3	235 - 240	1	
	2-Min Rest/B-Breath					
300	BENCH PRESS		3	270 - 280	3	miss 2 board
	Med Ball Chest Pass		5		3	
	25 rest- BB					
	1 Arm DB Row		6		3	
	25 rest- BB					
	Pike SWB Abs		5		3	
	Walking Band Lunge Jump		6		3	Drop
	Pair w/					
	Laying External Rot		6		3	
	Pair w/					
	1 S.A.S. R.G Lat P		10		3	
	GH HYPR		8		3	
	Pair w/					
	Iso Ball Groin Sqeeze		10S		3	
	Pair w/					
	Bam Bam		8		3	
	Inc Delt Lat Reb Drop		6		2	
	25 rest- BB					
	Hip FLXor ISO Pull		6		2	
	25 rest- BB					
75	DB Shoulder Press		10	50 - 55	2	oc-D+1
150	Rev Grip Tri Push		8	115 - 120	2	
	25 rest- BB					
	Bicep shock curls		6		2	
	25 rest- BB					
	Blackburn		6		2	

COACHING POINTS AND EXERCISE TUTORIAL

Box 1-2

-Some key points to remember and remind the athletes when performing the back squat: be sure to keep the back flat, chest up, and torso tight. The loads used on this day are heavier so be sure to be aware of technical breakdowns
-For the standing squat drop jump, pull the body into position using the anterior hip musculature; immediately upon impact with the ground, jump as high as possible
-For the Thors hammer, keep the elbow tucked into the side
Back Squat; Squat Drop Jump; Delt Bent Over Lateral Reactive Drop; Thors Hammer

Box 3-4

-Some key points to remember and remind the athletes when performing the bench press: set up as tight as possible on the bench, with an arched back and retracted scapula. The loads used here are heavier so be aware of technical breakdown
Bench Press ; Med Ball Pass; One Arm Dumbell Row; Pike Swiss Ball Abs

Box 5

-The biggest change is in the walking band lunge jump. The athlete will actually jump into the lunge drop and then explode forward with the band still attached to him.
--The walking drop lunge jump with a band is a highly reactive exercise; be sure not to put too much tension on the band as it will decrease the athlete's ability to generate force rapidly.
Walking Drop Lunge Jump; External Rotation Prone; Single Arm Supine Rev Grip Lat Pull

Box 6

-The iso ball groin squeeze is performed with a Swiss ball between the knees in an athletic stance; squeeze the knees together as hard as possible into the ball
Glute Ham Hyper; Isometric Ball Groin Squeeze; Bam Bams

Box 7

Incline Delt Drop; Hip Flexor Isometric Pull; DB Shoulder Press

Box 8

-During the bicep shock curl, the athlete must be sure to turn the palms down and away from the bar after they release; when bringing the hands back up, supinate(palm up) the hands and catch the bar rapidly
-The bicep shock curls develop explosiveness of the arms
Reverse Grip Tricep Push Down Adaptability ; Bicep Curl Shock; Blackburn

BLOCK THREE, WEDNESDAY

100%	Wednesday	2-Dec-10			
		REPS	LOAD	SETS	NOTES
500	Back Squat	5,3	250 - 335	1,1	
	2-Min Rest/B-Breath				
500	Back Squat	3	■ - 400	1	
	2-Min Rest/B-Breath				
500	Back Squat	3	440 - 465	4	
	Stding SQ Drop Jump	4		3	
	25 rest- BB				
	Delt BO Lat Reb Drop	4		3	
	25 rest- BB				
	Thors Hammer	12		3	
300	BENCH PRESS	5,3	150 - 200	1,1	
	2-Min Rest/B-Breath				
300	Bench Press	3	235 - 240	1	
	2-Min Rest/B-Breath				
300	BENCH PRESS	3	270 - 280	3	miss 2 board
	Med Ball Chest Pass	5		3	
	25 rest- BB				
	1 Arm DB Row	6		3	
	25 rest- BB				
	Pike SWB Abs	5		3	
	Walking Band Lunge Jump	6		3	Drop
	Pair w/				
	Laying External Rot	6		3	
	Pair w/				
	1 S.A.S. R.G Lat P	10		3	
	GH HYPR	8		3	
	Pair w/				
	Iso Ball Grion Sqeeze	10S		3	
	Pair w/				
	Bam Bam	8		3	
	Inc Delt Lat Reb Drop	6		2	
	25 rest- BB				
	Hip FLXor ISO Pull	6		2	
	25 rest- BB				
75	DB Shoulder Press	10	50 - 55	2	oc-D+1
150	Rev Grip Tri Push	8	115 - 120	2	
	25 rest- BB				
	Bicep shock curls	6		2	
	25 rest- BB				
	Blackburn	6		2	

COACHING POINTS AND EXERCISE TUTORIAL

*The same methods are used in coaching this maximal effort day.

Box 1-2

-Some key points to remember and remind the athletes when performing the back squat: be sure to keep the back flat, chest up, and torso tight. The loads used on this day are heavier so be sure to be aware of technical breakdowns
-For the standing squat drop jump, pull the body into position using the anterior hip musculature; immediately upon impact with the ground, jump as high as possible
-For the Thors hammer, keep the elbow tucked into the side.
Back Squat; Squat Drop Jump; Delt Bent Over Lateral Reactive Drop; Thors Hammer

Box 3-4

-Some key points to remember and remind the athletes when performing the bench press: set up as tight as possible on the bench, with an arched back and retracted scapula. The loads used here are heavier so be aware of technical breakdown.
Bench Press ; Med Ball Pass; One Arm Dumbell Row; Pike Swiss Ball Abs

Box 5

-The biggest change is in the walking band lunge jump. The athlete will actually jump into the lunge drop and then explode forward with the band still attached to him.
-The walking drop lunge jump with a band is a highly reactive exercise; be sure not to put too much tension on the band as it will decrease the athlete's ability to generate force rapidly.
Walking Drop Lunge Jump; External Rotation Prone; Single Arm Supine Rev Grip Lat Pull

Box 6

-In the glute ham hyper, more advanced athletes can focus on dropping as fast as they can to full extension and then rip themselves up. For less advanced athletes, continue to perform the standard glute ham method.
Glute Ham Hyper; Isometric Ball Groin Squeeze; Bam Bams

Box 7

Incline Delt Drop; Hip Flexor Isometric Pull; DB Shoulder Press

Box 8

Reverse Grip Tricep Push Down Adaptability ; Bicep Curl Shock; Blackburn

√ COACH'S CORNER

SINGLE LEG VERSUS DOUBLE LEG TRAINING: ADDRESSING THE CONTROVERSY
BY CAL DIETZ
EDITED BY BEN PETERSON

In the past several years, many controversial articles have been written about whether double leg training is superior to single leg training and even if bilateral exercises (i.e. heavy squats or leg presses) are necessary to achieve the same results. Keep in mind that results are relative to the particular sport you're training for. Some sports don't need very intensive measures to get these types of results. For example, I find that golf is a sport where if an athlete seems to be strong enough, he can reach his intended goals by doing mainly single leg work and those types of exercises to get the desired results. Please keep in mind that the following are my opinions as well as those of many other unnamed strength coaches.

So in regards to the single versus double leg debate, my thoughts immediately jump to getting results in testing. The testing results aren't necessarily getting strong in the back squat. These are based on 10s, 20s, pro agility, vertical jumps, and mainly the explosive sports and sports' tests. In review of my records over the last decade and different transitions that have happened for athletes from the double leg training to the single leg training, I researched and thought about as many instances as possible within our own system of training. This is what I found—I was unable to find any records, testing results, or performance results based upon an athlete who had trained in our system over one year and as much as three years with the double leg back squat or front squat methods that were able to reproduce results in testing and/or performance based sports such as track and field.

I will give one example and one example only. I had a very athletic female athlete who I considered late to mature physically. She was biomechanically gifted strength wise when she walked into the weight room. Her first test was a pro agility. Her numbers were a 4.91, no hand touch, pro agility. She simply ran a pro agility by getting her foot beyond the line. After fifteen to sixteen months of training including in-season training protocols, she was able to run a 4.32 in the pro agility without a hand touch. After a couple of years of severe wrist and shoulder injuries, we were unable to load the body with a double leg approach. The best results she could get in a pro agility after an entire summer of training extremely hard was a 4.65 pro agility.

This is an obvious and simple example of how I'm unable to reproduce efforts when single leg work is the main focus of a program. Trust me—I believe in single leg work. I use it in many of my programming methods, but I truly believe and have seen that I can't get the results with these particular methods by only using single leg work. Here is something we must think of when addressing single versus double leg work. It would almost be impossible to do, but if an Olympic lifting athlete removed all double leg work except in the clean and snatch movements, would he be able to hit maximal effort lifts? I believe we know the answer to this without answering it. So then we get back to addressing why particular double leg exercises produce superior results.

I truly believe the main reason is a systemic effect over the whole body with a very intense response to heavy loads(instability via single leg lifts decrease motor unit recruitment). Essentially, in my system, back squats rarely go over ten seconds in duration with a complete set, and it is a very intense three to ten seconds of squatting. It's more efficient to work the alactic system using bilateral lifts. When doing a single leg exercise, most people will raise the repetitions thereby stressing certain energy systems more than others due to the fact that both legs need to be exercised. For my system, which deals with many alactic and alactic aerobic sports, I've found that single leg lifts can't compare in intensity to their double leg counterparts. Please keep in mind, however, that one way to offset the exercise becoming so anaerobic lactic would be to do the left leg, rest thirty to forty seconds, and do the right leg. This will keep the emphasis alactic, though the intensity will still be reduced due to the inherent loading limitations of single leg exercises.

I have various methods of programming for the back squat and single leg work. Some of my programs have only squatting with minimal single leg work whereas other programs have minimal back squatting and mainly single leg work. Some of my methods use only single leg work. I truly believe that some of the most beneficial programs are the beginner variations where we'll back squat and do single leg work initially and then transfer to single leg work based upon loads and speed of the movement. I truly believe that one can pull back squats four to six weeks out of the main competition and time of performance and still keep relative strength to the sport's performance extremely high. Even if the athletes lose strength in the squatting motor skill, it doesn't mean they lose performance. It can actually mean the opposite if you're doing the right exercises in the latter part of the program to peak for performance.

4.8: FRIDAY, LOW INTENSITY (HIGH VOLUME)

LOADING

Friday is very similar to Monday with the exception that you replace the moderate intensity level with extra volume. By the sixth week of training and working out three to five days a week, it gets hard to drag your butt into a weight room and give it 100 percent. Returning to previous stimuli week after week often results in stagnant training gains. These are attributed not only to the athlete's body adapting to the stressor but also to a lack of interest from the athlete, which decreases his mental state of focus and intensity during training sessions. To try and keep the training level as high as possible, I've found that it works best to expand the list of methods used to keep the athlete's attention, focus, and intensity. Training means used on Friday include but aren't limited to bodybuilding methods, Strongman training, dinosaur training, and CrossFit methods.

These methods are applied by using the loading variables listed in table 4.13. Any area that is shaded signifies that it is a load that shouldn't be used on the low intensity/high volume day.

TABLE 4.13: FRIDAY LOADING (LOW INTENSITY)

% 1RM	MAXIMUM REPS POSSIBLE	HIGH QUALITY REPS (VOLUME)	SETS (OFF-SEASON)	SETS (IN-SEASON)
95 %	2			
92.5%	2–3			
90%	3–4			
87.5%	4			
85%	4–5			
82.5%	5			
80%	5–6	3–4	4–5	IN-SEASON VOLUME COMES FROM PRACTICE
77.5%	6–7	3–4	4–5	
75%	7–8	4–5	4–5	

When we take the loading variables from above and apply them to the triphasic methods outlined earlier in this section, the result is what you see in table 4.14. The loads for all three blocks remain the same. The target parameter for this mesocycle is general strength, so the stimulus (stress) placed on the nervous system must remain within the same range to promote the greatest levels of adaptation. The eccentric stress is reduced by one second per set during block one to offset some stress that is replaced by the extra volume of the workout. During block two, a three-second eccentric phase is added to a reduced isometric phase (as compared to its related Monday tempo) to again shift some of the stress from a higher intensity exercise to volume work performed during the remaining parts of the workout. At this point in the training week, it is unlikely that the athlete's nervous system is sufficiently primed to still handle the high levels of stress placed on it by longer duration eccentric and isometric phases. As a result, the workload is shifted from high intensity means to ones that apply stress through higher (lower intensity) volumes.

TABLE 4.14: FRIDAY TRIPHASIC LOADING PARAMETERS					
BLOCK	INTENSITY	LOAD	TEMPO	REPS	SETS
BLOCK 1 (ECCENTRIC)	HIGH VOLUME	75–80%	5:0:0:0	3–4	4–5
BLOCK 2 (ISOMETRIC)		75–80%	3:2:0:0	3–4	4–5
BLOCK 3 (CONCENTRIC)		75–80%	REACTIVE 0:0:0:0	3–4	4–5

The tempos and rep ranges outlined above are to be used primarily with the specialized methods of applying training means discussed earlier in this section. When programming for assistance work, don't worry about these tempos because additional emphasis on eccentric and isometric loading will overwork the neurological system of the athlete. As always, there are exceptions to this rule. As an athlete progresses and is able to handle ever higher stress loads, additional triphasic means can be programmed into some assistance work. For less advanced athletes, all assistance work should be performed within the loading parameters for that day within the undulated block, which is in this case 75–80 percent. For examples of assistance work that should be used to optimize performance gains and for suggested rep ranges of these exercises within each block, refer to the programs throughout this section.

SEQUENCING

The sequencing of these exercises is very similar to Monday's. One point to make here is select a training means that would be considered a less stressful version of the compound exercise chosen on Monday. For example, if the athlete performs a back squat on Monday, have him perform a back squat with weight releasers on Friday. Choose an exercise that is slightly less stressful, as the athlete and his nervous system are fatigued by this point and aren't able to handle high intensities any longer. Below is a second example of triphasic exercise sequencing using the bench press.

TABLE 4.15: FRIDAY TRIPHASIC EXERCISE SEQUENCING (BENCH PRESS)		
BLOCK 1 (ECCENTRIC)	BLOCK 2 (ISOMETRIC)	BLOCK 3 (CONCENTRIC)
BENCH PRESS ECCENTRIC TEMPO - 6:0:0:0	BENCH PRESS ISOMETRIC TEMPO - 0:3:0:0	BENCH PRESS CONCENTRIC TEMPO - 0:0:0:0
BENCH PRESS CLOSE GRIP ECCENTRIC TEMPO - 6:0:0:0	DB BENCH PRESS ISOMETRIC TEMPO - 0:3:0:0	DB BENCH PRESS WITH BANDS TEMPO - 0:0:0:0
	INCLINE DB PRESS ISOMETRIC TEMPO - 0:3:0:0	DB INCLINE PRESS TEMPO - 0:0:0:0
	BENCH PRESS CLOSE GRIP ISOMETRIC TEMPO - 0:3:0:0	CLOSE GRIP BENCH PRESS TEMPO - 0:0:0:0

WORKOUT

Below you will find Friday's workout for each block of the three-day above 80 percent model. Coaching points with their respective hyperlinks to the exercises are in the right-hand column. At the end of this section, you will find workouts for each block of a four-day, five-day, six-day, and two-day in-season model.

BLOCK ONE, FRIDAY

100%	FRIDAY	6-Nov-10			
		REPS	LOAD	SETS	NOTES
200	STEP UP	8	150 - 160	3	5:0:0:0:
	15 Rest-BB				
	INCLINE SIT UP	8		3	
	15 Rest-BB				
	Ball LG Curl	10		3	
90	DB INCLINE BENCH	15	60 - 65	3	oc-D+1
	15 Rest-BB				
75	DB Twist	15	50 - 55	3	
	15 Rest-BB				
	Jobes	6		3	4:0:0:0
200	Walking Lunge	8	150 - 160	3	Squeeze
	15 Rest-BB				
75	DB Fly	8	40 - 45	3	
	15 Rest-BB				
	Delt Lat Rebound Drop	8		3	
500	Glute Bar Lift	8	250 - 300	3	
	15 Rest-BB				
	Rope Circles	15		3	Each Way
	15 Rest-BB				
180	Gripper	15	115 - 125	3	
120	BAR CURL	8	85 - 90	2	
	15 Rest-BB				
150	TRI PUSH DOWN	8	105 - 115	2	
	15 Rest-BB				
	90 90 Groin ISO Hold	10		2	
60	Zotman Curl	6	45 - 50	2	
	15 Rest-BB				
	Speed Abduction	8		2	
	15 Rest-BB				
240	Close Grip Bench	6	60 - 70	2	3 Board
	Single Leg Iso DL	6 s		2	
	15 Rest-BB				
	Rope Vertical	15		2	
	15 Rest-BB				
	Full BCH Curl Up	8		2	

COACHING POINTS AND EXERCISE TUTORIAL

Box 1

-Notice that there isn't a French contrast method. A third day of this method can be applied with well trained athletes. However, make sure they aren't overworked.
-This particular program shows an example of athletes who may not be able to handle all the loading and shock that exists with the French contrast method, so we did a step-up with an eccentric component.
-Notice that the rest on this particular day is reduced to increase the work capacities of the athlete during this training cycle.
Step up; Incline sit up; Ball LG curl

Box 2

-Make sure to finish the oscillatory incline DB bench on a full rep
OC DB Incline Bench; DB twist; Jobes

Box 3

-The delt lat rebound drop develops the explosive capacity of the shoulder, and therefore must be done fast
Walking Lunge; DB Fly; Delt Lat Rebound Drop

Box 4

-The rope circles are done in various ways—in and out, down and up, and circles in multiple fashions. This is the work capacity component for the shoulder. I truly believe that it provides effective shock training for the posterior shoulder in aiding the athlete.
Glute bar lift; Rope circles; Gripper

Box 5

-The 90 90 groin iso hold is a prehab exercise for the adductors
Bar curl; Tri push down; 90 90 groin iso hold

Box 6

-Speed abduction: When the athlete pulls the foot in, the toes should come toward the midline of the body. As the athlete pushes the foot back out, the toes should be externally located during this movement.
Zottman curl; Speed abduction; Close grip bench

Box 7

-The single leg iso deadlift is one of the most effective strength builders in the deep position that I've ever used.
Single leg iso DL; Rope vertical; Full BCH curl up

BLOCK TWO, FRIDAY

100%	FRIDAY	20-Nov-10			
		REPS	LOAD	SETS	NOTES
225	Single Leg Squat	8	170 - 180	3	0:5:0:0
	15 Rest-BB				
	INCLINE SIT UP	8		3	
	15 Rest-BB				
	Ball LG Curl	10		3	
90	DB INCLINE BENCH	15	60 - 65	3	oc-D+1
	15 Rest-BB				
75	DB Twist	15	50 - 55	3	
	15 Rest-BB				
	Jobes	6		3	4:0:0:0
	Walking Drop Lunge Jump	8		3	
	15 Rest-BB				
75	DB Fly	8	40 - 45	3	
	15 Rest-BB				
	Delt Lat Rebound Drop	8		3	
500	Glute Bar Lift	8	250 - 300	3	
	15 Rest-BB				
	Rope Circles	15		3	Each Way
	15 Rest-BB				
180	Gripper	15	115 - 125	3	
120	BAR CURL	8	85 - 90	2	
	15 Rest-BB				
150	TRI PUSH DOWN	8	105 - 115	2	
	15 Rest-BB				
	90 90 Groin ISO Hold	10		2	
60	Zotman Curl	6	45 - 50	2	
	15 Rest-BB				
	Speed Abduction	8		2	
	15 Rest-BB				
240	Close Grip Bench	6	60 - 70	2	3 Board
	Single Leg Iso DL	6 s		2	
	15 Rest-BB				
	Rope Vertical	15		2	
	15 Rest-BB				
	Full BCH Curl Up	8		2	

COACHING POINTS AND EXERCISE TUTORIAL

Box 1
-Notice the change from a step-up to a single leg squat for the isometric. It isn't practical to do a step-up in the isometric phase or a step-up in the reactive phase.
Single Leg Squat; Incline sit up; Ball LG curl

Box 2
-Remember to finish the DB incline bench on a complete rep
OC DB Incline Bench; DB twist; Jobes

Box 3
-A key component for every plyometric and strength movement with the legs is to drive your foot through the ground.
-The walking drop lunge jump employs principles from the AFSM method, whereby an athlete needs to pull themselves down into position hard and fast, and immediately reverse the direction forward explosively
-The delt lat rebound drop develops the explosive capacity of the shoulder, and must therefore be done as fast as possible
Walking Drop Lunge Jump; DB Fly; Delt Lat Rebound Drop

Box 4
Glute bar lift; Rope circles; Gripper

Box 5
-The 90 90 groin iso hold is a prehab exercise for the adductors
Bar curl; Tri push down; 90 90 groin iso hold

Box 6
-Speed abduction: When the athlete pulls the foot in, the toes should come toward the midline of the body. As the athlete pushes the foot back out, the toes should be externally rotated.
Zottman curl; Speed abduction; Close grip bench

Box 7
-The single leg iso deadlift is one of the most effective strength builders in the deep position that I've ever used.
Single leg iso DL; Rope vertical;; Full BCH curl up

BLOCK THREE, FRIDAY

100%	FRIDAY	4-Dec-10	REPS	LOAD	SETS	NOTES
225	Single Leg Squat		8	170 - 180	3	
	15 Rest-BB					
	INCLINE SIT UP		8		3	
	15 Rest-BB					
	Ball LG Curl		10		3	
90	DB INCLINE BENCH		15	60 - 65	3	oc-D+1
	15 Rest-BB					
75	DB Twist		15	50 - 55	3	
	15 Rest-BB					
	Jobes		6		3	
	Walking Drop Lunge Jump		8		3	
	15 Rest-BB					
75	DB Fly		8	40 - 45	3	
	15 Rest-BB					
	Delt Lat Rebound Drop		8		3	
500	Glute Bar Lift		8	250 - 300	3	
	15 Rest-BB					
	Rope Circles		15		3	Each Way
	15 Rest-BB					
180	Gripper		15	115 - 125	3	
120	BAR CURL		8	85 - 90	2	
	15 Rest-BB					
150	TRI PUSH DOWN		8	105 - 115	2	
	15 Rest-BB					
	90 90 Groin ISO Hold		10		2	
60	Zotman Curl		6	45 - 50	2	
	15 Rest-BB					
	Speed Abduction		8		2	
	15 Rest-BB					
240	Close Grip Bench		6	60 - 70	2	3 Board
	Single Leg Iso DL		6 s		2	
	15 Rest-BB					
	Rope Vertical		15		2	
	15 Rest-BB					
	Full BCH Curl Up		8		2	

COACHING POINTS AND EXERCISE TUTORIAL

BOX 1

-Some points to keep in mind while doing the single leg squat: as the load increases, athletes are liable to decrease their range of motion; as such, it is important to constantly remind them to sink down towards ground, keeping the back flat and chest up
Single Leg Squat; Incline sit up; Ball LG curl

BOX 2

-The DB incline bench is performed in the oscillatory manner, and finishes on a complete rep
OC DB Incline Bench; DB twist; Jobes

BOX 3

-The walking drop lunge jump is performed without a band; the athlete, just as with any AFSM exercise, pulls themselves into position powerfully. After the athlete is in the lunge position, jump forward as far as possible. This is a highly reactive exercise
Walking Drop Lunge Jump; DB Fly; Delt Lat Rebound Drop

BOX 4

-Rope circles can be perfomed in many ways, such as side to side, up/down, and in/out
Glute bar lift; Rope circles; Gripper

BOX 5

-The 90 90 groin iso hold is a prehab exercise for the adductors
Bar curl; Tri push down; 90 90 groin iso hold

BOX 6

-Speed abduction: When the athlete pulls the foot in, the toes should come toward the midline of the body. As the athlete pushes the foot back out, the toes should be externally rotated.
Zottman curl; Speed abduction; Close grip bench

BOX 7

-The single leg iso deadlift is one of the most effective strength builders in the deep position that I've ever used.
Single leg iso DL; Rope vertical;; Full BCH curl up

√ COACH'S CORNER

ACCELERATED PLYOMETRICS
BY CAL DIETZ AND BEN PETERSON
EDITED BY DANIEL RAIMONDI

Approximately nine years ago, I was fortunate to come across a motion analysis system that our mechanical engineering department possessed. This device contained nine cameras placed systematically such that it could detect a multitude of human movements and joint angles to find out what was really going on in sport. While utilizing this system, I analyzed a number of athletes in the weight room and on the field with this elite camera system. To be clear, I couldn't set these cameras up myself. Our strength and conditioning staff had to have biomedical engineering students assemble the entire system in order to run these tests and analyze various movements.

One day while analyzing the data, I began to realize that during the second and third step in running and skating, I couldn't mimic the speed qualities that took place during those steps in the weight room by using conventional plyometric exercises. At that point it dawned on me to unload the human body while it did those jumping movements to mimic the speed at which the second, third, fourth, and fifth step in skating and running took place. Keep in mind, I usually use double leg plyometrics with this particular accelerated method because of the speed involved in the extension of the hips and knees. I realize that many strength coaches think single leg plyometrics are more sport-specific because sports are played mainly on one leg. This is an opinion I can't disagree with. However, what I will disagree with is that a single leg plyometric, as shown by this motion analysis machine, is so much slower in producing forces that it doesn't mimic what is taking place in sports. In real life, single leg plyometrics are beneficial in teaching the human body to be more explosive for the same reason that double leg plyometrics teach a constant load (body weight) to accelerate faster. With double leg plyometrics, it must be noted that because the weight per limb is distributed, there is a higher potential for developing speed because of the shorter amortization phase, and thus, a more explosive rebound.

Most coaches are incorrect in their programming because they place single leg plyometrics after double leg plyometrics. They believe this to be the logical training progression because the single leg requires more strength. Within a block scheme, the programming of plyometric jumps should look like this:

1. Single leg plyometrics
2. Double leg plyometrics
3. Single leg accelerated plyometrics
4. Double leg accelerated plyometrics

Right there you have four blocks of training utilizing the natural progression of least sport-specific to most sport-specific for peaking an athlete. Single leg plyometrics should be viewed more as a strength plyometric whereas double leg plyometrics develop speed. In closing, when using the accelerated plyometrics, one must keep in mind that to get the speed and explosive qualities to transfer to the sporting field, you must provide movements that mimic speed and joint angles of what is taking place in the sport you're training.

4.9: ABOVE 80 PERCENT THREE-DAY PROGRAM OVERVIEW

TABLE 4.16: UNDULATING BLOCK MODEL							
TRAINING WEEK:		DAY 1	DAY 2	DAY 3	DAY 4	DAY 5	DAY 6
3-DAY MODEL	FOCUS	TOTAL BODY	OFF	TOTAL BODY	OFF	TOTAL BODY	OFF
	LOAD	82–87%		90–97%		75–80%	
	MEANS APPLIED	TRIPHASIC		DYNAMIC		TRIPHASIC	

TABLE 4.17: ABOVE 80 PERCENT THREE-DAY CONDITIONING MODEL			
TRAINING DAY	**CONDITIONING GOAL**	**SPECIAL INSTRUCTIONS**	**EXAMPLE WORKOUT**
DAY 1	**Long Sprints *or* Short Sprints with Reduced Rest** (Speed Conditioning)	• Sprints over 15 seconds or • Sprints under 10, recovery under 20 seconds.	• High Quality Lactic Anaerobic Power Training Builder • Metabolic Injury Prevention Runs
DAY 2	**Short Sprints** (High Quality Speed)	• Sprints under 10 seconds • Full recovery; rest 90–120 seconds.	• Alactic High Quality Workout • Flying 60's • 16 Week Short Sprint Workouts • Cone Agility
DAY 3	**Longer Sprints *or* Continuous Running** (Oxidative Conditioning)	This day is purely work capacity focused	• Aerobic Work Capacity Training Builder • Game Speed Conditioning • Bike Conditioning • TrashBall

*Additional conditioning models for four-day, five-day, and six-day training models are shown in successive sections of this chapter.

BLOCK ONE (3-DAY): ABOVE 80% ECCENTRIC PHASE (2-3 WEEKS)

MONDAY — 2-Nov-10

100%	Exercise	REPS	LOAD	SETS	NOTES
500	Sport Back Squat	5,3	250 - 335	1,1	Pwr Cplx F8
	2-Min Rest/B-Breath				1 band Rollers
500	Sport Back Squat	3	390 - 400	1	pwr/cuban f8
	2-Min Rest/B-Breath				1 band Rollers
500	Sport Back Squat	3	415 - 440	3	6:0:0:0
	2-Min Rest/B-Breath				
	Hurdle Hop	5		3	Pull Down
	15 rest- BB				
	1/2 SQ JMP Weighted	4		3	reactive
	15 rest- BB				
	15 Yard Starts	1		3	4:00 Rest
300	BENCH PRESS	5,3	150 - 200	1,1	Ext Shock
	2-Min Rest/B-Breath				
300	Bench Press	3	- 240	1	coach see
	2-Min Rest/B-Breath				Ext Shock
300	BENCH PRESS	4	205 - 210	3	20C-d+1
	One Leg MB Side Toss	5		3	Pause
	25 rest- BB				
	1 Bent Arm S; LP Down	6		3	3:0:0:0
	25 rest- BB				
	90 90 Jump Twist	5		3	
500	Glute Bar Lift	8	250 - 300	3	
	25 rest- BB				
	Face Band Pulls	8		3	
	25 rest- BB				
75	1 Arm Lat Pull Supine	10	50 - 55	3	
	GH HYPR	6		3	
	25 rest- BB				
	Iso Ball Grion Sqeeze	10S		3	
	25 rest- BB				
	Round House	8		2	
75	DB Shoulder Press	10	50 - 55	2	oc-D+1
	25 rest- BB				
	Hip FLX BND Pulls	6		2	
	25 rest- BB				
105	Drag Curl	10	70 - 75	2	
45	DB Tri Pro Sup	8	35 - 35	2	
	25 rest- BB				
180	Chin up	6	135 - 145	2	
	25 rest- BB				
	Jobes ECC	6		2	4:0:0:0;

Wednesday — 4-Nov-10

100%	Exercise	REPS	LOAD	SETS	NOTES
500	Back Squat	5,3	250 - 335	1,1	
	2-Min Rest/B-Breath				
500	Back Squat	3	- 400	1	
	2-Min Rest/B-Breath				
500	Back Squat	3	440 - 465	4	
	Stding SQ Drop Jump	4		3	
	25 rest- BB				
	Delt BO Lat Reb Drop	4		3	
	25 rest- BB				
	Thors Hammer	12		3	
300	BENCH PRESS	5,3	150 - 200	1,1	
	2-Min Rest/B-Breath				
300	Bench Press	3	235 - 240	1	
	2-Min Rest/B-Breath				
300	BENCH PRESS	3	270 - 280	3	miss 2 board
	Med Ball Chest Pass	5		3	
	25 rest- BB				
	1 Arm DB Row	6		3	
	25 rest- BB				
	Pike SWB Abs	5		3	
200	DB Walking Lunge	4		3	Band
	Pair w/				
	Laying External Rot	6		3	Squeeze
	Pair w/				
	1 S.A.S. R.G Lat P	10		3	
	GH HYPR	8		3	
	Pair w/				
	Iso Ball Grion Sqeeze	10S		3	
	Pair w/				
	Bam Bam	8		3	
75	Inc Delt Lat Reb Drop	6		2	
	25 rest- BB				
	Hip FLXor ISO Pull	6		2	
	25 rest- BB				
75	DB Shoulder Press	10	50 - 55	2	
150	Rev Grip Tri Push	8	115 - 120	2	oc-D+1
	25 rest- BB				
	Bicep shock curls	6		2	
	25 rest- BB				
	Blackburn	6		2	

FRIDAY — 6-Nov-10

100%	Exercise	REPS	LOAD	SETS	NOTES
200	STEP UP	8	150 - 160	3	5:0:0:0:
	15 Rest-BB				
	INCLINE SIT UP	8		3	
	15 Rest-BB				
	Ball LG Curl	10		3	
90	DB INCLNE BENCH	15	60 - 65	3	oc-D+1
	15 Rest-BB				
75	DB Twist	15	50 - 55	3	
	15 Rest-BB				
	Jobes	6		3	4:0:0:0
200	Walking Lunge	8	150 - 160	3	Squeeze
	15 Rest-BB				
75	DB Fly	8	40 - 45	3	
	15 Rest-BB				
	Delt Lat Rebound Drop	8		3	
500	Glute Bar Lift	8	250 - 300	3	
	15 Rest-BB				
	Rope Circles	15		3	Each Way
	15 Rest-BB				
180	Gripper	15	115 - 125	3	
120	BAR CURL	8	85 - 90	2	
	15 Rest-BB				
150	TRI PUSH DOWN	8	105 - 115	2	
	15 Rest-BB				
	90 90 Groin ISO Hold	10		2	
60	Zotman Curl	6	45 - 50	2	
	15 Rest-BB				
	Speed Abduction	8		2	
	15 Rest-BB				
240	Close Grip Bench	6	60 - 70	2	3 Board
	Single Leg Iso DL	6 s		2	
	15 Rest-BB				
	Rope Vertical	15		2	
	15 Rest-BB				
	Full BCH Curl Up	8		2	

BLOCK TWO (3-DAY): ABOVE 80% ISOMETRIC PHASE (2-3 WEEKS)

MONDAY 16-Nov-10

100%	Exercise	REPS	LOAD	SETS	NOTES
500	Sport Back Squat	5,3	250 - 335	1,1	Pw/ Cuban F8
	No Rest/B-Breath				I band Rollers
500	Sport Back Squat	3	390 - 400	1	pw/cuban f8
	No Rest/B-Breath				I band Rollers
500	Sport Back Squat	3	390 - 400	3	0:5:0:0
	Hurdle Hop	5		3	Pull Down
	15 rest- BB				
	1/2 SQ JMP Weighted	4		3	reactive
	15 rest- BB				
	15 Yard Starts	T		3	
300	BENCH PRESS	5,3	150 - 200	1,1	Ext Shock
	No Rest/B-Breath				
300	Bench Press	3	240	1	coach see
	No Rest/B-Breath				Ext Shock
300	BENCH PRESS	4	205 - 210	3	2OC-d+1
	One Leg MB Side Toss	5		3	
	25 rest- BB				
	1 Bent Arm S. LP Down	6		3	
	25 rest- BB				
	90 90 Jump Twist	5		3	
500	Glute Bar Lift	8	250 - 300	3	
	25 rest- BB				
	Face Band Pulls	8		3	
	25 rest- BB				
75	1 Arm Lat Pull Supine	10	50 - 55	3	oc-A
	25 rest- BB				
	GH HYPR	6		3	
	25 rest- BB				
	Iso Ball Grion Sqeeze	10S		3	
	25 rest- BB				
	Round House	8	80 - 85	3	
75	DB Shoulder Press	10	50 - 55	2	oc-D+1
	25 rest- BB				
	Hip FLX BND Pulls	6	35 - 35	2	
	25 rest- BB				
120	Bar Curl	10	80 - 85	2	
45	DB Tri Pro Sup	8	35 - 35	2	
	25 rest- BB				
180	Chin up	6	135 - 145	2	
	25 rest- BB				
	Jobes ECC	6			4:0:0:0;

WEDNESDAY 18-Nov-10

100%	Exercise	REPS	LOAD	SETS	NOTES
500	Back Squat	5,3	250 - 335	1,1	
	2-Min Rest/B-Breath				
500	Back Squat	3	400	1	
	2-Min Rest/B-Breath				
500	Back Squat	3	440 - 465	4	
	Stding SQ Drop Jump	4		3	Pull Down
	25 rest- BB				
	Deft BO Lat Reb Drop	4		3	
	25 rest- BB				
	Thors Hammer	12		3	
300	BENCH PRESS	5,3	150 - 200	1,1	
	2-Min Rest/B-Breath				
300	Bench Press	3	235 - 240	1	
	2-Min Rest/B-Breath				
300	BENCH PRESS	3	270 - 280	3	miss 2 board
	Med Ball Chest Pass	5		3	
	25 rest- BB				
	1 Arm DB Row	6		3	
	25 rest- BB				
	Pike SWB Abs	5		3	
	Walking Band Lungs Jump	6		3	Drop
	Pair w/				
	Laying External Rot	6		3	
	Pair w/				
	1.S.A.S. R.G Lat P	10		3	
	GH HYPR	8		3	
	Pair w/				
	Iso Ball Grion Sqeeze	10S		3	
	Pair w/				
	Bam Bam	8		3	
	Inc Delt Lat Reb Drop	6		3	
	25 rest- BB				
	Hip FLXor ISO Pull	6		2	
	25 rest- BB				
75	DB Shoulder Press	10	50 - 55	2	oc-D+1
150	Rev Grip Tri Push	8	115 - 120	2	
	25 rest- BB				
	Bicep shock curls	6		2	
	25 rest- BB				
	Blackburn	6		2	

FRIDAY 20-Nov-10

100%	Exercise	REPS	LOAD	SETS	NOTES
225	Single Leg Squat	8	170 - 180	3	0:5:0:0
	15 Rest- BB				
	INCLINE SIT UP	8		3	
	15 Rest- BB				
	Ball LG Curl	10		3	
90	DB INCLINE BENCH	15	60 - 65	3	oc-D+1
	15 Rest- BB				
75	DB Twist	15	50 - 55	3	
	15 Rest- BB				
	Jobes	6		3	4:0:0:0
	Walking Drop Lunge Jump	8		3	
	2-Min Rest/B-Breath				
75	DB Fly	8	40 - 45	3	
	15 Rest- BB				
	Delt Lat Rebound Drop	8		3	
500	Glute Bar Lift	8	250 - 300	3	
	15 Rest- BB				
	Rope Circles	15		3	Each Way
	15 Rest- BB				
180	Gripper	15	115 - 125	3	
120	BAR CURL	8	85 - 90	2	
	15 Rest- BB				
150	TRI PUSH DOWN	8	105 - 115	2	
	15 Rest- BB				
	90 90 Groin ISO Hold	10		2	
60	Zotman Curl	6	45 - 50	2	
	15 Rest- BB				
	Speed Abduction	8		2	
	15 Rest- BB				
240	Close Grip Bench	6	60 - 70	2	3 Board
	Single Leg Iso DL	6 s		2	
	15 Rest- BB				
	Rope Vertical	15		2	
	15 Rest- BB				
	Full BCH Curl Up	8		2	

BLOCK THREE (3-DAY): ABOVE 80% CONCENTRIC PHASE (2-3 WEEKS)

MONDAY — 30-Nov-10

100%		REPS	LOAD	SETS	NOTES
500	Sport Back Squat	5,3	250 - 335	1,1	Pwr Cuban F8
	2-Min Rest/B-Breath				
500	Sport Back Squat	3	390 - 400	1	pwr cuban f8 / I band Rollers
	2-Min Rest/B-Breath				
500	Sport Back Squat	3	415 - 440	3	I band Rollers
	Hurdle Hop	5		3	0:0:0:0 Pull Down
	15 rest- BB				
	1/2 SQ JMP Weighted	4		3	reactive
	15 rest- BB				
	15 Yard Starts	1		3	4:00 Rest
300	BENCH PRESS	5,3	150 - 200	1,1	Ext Shock
	2-Min Rest/B-Breath				
300	Bench Press	3	- 240	1	coach see
	2-Min Rest/B-Breath				
300	BENCH PRESS	4	205 - 210	3	Ext Shock / 2OC-d+1
	One Leg MB Side Toss	5		3	
	25 rest- BB				
	Face Band Pulls	8		3	
	25 rest- BB				
	90 90 Jump Twist	5		3	
500	Glute Bar Lift	8	250 - 300	3	
	25 rest- BB				
75	1 Arm Lat Pull Supine	10	50 - 55	3	
	GH HYPR	6		3	oc-A
	25 rest- BB				
	Iso Ball Groin Sqeeze	10S		3	
	25 rest- BB				
	Round House	8		3	
75	DB Shoulder Press	10	80 - 85	2	oc-D+1
	25 rest- BB				
	Hip FLX BND Pulls	6		2	
	25 rest- BB				
120	Bar Curl	10	135 - 145	2	
45	DB Tri Pro Sup	8	35 - 35	2	
	25 rest- BB				
180	Chin up	6		2	
	25 rest- BB				
	Jobes ECC	6		2	4:0:0:0;

Wednesday — 2-Dec-10 (100.0%)

100%		REPS	LOAD	SETS	NOTES
500	Back Squat	5,3	250 - 335	1,1	
	2-Min Rest/B-Breath				
500	Back Squat	3	- 400	1	
	2-Min Rest/B-Breath				
500	Back Squat	3	440 - 465	4	
	Stding SQ Drop Jump	4		3	
	25 rest- BB				
	Delt BO Lat Reb Drop	4		3	
	25 rest- BB				
	Thors Hammer	12		3	
300	BENCH PRESS	5,3	150 - 200	1,1	
	2-Min Rest/B-Breath				
300	Bench Press	3	235 - 240	1	
	2-Min Rest/B-Breath				
300	BENCH PRESS	3	270 - 280	3	miss 2 board
	Med Ball Chest Pass	5		3	
	25 rest- BB				
	1 Arm DB Row	6		3	
	25 rest- BB				
	Pike SWB Abs	5		3	
	Walking Band Lunge Jump	6		3	Drop
	Pair w/				
	Laying External Rot	6		3	
	Pair w/				
	1 S.A.S. R.G LatP	10		3	
	GH HYPR	8		3	
	Pair w/				
	Iso Ball Groin Sqeeze	10S		3	
	Pair w/				
	Bam Bam	8		3	
	Inc Delt Lat Reb Drop	6		2	
	25 rest- BB				
	Hip FLXor ISO Pull	6		2	
	25 rest- BB				
75	DB Shoulder Press	10	50 - 55	2	
150	Rev Grip Tri Push	8	115 - 120	2	oc-D+1
	25 rest- BB				
	Bicep shock curls	6		2	
	25 rest- BB				
	Blackburn	6		2	

FRIDAY — 4-Dec-10 (100%)

100%		REPS	LOAD	SETS	NOTES
225	Single Leg Squat	8	170 - 180	3	
	INCLINE SIT UP	8		3	
	15 Rest- BB				
	Ball LG Curl	10		3	
	15 Rest- BB				
90	DB INCLINE BENCH	15	60 - 65	3	oc-D+1
	15 Rest- BB				
75	DB Twist	15	50 - 55	3	
	15 Rest- BB				
	Jobes	6		3	
	Walking Drop Lunge Jump	8		3	
	15 Rest- BB				
75	DB Fly	8	40 - 45	3	
	15 Rest- BB				
	Delt Lat Rebound Drop	8		3	
500	Glute Bar Lift	8	250 - 300	3	
	Rope Circles	15		3	Each Way
	15 Rest- BB				
180	Gripper	15	115 - 125	3	
120	BAR CURL	8	85 - 90	2	
	15 Rest- BB				
150	TRI PUSH DOWN	8	105 - 115	2	
	15 Rest- BB				
	90 90 Groin ISO Hold	10		2	
60	Zotman Curl	6	45 - 50	2	
	15 Rest- BB				
	Speed Abduction	8		2	
	15 Rest- BB				
240	Close Grip Bench	6	60 - 70	2	3 Board
	Single Leg Iso DL	6 s		2	
	15 Rest- BB				
	Rope Vertical	15		2	
	15 Rest- BB				
	Full BCH Curl Up	8		2	

4.10: TRIPHASIC Q&A

By now, I'm sure that you have some questions regarding the triphasic method as it pertains to its application and sequencing within an undulated block model. In an effort to try and stave off some of this confusion, below you will find answers to the five most asked questions that I receive regarding triphasic training.

QUESTION 1: DO YOU TRAIN YOUR ATHLETES WITH UPPER BODY TRIPHASIC MEANS AT ALL?

The triphasic method can be used with athletes in most sports. I've found great success using the triphasic method in posterior parts of the shoulder for baseball pitchers and also for athletes who play racket based sports. This sequencing of exercises in the triphasic nature helps absorption/ deceleration of force and prevents a number of shoulder problems. The lists of upper body triphasic methods are endless and reasons for using it are necessary to prevent injury.

QUESTION 2: CAN YOU TRAIN BOTH THE UPPER AND LOWER BODY WITH TRIPHASIC MEANS AT THE SAME TIME?

The short answer is "yes," but there are a few key factors that you must keep in mind. The first is that when you implement the triphasic method into your strength training program, your athletes must have some training base to begin with in order to achieve optimal results. If this is the very first training session or block that your athletes are completing, the results will be limited. When using a three-day program, the upper and lower body must be done on the same day. You can do the triphasic on both body parts. However, the fitness levels of the athletes and work capacity must be very high. I have trained athletes who could only do the lower body work because of their fitness levels and have gotten great results. What we saw with this group was that their upper body still made strength gains that are of the reactive nature as the lower body would have in this phase. Let me explain—when you're training the legs, you're training a large portion of your nervous system. The nervous system isn't limb specific. It is the entire system that you're training. So if you're just doing the legs, you're training the upper body with the triphasic method and gaining strength eccentrically and isometrically. With a six-day program, your athletes again will have to have a training method and work capacity already in place in order to implement the triphasic six-day plan. It can be done and you actually can have your athletes complete all this in the triphasic method during this time frame if they are in excellent shape and have great work capacity. If they aren't in shape, you will most likely just want to implement the triphasic method in your core lifts such as the back squat and bench press. So for building a multi-level strength training program, a separation of abilities could be as simple as implementing the triphasic methods with your core lifts. Then at the next level, implement your triphasic with some of the lifts beyond the "core," and at the most advanced levels, implement the triphasic methods with all your lifts. This would most likely be a second-, third-, or fourth-year period.

QUESTION 3: CAN YOU USE A DEADLIFT AS THE MAIN COMPONENT EXERCISE WHEN TRAINING FOR TRIPHASIC ADAPTION?

A deadlift isn't often used due to the nature of the lift and the positions that must be held with the deadlift. The purpose of triphasic training is to help with the transition of force. In the deadlift, one doesn't have a transition of force that takes place. We've always seen the best adaptations occur with the back or front squat, as they teach the human to be more reactive.

QUESTION 4: WHY DO YOU CHOOSE THE BACK SQUAT AS THE MAIN COMPOUND EXERCISE IN YOUR TRIPHASIC MICROCYCLE? ARE THERE EXCEPTIONS FOR SPECIFIC ATHLETE POPULATIONS?

The main reason that I stated above for the back squat is that it is a reactive exercise and one that can make an athlete extremely strong quickly with few weak links. I have seen the back squat with the triphasic method get rid of many weak links that exist in someone's back squat technique. Due to the nature of the global, systemic training effects, the back squat was chosen. This is one of the best exercises for strengthening the glutes, quads, hamstrings, lower back, upper back, and core. A large amount of training can take place with just this single exercise. There are always exceptions to every rule and you may have to modify this based on if the athletes are injured or have an anthropometrical limitation. This is when the single leg lifts will be utilized in training.

QUESTION 5: WHAT IS THE BEST EXERCISE SEQUENCE YOU HAVE FOUND THAT TRAINS THE TRIPHASIC MUSCLE ACTION OF YOUR ATHLETES?

This essentially comes back to the larger muscle groups and readdressing the issue that we aren't necessarily training the muscles but rather the entire nervous system. The more motor units that can be recruited with a particular exercise the better. The overall selection and choice of that exercise would be superior because you're creating a systemic adaption to the stress placed on the organism from the triphasic methods. The best sequencing therefore would be something that involves larger muscle groups being recruited through the exercises being used.

QUESTION 6: WHAT PROGRESSIONS SHOULD I USE WITH OTHER EXERCISES DURING THE TRIPHASIC MESOCYCLE TO MAXIMIZE PERFORMANCE?

TABLE 4.18: ABOVE 80 PERCENT TRIPHASIC EXERCISE SEQUENCING

EXERCISE	BLOCK 1 (ECCENTRIC)	BLOCK 2 (ISOMETRIC)	BLOCK 3 (CONCENTRIC)
FRONT SQUAT	FRONT SQUAT ECCENTRIC	FRONT SQUAT ISOMETRIC	FRONT SQUAT
LEG PRESS	LEG PRESS SINGLE LEG ECCENTRIC	LEG PRESS SINGLE LEG ISOMETRIC	SINGLE LEG PRESS
DB ROW	DUMBBELL ROW ECCENTRIC	DUMBBELL ROW ISOMETRIC	ONE ARM DUMBBELL ROW
BAND JUMPS	ACCELERATED BAND SQUAT JUMP PAUSE	ACCELERATED BAND SQUAT JUMP	ACCELERATED BAND SQUAT JUMP REACTIVE
RDL	RDL DUMBBELL ECCENTRIC	RDL DUMBBELL ISOMETRIC	RDL DUMBBELL
DB LUNGE	DUMBBELL WALKING LUNGE WITH PAUSE	DUMBBELL WALKING LUNGE	DUMBBELL WALKING LUNGE SWITCH
BENCH PRESS	BENCH PRESS ECCENTRIC	BENCH PRESS ISOMETRIC	BENCH PRESS REACTIVE
HIP FLEXOR	HIP FLEXOR ECCENTRIC PRONE	HIP FLEXOR ISOMETRIC PULL	HIP FLEXOR PRONE CONTRALATERAL

4.11: ABOVE 80 PERCENT FOUR-DAY PROGRAM

It's important to have a firm understanding of the above 80 percent mesocycle and all that it entails—its blocks, triphasic means, specialized training methods, and loading parameters. Over the years of teaching this system to hundreds of coaches, I've found that the three-day model best explains the triphasic undulating block method because it allows for the person learning to focus on fewer moving parts. That said, most coaches don't use a three-day training model. Most coaches now train their athletes on a four- or five-day model and sometimes even a six-day model (if you're of Bulgarian decent!). That's great! Because we've already learned how important it is to maximally stress the athlete, clearly five days of training is more taxing than three days.

On the following page, you will find how to take the three-day model and extrapolate it to a four-day model. In table 4.19, day one loading parameters are in white, day two loading parameters are in light gray, and day three loading parameters are in dark gray. Notice in the four-day model that there isn't a dark gray day. In this mesocycle, day three loading parameters (signified by the dark gray) are the "volume" days of the week. In a four-day model, there aren't enough training days to give each focus its own volume day. Instead of sacrificing a high intensity day of training, extra volume work is placed at the end of training days two and five of the week. As you will see when you look at the example workout, at the end of both upper body days, a box of deadlifts is added to the end of the workout. Intensity is moderate (75–80 percent) with the volume slightly increased. This allows the athlete to add some needed volume training without sacrificing the nervous system or accumulating fatigue.

TABLE 4.19: ABOVE 80 PERCENT THREE-DAY VERSUS FOUR-DAY MODEL

TRAINING WEEK:		DAY 1	DAY 2	DAY 3	DAY 4	DAY 5	DAY 6
THREE-DAY MODEL	FOCUS	TOTAL BODY	OFF	TOTAL BODY	OFF	TOTAL BODY	OFF
	LOAD	82–87%		90–97%		75–80%	
	MEANS APPLIED	TRIPHASIC		DYNAMIC		TRIPHASIC	
FOUR-DAY MODEL	FOCUS	LOWER BODY	UPPER BODY	OFF	LOWER BODY	UPPER BODY	OFF
	LOAD	82–87%	82–87%		90–97%	90–97%	
	MEANS APPLIED	TRIPHASIC			DYNAMIC		

Two other important aspects of training that can't be forgotten are speed work and conditioning. Below is a table that shows where in the training week each should be emphasized along with special instructions and example workouts.

TABLE 4.20: ABOVE 80 PERCENT FOUR-DAY CONDITIONING MODEL

TRAINING DAY	CONDITIONING GOAL	SPECIAL INSTRUCTIONS	EXAMPLE WORKOUT
DAY 1	**Short Sprints** (High Quality Speed)	• Sprints under 10 seconds • Full recovery; rest 90–120 seconds	• Alactic High Quality Workout • Flying 60's • 16 Week Short Sprint Workouts • Cone Agility
DAY 2	**Long Sprints *or* Short Sprints w/ Reduced Rest** (Speed Conditioning)	• Sprints over 15 seconds or • Sprints under 10, recovery under 20 seconds	• High Quality Lactic Anaerobic Power Training Builder • Metabolic Injury Prevention Runs

TABLE 4.20: ABOVE 80 PERCENT FOUR-DAY CONDITIONING MODEL

TRAINING DAY	CONDITIONING GOAL	SPECIAL INSTRUCTIONS	EXAMPLE WORKOUT
DAY 3	**Short Sprint** (High Quality Speed)	• Sprints under 10 seconds • Full recovery; rest 90–120 seconds	• Alactic High Quality Workout • Flying 60s • 16 Week Short Sprint Workouts • Cone Agility
DAY 4	**Longer Sprints *or* Continuous Running** (Oxidative Conditioning)	This day is purely work capacity focused	• Aerobic Work Capacity Training Builder • Game Speed Conditioning • Bike Conditioning • TrashBall

Finally, we need to talk about the different exercises, methods, and means I use in a four-day program that I don't use and didn't show you in the three-day program. By this point, however, I'm sure you're probably a little tired of reading, and I'm certainly tired of writing. So I thought this would be a good point in the book to change it up a little. Instead of reading, let's try listening and watching.

Below is a hyperlink that will take you to a video series where I walk you through the four-day program, explaining some of the exercises and why I use them. I recommend having the program next to you while you watch, so you can follow along and take notes. In advance, yes, my hair is a mess; no, I didn't shave even though my wife told me to; and yes, I am a little heavy right now. We filmed this right around Christmas time, so I had access to cookies galore. No fat jokes, please.

FOUR-DAY ABOVE 80 PERCENT TRIPHASIC VIDEO

BLOCK ONE (4-DAY): ABOVE 80% ECCENTRIC PHASE (2-3 WEEKS)

Day one

100%	Exercise	REPS	LOAD	SETS	NOTES
			28-Dec-09		4-Jan-10
500	Back Squat	5	225 - 275	1	
	Pair w/				
500	Back Squat	3	295 - 325	1	Pr/2 Neck
	Pair w/				
500	Back Squat	1	390 - 400	1	Each Leg
	Pair w/				
500	Back Squat	2	415 - 425	4	5:0:0:0 Box
	Hurdle Hop	6		4	
	Acc Band Jump	8		4	Reactive
	90 90 Groin ISO Hold	10S		3	5:0:0:0 Bands
	GH HYPR Incline	5		3	0:5:0:0
	INC STEP Up Toe Raise	6			
	Hip Flex Ecc Prone	6		4	3:0:0:0
	BO DB Push Back	8		4	
	Supine Glt Ham Blk Iso	180s		1	
	H-Sq Sh Bi Trap	180s		1	
	Glute Ham Back Cav Iso	180s		1	
300	Power Clean	5	195 - 210	1	
	Pair w/				
300	Power Clean	4	220 - 225	3	
	3:00 Core Test				
	SWB Down TW	8		2	
	GH HANG	120s		1	
	Rollers Glutes & Hams	120s		1	
	LAYING RELAXATION	120s		1	

Day 2

100%	Exercise	REPS	LOAD	SETS	NOTES
			30-Dec-09		6-Jan-10
300	BENCH PRESS	5	135 - 165	1	Pr/ Gripper
	Pair w/				
300	BENCH PRESS	3	175 - 195	1	Pr/ Gripper
	Pair w/				
300	BENCH PRESS	1	235 - 240	1	Pr/ Gripper
300	BENCH PRESS	2	250 - 255	4	
38	DB Rear Delt	9	25 - 30	4	0:4:0:0
	Leg Press Calf Raise	10		4	Rest 1:30
53	DB Incline Fly	8	40 - 40	3	5:0:0:0
105	DB BO Row	6	85 - 85	3	3:0:0:0
	Pair w/				
	Delt Lat Rebound Drop	10		3	
90	JM DB Press	8	65 - 70	4	
	Pair w/				
120	Bar Curl	1,7,1,1	85 - 95	4	
	Pair w/				
	Chest Rev Grip Iso	180s		1	
	Supine Glt Ham Blk Iso	180s			
	H-Sq Sh Bi Trap	120s		1	
	Pair w/				
500	DeadLift	5	325 - 350	1	
	Pair w/				
500	DeadLift	1	390 - 400	1	
	Pair w/				
500	DeadLift	8	350 - 375	4	
	3:00 Core Test				
	SWB Down TW	8		2	
	GH HANG	120s		1	
	Rollers Quads & Back	120s		1	
	LAYING WALL SHAKES	120s		1	Relax Mouth

Day 3

100%	Exercise	REPS	LOAD	SETS	NOTES
			20-Oct-09		27-Oct-09
	BAL SNGL LG SQ	5		2	
	Pair w/				
	Lat Pull And Press	5		2	0:0:0:0
	Leg Press Calf Raise	10		2	Each Leg
500	Back Squat	5	225 - 275	1	
	Pair w/				
500	Back Squat	3	295 - 325	1	
	Pair w/				
500	Back Squat	1	390 - 400	1	
500	Back Squat	1	440 - 465	5	
	1/2 SQ JMP Weighted	5		5	
	Pair w/				
	Face Band Pull Apart	8		4	
	90 90 Groin ISO Hold	10S		3	3:0:0:0
	Pair w/				
300	Rever Hyper	5	150 - 180	3	
	Pair w/				
200	DB Walking Lunge	6	150 - 160	3	
	H-Sq Sh Bi Trap	180s			
	Glute Ham Back Cav Iso	180s			
	Supine Glt Ham Blk Iso	180s			
300	Power Clean	5	195 - 210	1	
	Pair w/				
300	Power Clean	4	220 - 225	3	
	3:00 Core Test				
	SWB Down TW	8		2	
	GH HANG	120s		1	
	Rollers Glutes & Hams	120s			
	LAYING RELAXATION	120s		1	

Day 4

100%	Exercise	REPS	LOAD	SETS	NOTES
			22-Oct-09		29-Oct-09
300	BENCH PRESS	5	135 - 165	1	
	Pair w/				
300	BENCH PRESS	3	175 - 195	1	
	Pair w/				
300	BENCH PRESS	1	235 - 240	1	
300	BENCH PRESS	1,1	265 - 270	4	0:0:0:20
	Rack Band Push Up	5		4	
	Pair w/				
	KA DI Pattern	8		4	Rest 1:30
120	DB BENCH	9,7,5	85 - 95	3	5:0:0:0
	Pair w/				
	KA Squat Twist	6		3	3:0:0:0
	Pair w/				
	Incline Rear Delt	10		3	
90	JM DB Press	8	65 - 70	4	
	Pair w/				
60	Incline Hammer Curls	8	40 - 45	4	
	Pair w/				
	Chest Rev Grip Iso	180s		1	
	Supine Glt Ham Bk Iso	180s		1	
	H-Sq Sh Bi Trap	120s		1	
	Pair w/				
500	DeadLift	5	325 - 350	1	
	Pair w/				
500	DeadLift	1	390 - 400	1	
	Pair w/				
500	DeadLift	3	440 - 465	4	
	3:00 Core Test				
	SWB Down TW	8		2	
	GH HANG	120s		1	
	Rollers Quads & Back	120s		1	
	LAYING WALL SHAKES	120s		1	Relax Mouth

BLOCK ONE (4-DAY): ABOVE 80% ECCENTRIC PHASE HYPERLINKS

Day 1	Exercise Hyperlink	Day 2	Exercise Hyperlink	Day 3	Exercise Hyperlink	Day 4	Exercise Hyperlink
Box 1	Back Squat	Box 1	Bench Press	Box 1	Balance Single Leg Squat Lat Pull and Press Leg Press Calf Raise	Box 1	Bench Press
Box 2	Back Squat Eccentric Hurdle Hop Accelerated Band Jump	Box 2	Bench Press Dumbbell Rear Leg Press Calf Raise	Box 2	Back Squat	Box 2	Bench Press Rack Band Push Up KA D1 Pattern
Box 3	90 90 Groin ISO Hold GH HYPR Incline Incline Step Up Toe Raises	Box 3	Dumbbell Incline Fly Dumbell Bent Over Row Delt Lateral Rebound Drop	Box 3	Back Squat Half Squat Jump Weighted Face Band Pulls	Box 3	Eccentric DB Press KA Squat Twist Dumbbell Rear
Box 4	Hip Flex Ecc Prone Dumbbell Push Backs Supine Glute Ham Back Iso	Box 4	JM Dumbbell Press Bar Curl Chest Reverse Grip ISO	Box 4	90 90 Groin ISO Hold Reverse Hyper DB Walking Lunge	Box 4	JM Dumbbell Press Incline Hammer Curl Chest Rev Grip Iso
Box 5	H-Sq Sh Bi Trap Glute Ham Back Cav Iso	Box 5	Supine Glute Ham Back Iso H-Sq Sh Bi Trap	Box 5	H-Sq Sh Bi Trap Glute Ham Back Cav Iso Supine Glute Ham Back Iso	Box 5	Glute Ham Back Cav Iso Sq Trap Sh Bi Hold
Box 6	Power Clean	Box 6	Deadlift	Box 6	Power Clean	Box 6	Deadlift
Box 7	3:00 Core Test SWB Down TW	Box 7	3:00 Core Test Swiss Ball Down Twist	Box 7	3:00 Core Test SWB Down TW	Box 7	3:00 Core Test SWB Down TW
Box 8	GH HANG Rollers Glutes and Hams Laying Relaxation	Box 8	Glute Ham Hang Rollers Quads & Back Laying Wall Shakes	Box 8	GH HANG Rollers Glutes and Hams Laying Relaxation	Box 8	Glute Ham Hang Rollers Quads & Back Laying Wall Shakes

BLOCK TWO (4-DAY): ABOVE 80% ISOMETRIC PHASE (2-3 WEEKS)

Day one — 18-Jan-10 / 25-Jan-10

100%		REPS	LOAD	SETS	NOTES
500	Back Squat	5	225 - 275	1	
	Pair w/				
500	Back Squat	3	295 - 325	1	Flw-2 Neck
	Pair w/				
500	Back Squat	1	390 - 400	1	Each Leg
500	Back Squat	2	415 - 425	4	0:4:0:0
	Pair w/				
	Hurdle Hop	6		4	
	Acc Band Jump	8		4	Reactive
	90 90 Groin ISO Hold	10S		3	0:4:0:0
	Pair w/				Bands
	GH HYPR Incline	5		3	0:5:0:0
	Pair w/				
	INC STEP Up Toe Raise	6		3	
	Hip Flex Ecc Prone	6		4	0:4:0:0
	Pair w/				
	BO DB Push Back	8		4	
	Pair w/				
	Supine Glt Ham Bk Iso	180s		1	
	H-Sq Sh Bi Trap	180s		1	
	Glute Ham Back Cav Iso	180s		1	
300	Power Clean	5	195 - 210	1	
	Pair w/				
300	Power Clean	4	220 - 225	3	
	3:00 Core Test				
	SWB Down TW	8		2	
	GH HANG	120S		1	
	Pair w/				
	Rollers Glutes & Hams	120S		1	
	Pair w/				
	LAYING RELAXATION	120S		1	

Day 2

100%		REPS	LOAD	SETS	NOTES
300	BENCH PRESS	5	135 - 165	1	P/ Gripper
	Pair w/				
300	BENCH PRESS	3	175 - 195	1	P/ Gripper
	Pair w/				
300	BENCH PRESS	1	235 - 240	1	P/ Gripper
300	BENCH PRESS	2	250 - 255	4	0:4:0:0
38	DB Rear Delt	9	25 - 30	4	3:0:0:0
	Pair w/				
	Leg Press Calf Raise	10		4	Rest 1:30
53	DB Incline Fly	8	40 - 40	3	0:4:0:0
	Pair w/				
105	DB BO Row	6	70 - 75	3	0:4:0:0
	Pair w/				
	Delt Lat Rebound Drop	10		3	
90	JM DB Press	8	65 - 70	4	
	Pair w/				
120	Bar Curl	4,7,6,5	85 - 95	4	
	Chest Rev Grip Iso	180s		1	
	Supine Glt Ham Bk Iso	180s		1	
	H-Sq Sh Bi Trap	180s		1	
	3:00 Core Test				
	SWB Down TW	8		2	
	GH HANG	120s		1	
	Pair w/				
	Rollers Quads & Back	120s		1	
	Pair w/				
	LAYING WALL SHAKES	120s		1	Relax Mouth

Day 3

100%		REPS	LOAD	SETS	NOTES
	BAL SNGL LG SQ	5		2	
	Pair w/				
	Lat Pull And Press	5		2	0:0:0:0
	Pair w/				
	Leg Press Calf Raise	10		2	Each Leg
500	Back Squat	5	225 - 275	1	
500	Back Squat	3	295 - 325	1	
	Pair w/				
500	Back Squat	1	390 - 400	1	
500	Back Squat	1	440 - 465	5	
	1/2 SQ JMP Weighted	5		5	
	Pair w/				
	Face Band Pull Apart	8		4	
	90 90 Groin ISO Hold	10S		3	0:4:0:0
300	Rever Hyper	5	150 - 180	3	
	Pair w/				
200	DB Walking Lunge	6	150 - 160	3	
	H-Sq Sh Bi Trap	180s		1	
	Glute Ham Back Cav Iso	180s		1	
	Supine Glt Ham Bk Iso	180s		1	
300	Power Clean	5	195 - 210	1	
	Pair w/				
300	Power Clean	4	220 - 225	3	
	3:00 Core Test				
	SWB Down TW	8		2	
	GH HANG	120S		1	
	Pair w/				
	Rollers Glutes & Hams	120S		1	
	Pair w/				
	LAYING RELAXATION	120S		1	

Day 4

100%		REPS	LOAD	SETS	NOTES
300	BENCH PRESS	5	135 - 165	1	
	Pair w/				
300	BENCH PRESS	3	175 - 195	1	
	Pair w/				
300	BENCH PRESS	1	235 - 240	1	0:0:0:20
300	BENCH PRESS	1,1	265 - 270	4	
	Rack Band Push Up	5		4	
	KA Di Pattern	8		4	Rest 1:30
120	DB BENCH	9,7,5	85 - 95	3	0:4:0:0
	KA Squat Twist	6		3	0:4:0:0
	Incline Rear Delt	10		3	
90	JM DB Press	8	65 - 70	4	
	Pair w/				
60	Incline Hammer Curls	8	40 - 45	4	
	Pair w/				
	Chest Rev Grip Iso	180s		1	
	Supine Glt Ham Bk Iso	180s		1	
	H-Sq Sh Bi Trap	180s		1	
500	DeadLift	5	325 - 350	1	
500	DeadLift	1	390 - 400	1	Coach Watch
500	DeadLift	3	440 - 465	4	
	3:00 Core Test				
	SWB Down TW	8		2	
	GH HANG	120S		1	Relax Mouth
	Pair w/				
	Rollers Quads & Back	120S		1	
	LAYING WALL SHAKES	120S		1	Relax Mouth

BLOCK TWO (4-DAY): ABOVE 80% ISOMETRIC PHASE
HYPERLINKS

Day 1	Exercise Hyperlink	Day 2	Exercise Hyperlink	Day 3	Exercise Hyperlink	Day 4	Exercise Hyperlink
Box 1	Back Squat	Box 1	Bench Press	Box 1	Balance Single Leg Squat Lat Pull and Press Leg Press Calf Raise	Box 1	Bench Press
Box 2	Back Squat Isometric Hurdle Hop Accelerated Band Jump	Box 2	Bench Press Dumbbell Rear Leg Press Calf Raise	Box 2	Back Squat	Box 2	Bench Press Rack Band Push Up KA D1 Pattern
Box 3	90 90 Groin ISO Hold GH HYPR Incline Isometric Incline Step Up Toe Raises	Box 3	Dumbbell Incline Fly Dumbell Bent Over Row Delt Lateral Rebound Drop	Box 3	Back Squat Half Squat Jump Weighted Face Band Pulls	Box 3	Isometric DB Press KA Squat Twist Dumbbell Rear
Box 4	Hip Flex Prone Isometric Dumbbell Push Backs Supine Glute Ham Back Iso	Box 4	JM Dumbbell Press Bar Curl Chest Reverse Grip ISO	Box 4	90 90 Groin ISO Hold Reverse Hyper DB Walking Lunge	Box 4	JM Dumbbell Press Incline Hammer Curl Chest Rev Grip Iso
Box 5	Hip Flex Prone Isometric Dumbbell Push Backs	Box 5	Supine Glute Ham Back Iso H-Sq Sh Bi Trap	Box 5	H-Sq Sh Bi Trap Glute Ham Back Cav Iso Supine Glute Ham Back Iso	Box 5	Supine Glute Ham Back Iso Sq Trap Sh Bi Hold
Box 6	Power Clean	Box 6		Box 6	Power Clean	Box 6	Deadlift
Box 7	3:00 Core Test SWB Down TW	Box 7	3:00 Core Test Swiss Ball Down Twist	Box 7	3:00 Core Test SWB Down TW	Box 7	3:00 Core Test SWB Down TW
Box 8	GH HANG Rollers Glutes and Hams Laying Relaxation	Box 8	Glute Ham Hang Rollers Quads & Back Laying Wall Shakes	Box 8	GH HANG Rollers Glutes and Hams Laying Relaxation	Box 8	Glute Ham Hang Rollers Quads & Back Laying Wall Shakes

BLOCK THREE (4-DAY): ABOVE 80% CONCENTRIC PHASE (2-3 WEEKS)

Day one

100%	Exercise	REPS	LOAD	SETS	NOTES
500	Back Squat	5	225 - 275	1	
	Pair w/				
500	Back Squat	3	295 - 325	1	P/v-2 Neck
	Pair w/				
500	Back Squat	1	390 - 400	1	
500	Back Squat	2	415 - 425	4	
	Power Step up	6		4	
	Cycle Kicks	8		4	Reactive
	90 90 Groin ISO Hold	10S		3	
	3 - WY HAM Touch	6		3	0:0:0:0
200	Walking Lunge	6	150 - 160	3	Drop Jump
	Hip Flex Ecc Prone	6		4	0:0:0:0
	BO DB Push Back	8		4	
	Supine Glt Ham Bk Iso	60S		1	
		180s	60% -	1	
	Glute Ham Back Cav Iso	60S		1	
	3:00 Core Test				
	SWB Down TW	8		2	
	GH HANG	120S		1	Relax Mouth
	Pair w/				
	Rollers Glutes & Hams	120S		1	
	Pair w/				
	LAYING RELAXATION	120S		1	

Day 2

100%	Exercise	REPS	LOAD	SETS	NOTES
300	BENCH PRESS	5	135 - 165	1	P/ Gripper
	Pair w/				
300	BENCH PRESS	3	175 - 195	1	P/ Gripper
	Pair w/				
300	BENCH PRESS	1	235 - 240	1	P/ Gripper
300	BENCH PRESS	2	250 - 255	4	
38	DB Rear Delt	9	25 - 30	4	0:4:0:0
	Leg Press Calf Raise	10		4	Rest 1:30
53	DB Incline Fly	8	40 - 40	3	5:0:0:0
105	DB BO Row	6	85 - 85	3	3:0:0:0
	Side DELT Raise	10		3	
90	JM DB Press	8	65 - 70	4	
120	Bar Curl	MAX	85 - 95	4	
	Chest Rev Grip Iso	180S		1	
	Supine Glt Ham Bk Iso	180s		1	
	Pair w/				
		120S	40% -	1	
	Pair w/				
	3:00 Core Test				
	SWB Down TW	8		2	
	GH HANG	120S		1	Relax Mouth
	Pair w/				
	Rollers Quads & Back	120S		1	
	Pair w/				
	LAYING WALL SHAKES	120S		1	Relax Mouth

Day 3

100%	Exercise	REPS	LOAD	SETS	NOTES
500	Glute Bar Lift	8	250 - 300	2	
	Pair w/				
	Lat Pull And Press	5		2	0:0:5:0
	Pair w/				
	3 - WY HAM Touch	9		2	Each Leg
500	Back Squat	5	225 - 275	1	
	Pair w/				
500	Back Squat	3	295 - 325	1	
	Pair w/				
500	Back Squat	1	390 - 400	1	Sport Squat
500	Back Squat	3	450 - 465	3	
	Acc Band Jump	5		4	
	Pair w/				
	KA bent over rows	8		4	
	90 90 Groin ISO Hold	10S		3	
225	DB RDL InLine	5	115 - 135	3	
200	DB Walking Lunge	6	150 - 160	3	
		180s	60% -	1	
	Glute Ham Back Cav Iso	60S		1	
	Pair w/				
	Supine Glt Ham Bk Iso	60S		1	
	Core Workout 7				
		8	70% - 75%	2	
	GH HANG	120S		1	
	Pair w/				
	Rollers Glutes & Hams	120S		1	
	Pair w/				
	LAYING RELAXATION	120S		1	

Day 4

100%	Exercise	REPS	LOAD	SETS	NOTES
300	BENCH PRESS	5	135 - 165	1	
	Pair w/				
300	BENCH PRESS	3	175 - 195	1	
	Pair w/				
300	BENCH PRESS	1	235 - 240	1	
300	BENCH PRESS	3	270 - 280	3	0:0:0:20
	Clap Push Up	5		4	
	Rear DELT	8		4	Rest 1:30
120	DB BENCH	9,7,5	85 - 95	3	
	Pair w/				
105	DB BO Row	6	85 - 85	3	
210	DB Shrug	10	135 - 145	3	
90	JM DB Press	8	65 - 70	4	
60	Incline Hammer Curls	8	40 - 45	4	
	Chest Rev Grip Iso	60S		1	
	Supine Glt Ham Bk Iso	60S		1	
	Pair w/				
	Core Workout 4				
		8	70% - 75%	2	
	GH HANG	120S		1	Relax Mouth
	Pair w/				
	Rollers Quads & Back	120S		1	
	Pair w/				
	LAYING WALL SHAKES	120S		1	Relax Mouth

BLOCK THREE (4-DAY): ABOVE 80% CONCENTRIC PHASE HYPERLINKS

Day 1	Exercise Hyperlink	Day 2	Exercise Hyperlink	Day 3	Exercise Hyperlink	Day 4	Exercise Hyperlink
Box 1	Back Squat	Box 1	Bench Press	Box 1	Glute Bar Lift / Lat Pull and Press / 3- Way Ham Touch	Box 1	Bench Press
Box 2	Back Squat / Power Step up / Cycle Kicks	Box 2	Bench Press / Dumbbell Rear / Leg Press Calf Raise	Box 2	Back Squat	Box 2	Bench Press / Clap Push-Up / Dumbbell Rear
Box 3	90 90 Groin ISO Hold / 3- Way Ham Touch / Walking Drop Lunge Jumps	Box 3	Dumbbell Incline Fly / Dumbell Bent Over Row / Delt Lateral Rebound Drop	Box 3	Sport back Squat / Accelerated Band Jump / KA Bent Over Rows	Box 3	DB Bench / Dumbell Bent Over Row / DB Shrugs
Box 4	Prone Bench Hip Flex / Dumbbell Push Backs / Supine Glute Ham Back Iso	Box 4	JM Dumbbell Press / Bar Curl / Chest Reverse Grip ISO	Box 4	90 90 Groin ISO Hold / DB RDL Inline / DB Walking Lunge	Box 4	JM Dumbbell Press / Incline Hammer Curl / Chest Rev Grip Iso
Box 5	Glute Ham Back Cav Iso	Box 5	Supine Glute Ham Back Iso	Box 5	Glute Ham Back Cav Iso / Supine Glute Ham Back Iso	Box 5	Glute Ham Back Cav Iso
Box 6	3:00 Core Test / SWB Down TW	Box 6	3:00 Core Test / Swiss Ball Down Twist	Box 6		Box 6	
Box 7	GH HANG / Rollers Glutes and Hams / Laying Relaxation	Box 7	Glute Ham Hang / Rollers Quads & Back / Laying Wall Shakes	Box 7	GH HANG / Rollers Glutes and Hams / Laying Relaxation	Box 7	Glute Ham Hang / Rollers Quads & Back / Laying Wall Shakes
Box 8		Box 8		Box 8		Box 8	

4.12: ABOVE 80 PERCENT FIVE-DAY PROGRAM

The table below shows how to take what you learned about the three-day model and convert it to a five-day training platform. In the table, day one loading parameters are in white, day two loading parameters are in light gray, and day three loading parameters are in dark gray.

TABLE 4.21: ABOVE 80 PERCENT THREE-DAY VERSUS FIVE-DAY MODEL							
TRAINING WEEK:		DAY 1	DAY 2	DAY 3	DAY 4	DAY 5	DAY 6
THREE-DAY MODEL	FOCUS	TOTAL BODY	OFF	TOTAL BODY	OFF	TOTAL BODY	OFF
	LOAD	82–87%		90–97%		75–80%	
	MEANS APPLIED	TRIPHASIC		DYNAMIC		TRIPHASIC	
FIVE-DAY MODEL	FOCUS	LOWER BODY	UPPER BODY	LOWER BODY	UPPER BODY	TOTAL BODY	OFF
	LOAD	82–87%	82–87%	90–97%	90–97%	75–80%	
	MEANS APPLIED	TRIPHASIC		DYNAMIC		TRIPHASIC	

Two other important aspects of training that can't be forgotten are speed work and conditioning. On the next page, table 4.22 shows where in the training week each should be emphasized along with special instructions and example workouts.

TABLE 4.22: ABOVE 80 PERCENT FIVE-DAY CONDITIONING MODEL			
TRAINING DAY	CONDITIONING GOAL	SPECIAL INSTRUCTIONS	EXAMPLE WORKOUT
DAY 1	**Short Sprints** (High Quality Speed)	• Sprints under 10 seconds • Full recovery; rest 90–120 seconds	• Alactic High Quality Workout • Flying 60s • 16 Week Short Sprint Workouts • Cone Agility
DAY 2	**Long Sprints *or* Short Sprints w/ Reduced Rest** (Speed Conditioning)	• Sprints over 15 seconds or • Sprints under 10, recovery under 20 seconds	• High Quality Lactic Anaerobic Power Training Builder • Metabolic Injury Prevention Runs
DAY 3	**Short Sprints** (High Quality Speed)	• Sprints under 10 seconds • Full recovery; rest 90–120 seconds	• Alactic High Quality Workout • Flying 60's • 16 Week Short Sprint Workouts • Cone Agility
DAY 4	**Short Sprints** (Anaerobic Conditioning)	• Sprints under 10 seconds • Limited recovery; 45–60 seconds	• Work Capacity Alactic Anaerobic Training Builder • Flying 60's • 16 Week Short Sprint Workouts • Cone Agility
DAY 5	**Longer Sprints *or* Continuous Running** (Oxidative Conditioning)	This day is purely work capacity focused	• Aerobic Work Capacity Training Builder • Game Speed Conditioning • Bike Conditioning • TrashBall

Finally, we need to talk about the different exercises, methods, and means I use in a five-day program that I don't use and didn't show you in the three-day program. The following hyperlink will take you to a video that explains the five-day program.

FIVE-DAY ABOVE 80 PERCENT TRIPHASIC VIDEO

BLOCK ONE (5-DAY): ABOVE 80% ECCENTRIC PHASE (LOWER BODY)

Monday - Day One (27-Jun-11 / 4-Jul-11)

%100	Exercise	REPS	LOAD	SETS	NOTES
400	FRONT SQUAT	5	180 - 220	1	Plv~2 Neck
400	Pair w/				Roller-I Band
400	FRONT SQUAT	3	235 - 260	1	Plv~2 Neck
400	Pair w/				Roller- HAM
400	FRONT SQUAT	1	310 - 320	1	Plv~2 Neck
400	FRONT SQUAT	3	330 - 350	5	3:0:0:0
225	Lat Pull Down	10	145 - 160	5	Rest 45
	Cuban PRSS INC F8	10		5	
200	DB Walking Lunge	8	140 - 150	4	Pause
	Pair w/				Toes
105	DB BO Row	10	70 - 75	4	Rest 45
360	Shrug	12	235 - 250	4	Chin Down
500	RDL	6	375 - 400	4	0:2:0:0
	Pair w/				Rest 45
60	Incline Hammer Curls	8	40 - 45	4	
	Pair w/				Rest 45
	Full BCH Curl Up	8		4	
	Ball LG Curl	8		3	
	Pair w/				Rest 45
	90 90 Groin ISO Hold	12		3	
120	Ez Bar Curl	10	85 - 90	3	Rest 45
360	Shrug	FFFF	235 - 125	4	Chin Down
	Closed Lunge Y EMOTIV	10		3	Rest 30
	Pair w/				Rest 30
	Wrist Flexion	10		3	LS Failure
	Sq Trap Sh Bi Hold	180s		1	Rest 1:30
	Glute Ham Back Cav Iso	180s	60% -	1	
	GH HANG	120S		1	Relax Mouth
	Rollers Glutes & Hams	120S			
	Partner Leg Walks	120S		1	

Wednesday - Day Three (29-Jun-11 / 6-Jul-11)

%100	Exercise	REPS	LOAD	SETS	NOTES
500	Back Squat	5	225 - 275	1	Plv~2 Neck
	Pair w/				Roller-I Band
500	Back Squat	3	295 - 325	1	Plv~2 Neck
	Pair w/				Roller- HAM
500	Back Squat	1	390 - 400	1	Plv~2 Neck
500	Back Squat	3	440 - 465	5	0:0:0:0
105	1 Arm Lat Pull Down	10	70 - 75	5	Rest 1:30
	Delt Lat Rebound Drop	8		5	
200	STEP UP	5	160 - 165	4	Rest 45
	Pair w/				
75	DB Twist	10	50 - 55	4	Rest 45
	Pair w/				
210	DB Shrug	12	135 - 145	4	
200	DB RDL InLine	6	150 - 160	4	0:2:0:0
	Pair w/				Rest 45
60	Zotman Curl	8	40 - 45	4	Rest 45
	INCLINE SIT UP	8		4	
	Glute Bar Lifts	6		3	Rest 45
120	BAR CURL	10	85 - 90	3	Rest 45
	BND Adduction	12		3	
360	Shrug	FFFF	235 - 125	4	Chin Down
	PRTNR Abs	10		3	Rest 45
	Pair w/				Rest 45
	Bam Bam	10		3	
	Sq Trap Sh Bi Hold	180s		1	Rest 1:30
	Glute Ham Back Cav Iso	180s	60% -	1	
	GH HANG	120S		1	Relax Mouth
	Rollers Glutes & Hams	120S		1	
	Partner Leg Walks	120S		1	Relax Mouth

Friday - Day Five (1-Jul-11 / 8-Jul-11)

%100	Exercise	REPS	LOAD	SETS	NOTES
390	Deadlift	5	175 - 215	1	Plv~2 Neck
	Pair w/				Roller-I Band
390	Deadlift	3	230 - 255	1	Plv~2 Neck
	Pair w/				Roller- HAM
390	Deadlift	1	305 - 310	1	Plv~2 Neck
390	Deadlift	6	295 - 310	4	Rest 1:00
180	Pull up	8	125 - 135	4	Rest 1:30
	Cuban PRSS INC F8	8		5	3:0:0:0
225	Single Leg Squat	5	180 - 185	4	Rest 45
	Pair w/				
105	DB BO Row	10	70 - 75	4	Rest 45
	Pair w/				
210	DB Shrug	12	135 - 145	4	
	Assist Nordic Ham Curl	6		4	Rest 30
	Pair w/				
60	DB Curl	8	40 - 45	4	Rest 30
	INCLINE SIT UP	8		4	
	Glute Bar Lift	10	65% - 70%	3	Rest 30
	Pair w/				
105	Revs Curl	10	75 - 80	3	Rest 30
	Iso Ball Grion Sqeeze	10S		3	
300	BENCH PRESS	FFFF	195 - 105	4	Rest Bt 45
75	DB Shoulder Press	FFFF	50 - 25	4	Rest 1:30 / OC Press
	Pair w/				Rest 1:30
150	TRI PUSH DOWN	FFFF	100 - 55	4	Rest BT 45
	Sq Trap Sh Bi Hold	180s		1	Rest 1:30
	Glute Ham Back Cav Iso	180s	60% -	1	
	GH HANG	120S		1	Relax Mouth
	Rollers Glutes & Hams	120S		1	
	Partner Leg Walks	120S		1	Relax Mouth

BLOCK ONE (5-DAY): ABOVE 80% ECCENTRIC PHASE HYPERLINKS

Day 1	Exercise Hyperlink	Day 3	Exercise Hyperlink	Day 5	Exercise Hyperlink
Box 1	FRONT SQUAT P/w-2 Neck	Box 1	Back Squat P/w-2 Neck	Box 1	Deadlift P/w-2 Neck
Box 2	Eccentric Front Squat Lat Pull Down Cuban PRSS INC F8	Box 2	Back Squat 1 Arm Lat Pull Down Delt Lat Rebound Drop	Box 2	Deadlift Pull up Cuban PRSS INC F8
Box 3	DB Walking Lunge DB BO Row Shrug	Box 3	STEP UP DB Twist DB Shrug	Box 3	Single Leg Squat DB BO Row DB Shrug
Box 4	RDL Incline Hammer Curls Full BCH Curl Up	Box 4	DB RDL InLine Zotman Curl INCLINE SIT UP	Box 4	Assist Noridic Ham Curl DB Curl INCLINE SIT UP
Box 5	Ball LG Curl 90 90 Groin ISO Hold Ez Bar Curl	Box 5	Glute Bar Lifts BAR CURL BND Adduction	Box 5	Glute Bar Lift Revs Curl Iso Ball Grion Sqeeze
Box 6	Shrug Closed Lunge V BND TW Wrist Flexion	Box 6	Shrug PRTNR Abs Bam Bam	Box 6	BENCH PRESS DB Shoulder Press TRI PUSH DOWN
Box 7	Sq Trap Sh Bi Hold Glute Ham Back Cav Iso	Box 7	Sq Trap Sh Bi Hold Glute Ham Back Cav Iso	Box 7	Sq Trap Sh Bi Hold Glute Ham Back Cav Iso
Box 8	GH HANG Rollers Glutes and Hams Partner Leg Walks	Box 8	GH HANG Rollers Glutes and Hams Partner Leg Walks	Box 8	GH HANG Rollers Glutes and Hams Partner Leg Walks

BLOCK ONE (5-DAY): ABOVE 80% ECCENTRIC PHASE (UPPER BODY)

Tuesday - Day Two

100%		27-Jun-11	4-Jul-11		
		REPS	LOAD	SETS	NOTES
300	BENCH PRESS	5	135 - 165	1	Plw-2 Neck
	Pair w/				Rest 30
300	BENCH PRESS	3	175 - 195	1	
	Pair w/				Rest 1:00
300	BENCH PRESS	1	235 - 240	1	Plw-2 Neck
300	BENCH PRESS	10	195 - 210	5	
	Pair w/				Rest 45
38	DB Rear Delt	10	25 - 25	5	
		12		5	Rest 30
	Calf Raises	12		5	
90	DB INCLINE BENCH	12,*,*	60 - 70	3	Increase Wgt
	Pair w/				Rest 30
	Infraspinatus	12		3	3:0:0:10
	Pair w/				Rest 30
38	DB Side Lat Raise	12	25 - 25	3	
	Jerk Support Iso	10S	60% -	3	
	Pair w/				Rest 30
	Hip FLX BND Pulls	6		3	
	Pair w/				Rest 30
	Glute Swings	10		3	
105	JM DB Press	10	70 - 75	3	0:2:0:0
	Pair w/				Rest 30
	BND Abduction	10		3	
	Pair w/				Rest 30
	Spider Flips	12		3	
360	Shrug	FFFF	235 - 125	4	
	Closed Lunge Y BND TW	10		3	Rest 30
	Pair w/				Rest 30
	Wrist Flexion	10		3	LS Failure
	Chest Rev Grip Iso	180s		1	
	ISO SPLIT	30s -	40% -	1	Each Leg
	GH HANG	120S		1	Relax Mouth
	Pair w/				
	Rollers Glutes & Hams	120S		1	
	Pair w/				
	Partner Back walk	120S		1	

Thursday

100%		29-Jun-11	6-Jul-11		
		REPS	LOAD	SETS	NOTES
300	BENCH PRESS	5	135 - 165	1	Plw-2 Neck
	Pair w/				Rest 30
300	BENCH PRESS	3	175 - 195	1	Plw-2 Neck
	Pair w/				Rest 1:00
300	BENCH PRESS	1	235 - 240	1	Plw-2 Neck
300	BENCH PRESS	12	195 - 210	5	
	Med Ball Chest Pass	5		5	Rest 45
	INC OH Sit Up	10		4	Rest 30
53	DB Incline Fly	9,7,5	35 - 40	3	
	Pair w/				Rest 30
60	Arnold Press	12	40 - 40	3	
	Pair w/				Rest 30
165	Dynamic Lat Pull	20	100 - 105	3	
270	Close Grip Bench	12	190 - 205	3	4 Board
	Hip Flex Ecc Prone	10S		3	Rest 30
	90 90 Glute ISO Hold	10S		3	Rest 30
60	DB Tri Floor Press	10	40 - 40	3	0:2:0:0
	Iso Abduction Hold	10S		3	Rest 30
	Round House	12		3	
	Wrist Flexion	12		2	Rest 30
	Pair w/				Rest 30
	PRTNR Abs	8		2	Rest 30
	Pair w/				
	SWB Up TW	8		2	
	Chest Rev Grip Iso	180s		1	
	GH HANG	120S		1	Relax Mouth
	Pair w/				
	Rollers Quads & Back	120S		1	
	Pair w/				
	LAYING WALL SHAKES	120S		1	Relax Mouth

BLOCK ONE (5-DAY): ABOVE 80%
ECCENTRIC PHASE HYPERLINKS

Day 2	Exercise Hyperlink	Day 4	Exercise Hyperlink
Box 1	BENCH PRESS P/w-2 Neck	Box 1	BENCH PRESS P/w-2 Neck
Box 2	BENCH PRESS DB Rear Delt Calf Raises	Box 2	BENCH PRESS Med Ball Chest Pass INC OH Sit Up
Box 3	DB INCLINE BENCH Infraspinatus DB Side Lat Raise	Box 3	DB Incline Fly Arnold Press Dynamic Lat Pull
Box 4	Jerk Support Iso Hip FLX BND Pulls Glute Swings	Box 4	Close Grip Bench Hip Flex Ecc Prone 90 90 Glute ISO Hold
Box 5	JM DB Press BND Abduction Spider Flips	Box 5	DB Tri Floor Press Iso Abduction Hold Round House
Box 6	Shrug Closed Lunge V BND TW Wrist Flexion	Box 6	Wrist Flexion PRTNR Abs SWB Up TW
Box 7	Chest Rev Grip Iso ISO SPLIT	Box 7	Chest Rev Grip Iso
Box 8	GH HANG Rollers Glutes and Hams Partner Back walk	Box 8	GH HANG Rollers Quads & Back LAYING WALL SHAKES

BLOCK TWO (5-DAY): ABOVE 80% ISOMETRIC PHASE (LOWER BODY)

Monday - Day One

Dates: 1-Aug-11, 8-Aug-11

100%	Exercise	REPS	LOAD	SETS	NOTES
400	FRONT SQUAT	5	180 - 220	1	Plw-2 Neck
	Pair w/				Roller-I Band
400	FRONT SQUAT	3	235 - 260	1	Plw-2 Neck
	Pair w/				Roller- HAM
400	FRONT SQUAT	1	310 - 320	1	Plw-2 Neck
400	FRONT SQUAT	3	330 - 350	5	0:3:0:0
225	Lat Pull Down	6	160 - 170	5	Rest 45
	Pair w/				Rest 45
	Cuban PRSS INC F8	10		5	
200	DB Walking Lunge	6	150 - 160	4	Pause
					Toes
105	DB BO Row	10	70 - 75	4	Rest 45
	Pair w/				Rest 45
360	Shrug	8	250 - 270	4	Chin Down
500	RDL	4	400 - 415	4	0:2:0:0
	Pair w/				Rest 45
60	Incline Hammer Curls	6	45 - 50	4	Rest 45
	Pair w/				Rest 45
	Full BCH Curl Up	8		4	
	Ball LG Curl	8		3	Rest 45
	90 90 Groin ISO Hold	12		3	Rest 30
	Pair w/				Rest 30
120	Ez Bar Curl	10	85 - 90	3	LS Failure
360	Shrug	FFFF	235 - 125	4	Chin Down
	Closed Lunge Y BND Tw	10		3	Rest 45
	Pair w/				Rest 30
	Wrist Flexion	10		3	LS Failure
	Sq Trap Sh BI Hold	180s		1	Rest 1:30
	Glute Ham Back Cav Iso	180s	60% -	1	
	GH HANG	120S		1	Relax Mouth
	Pair w/				
	Rollers Glutes & Hams	120S		1	
	Pair w/				
	Partner Leg Walks	120s		1	

Wednesday - Day Three

Dates: 3-Aug-11, 10-Aug-11

100%	Exercise	REPS	LOAD	SETS	NOTES
500	Back Squat	5	225 - 275	1	Plw-2 Neck
	Pair w/				Roller-I Band
500	Back Squat	3	295 - 325	1	Plw-2 Neck
	Pair w/				Roller- HAM
500	Back Squat	1	390 - 400	1	Plw-2 Neck
500	Back Squat	1	440 - 465	5	0:0:0:0
105	1 Arm Lat Pull Down	8	75 - 80	5	Rest 1:30
	Delt Lat Rebound Drop	8		5	Rest 45
200	STEP UP	3	175 - 185	4	Increase Vgt
	Pair w/				Rest 45
165	Dynamic Lat Pull	10	105 - 115	4	Rest 45
	Pair w/				Rest 45
210	DB Shrug	12	135 - 145	4	
	Assist Nordic Ham Curl	6		4	0:2:0:0
	Pair w/				Rest 45
60	DB Curl	6	45 - 50	4	Rest 45
	Pair w/				Rest 45
	INCLINE SIT UP	8		4	
	Glute Bar Lifts	6		3	Rest 45
120	BAR CURL	8	90 - 95	3	Rest 45
	Pair w/				Rest 45
360	BND Adduction	12		3	Chin Down
360	Shrug	FFFF	235 - 125	4	Rest 45
	PRTNR Abs	10		3	
	Pair w/				Rest 45
	Bam Bam	10		3	
	Sq Trap Sh BI Hold	180s		1	Rest 1:30
	Glute Ham Back Cav Iso	180s	60% -	1	
	GH HANG	120S		1	Relax Mouth
	Pair w/				
	Rollers Glutes & Hams	120S		1	
	Pair w/				
	Partner Leg Walks	120s		1	Relax Mouth

Friday - Day Five

Dates: 5-Aug-11, 12-Aug-11

100%	Exercise	REPS	LOAD	SETS	NOTES
390	Deadlift	5	175 - 215	1	Plw-2 Neck
	Pair w/				Roller-I Band
390	Deadlift	3	230 - 255	1	Plw-2 Neck
	Pair w/				Roller- HAM
390	Deadlift	1	305 - 310	1	Plw-2 Neck
390	Deadlift	5	295 - 310	4	
180	Pull up	8	125 - 135	4	Rest 1:00
	Pair w/				Rest 1:30
	Cuban PRSS INC F8	8		5	
225	Single Leg Squat	5	180 - 185	4	3:0:0:0
	Pair w/				Rest 45
105	DB BO Row	6	80 - 85	4	Rest 45
	Pair w/				Rest 45
210	DB Shrug	12	135 - 145	4	
	Assist Nordic Ham Curl	6		4	Rest 30
	Pair w/				Rest 30
120	Bar Curl	8	85 - 90	4	Rest 30
	Pair w/				Rest 30
	INCLINE SIT UP	8		4	
	Glute Bar Lifts	10		3	Rest 30
	Pair w/				Rest 30
105	Revs Curl	10	75 - 80	3	Rest 30
	Pair w/				Rest 30
	Iso Ball Groin Sqeeze	10S			
300	BENCH PRESS	FFFF	195 - 105	4	Rest Bt 45
					Rest 1:30
75	DB Shoulder Press	FFFF	50 - 25	4	OC Press
					Rest 1:30
150	TRI PUSH DOWN	FFFF	100 - 55	4	Rest BT 45
	Sq Trap Sh BI Hold	180s		1	
					Rest 1:30
	Glute Ham Back Cav Iso		60% -	1	
	GH HANG	120S		1	Relax Mouth
	Pair w/				
	Rollers Glutes & Hams	120S		1	
	Pair w/				
	Partner Leg Walks	120S		1	Relax Mouth

BLOCK TWO (5-DAY): Above 80% Isometric Phase
Hyperlinks

Day 1	Exercise Hyperlink	Day 3	Exercise Hyperlink	Day 5	Exercise Hyperlink
Box 1	FRONT SQUAT P/w-2 Neck	Box 1	Back Squat P/w-2 Neck	Box 1	Deadlift P/w-2 Neck
Box 2	Isometric Front Squat Lat Pull Down Cuban PRSS INC F8	Box 2	Back Squat 1 Arm Lat Pull Down Delt Lat Rebound Drop	Box 2	Deadlift Pull up Cuban PRSS INC F8
Box 3	DB Walking Lunge DB BO Row Shrug	Box 3	STEP UP Dynamic Lat Pull DB Shrug	Box 3	Single Leg Squat DB BO Row DB Shrug
Box 4	RDL Incline Hammer Curls Full BCH Curl Up	Box 4	Assist Noridic Ham Curl DB Curl INCLINE SIT UP	Box 4	Assist Noridic Ham Curl Bar Curl INCLINE SIT UP
Box 5	Ball LG Curl 90 90 Groin ISO Hold Ez Bar Curl	Box 5	Glute Bar Lifts BAR CURL BND Adduction	Box 5	Glute Bar Lifts Revs Curl Iso Ball Grion Sqeeze
Box 6	Shrug Closed Lunge V BND TW Wrist Flexion	Box 6	Shrug PRTNR Abs Bam Bam	Box 6	BENCH PRESS DB Shoulder Press TRI PUSH DOWN
Box 7	Sq Trap Sh Bi Hold Glute Ham Back Cav Iso	Box 7	Sq Trap Sh Bi Hold Glute Ham Back Cav Iso	Box 7	Sq Trap Sh Bi Hold Glute Ham Back Cav Iso
Box 8	GH HANG Rollers Glutes and Hams Partner Leg Walks	Box 8	GH HANG Rollers Glutes and Hams Partner Leg Walks	Box 8	GH HANG Rollers Glutes and Hams Partner Leg Walks

BLOCK TWO (5-DAY): ABOVE 80% ISOMETRIC PHASE (UPPER BODY)

Tuesday Day Two

%100↑		2-Aug-11 REPS	LOAD	9-Aug-11 SETS	NOTES
300	BENCH PRESS	5	135 - 165	1	Plw-2 Neck
	Pair w/				Rest 30
300	BENCH PRESS	3	175 - 195	1	Plw-2 Neck
	Pair w/				Rest 1:00
300	BENCH PRESS	1	235 - 240	1	Plw-2 Neck
300	BENCH PRESS	1,1	240 - 250	5	
	Pair w/				Rest 45
38	DB Rear Delt	10	25 - 25	5	
	Pair w/				Rest 30
	Calf Raises	12		5	
90	DB INCLINE BENCH	6	70 - 75	3	Increase Wgt
	Infraspinatus	12		3	3:0:0:10
	Pair w/				Rest 30
38	DB Side Lat Raise	12	25 - 25	3	
195	Push Press	10S	115 -	3	
	Pair w/				Rest 30
	Hip FLX BND Pulls	6		3	
	Pair w/				Rest 30
	Glute Swings	10		3	
105	JM DB Press	10	70 - 75	3	0:2:0:0
	Pair w/				Rest 30
	BND Abduction	10		3	
	Pair w/				Rest 30
	Spider Flips	12		3	
360	Shrug	FFFF	235 - 125	4	
	Closed Lunge VBND Tw	10		3	Rest 30
	Pair w/				Rest 30
	Wrist Flexion	10		3	LS Failure
	Chest Rev Grip Iso	180s		1	
	ISO SPLIT	30s	40% -	1	Each Leg
	GH HANG	120S		1	Relax Mouth
	Pair w/				
	Rollers Glutes & Hams	120S		1	
	Pair w/				
	Partner Back walk	120S		1	

Thursday - Day four

%100↑		4-Aug-11 REPS	LOAD	11-Aug-11 SETS	NOTES
300	BENCH PRESS	5	135 - 165	1	Plw-2 Neck
	Pair w/				Rest 30
300	BENCH PRESS	3	175 - 195	1	Plw-2 Neck
	Pair w/				Rest 1:00
300	BENCH PRESS	1	235 - 240	1	Plw-2 Neck
300	BENCH PRESS	1,1	265 - 280	5	
	Pair w/				Rest 45
	Med Ball Chest Pass	5		5	
	Pair w/				Rest 30
	INC OH Sit Up	10		4	
105	DB BENCH	6,5,4	85 - 95	3	Rest 30
60	Arnold Press	12	40 - 40	3	
	Pair w/				Rest 30
165	Dynamic Lat Pull	20	100 - 105	3	
270	Close Grip Bench	12	190 - 205	3	4 Board
	Pair w/				Rest 30
	Hip Flex Ecc Prone	10S		3	
	Pair w/				Rest 30
	90 90 Glute ISO Hold	10S		3	
60	DB Tri Floor Press	10	40 - 40	3	0:2:0:0
	Pair w/				Rest 30
	Iso Abduction Hold	10S		3	
	Round House	12		3	Rest 30
	Wrist Flexion	12		2	Rest 30
	Pair w/				
	PRTNR Abs	8		2	Rest 30
	Pair w/				
	SWB Up TW	8		2	
	Chest Rev Grip Iso	180s		1	
	GH HANG	120S		1	Relax Mouth
	Pair w/				
	Rollers Quads & Back	120S		1	
	Pair w/				
	LAYING WALL SHAKES	120S		1	Relax Mouth

BLOCK TWO (5-DAY): ABOVE 80% ISOMETRIC PHASE HYPERLINKS

Day 2	Exercise Hyperlink	Day 4	Exercise Hyperlink
Box 1	BENCH PRESS P/w-2 Neck	Box 1	BENCH PRESS P/w-2 Neck
Box 2	BENCH PRESS DB Rear Delt Calf Raises	Box 2	BENCH PRESS Med Ball Chest Pass INC OH Sit Up
Box 3	DB INCLINE BENCH Infraspinatus DB Side Lat Raise	Box 3	DB BENCH Arnold Press Dynamic Lat Pull
Box 4	Push Press Hip FLX BND Pulls Glute Swings	Box 4	Close Grip Bench Hip Flex Ecc Prone 90 90 Glute ISO Hold
Box 5	JM DB Press BND Abduction Spider Flips	Box 5	DB Tri Floor Press Iso Abduction Hold Round House
Box 6	Shrug Closed Lunge V BND TW Wrist Flexion	Box 6	Wrist Flexion PRTNR Abs SWB Up TW
Box 7	Chest Rev Grip Iso ISO SPLIT	Box 7	Chest Rev Grip Iso
Box 8	GH HANG Rollers Glutes and Hams Partner Back walk	Box 8	GH HANG Rollers Quads & Back LAYING WALL SHAKES

BLOCK THREE (5-DAY): ABOVE 80% CONCENTRIC PHASE(LOWER BODY)

Monday (100%)

Exercise	REPS	LOAD	SETS	NOTES
400 FRONT SQUAT no Rest BB	5	180 - 220	1	P/w-2 Neck
				Iband
400 FRONT SQUAT no Rest BB	3	235 - 260	1	P/w-2 Neck
				Iband
400 FRONT SQUAT	1	310 - 320	1	P/w-2 Neck
400 FRONT SQUAT	3	330 - 350	5	0:0:0:0
2:15/30 Rest BB				Rest 1:30
Drop Box Jump	4		5	Reactive
30Rest BB				
Hip FLX BND Pulls	8		3	
200 STEP UP	4	160 - 165	4	Reactive
30Rest BB				
GH HYPR Incline	6		4	0:4:0:0
30Rest BB				Reactive
Speed Adduction	10		3	
500 RDL	5	400 - 415	3	0:0:0:0
30Rest BB				+ Shrug
ANT TIB BND	10		3	
30Rest BB				
90 90 Glute ISO Hold	10S		3	
Closed Lunge V BND TW	10		2	Rest 1:00
Pair w/				
SWB TW Band	10		2	
Pair w/				
GH HANG	120S		1	Relax Mouth
Pair w/				Twist
Rollers Glutes & Hams	120S		1	
Pair w/				
Traction				

Wednesday (100%)

Exercise	REPS	LOAD	SETS	NOTES
Back Squat	5	225 - 275	1	P/w-2 Neck
				Iband
Back Squat	3	295 - 325	1	P/w-2 Neck
				Iband
Back Squat	3	- 400	1	P/w-2 Neck
Back Squat	1	450 - 465	4	
2:15/30 Rest BB				Rest 2:30
USSR Plyo BX Pause	4		4	Pause
30Rest BB				Each Leg
Speed Adduction	6		4	Rest 1:00
SL Leg Press	5	310 - 320	3	
30Rest BB				
Assist Nordic Ham Curl	6		3	Bands
30Rest BB				
90 90 Glute ISO Hold	10S		3	
ANT TIB BND	10		3	
30Rest BB				
PRTNR BND Abs	5		3	
30Rest BB				
90 90 Band Twist	8		3	Each Side
GH HANG	120S		1	Relax Mouth
Pair w/				
Rollers Quads & Back	120S		1	
Pair w/				
LAYING WALL SHAKES	[▸]		1	Relax Mouth

Friday (100%)

Exercise	REPS	LOAD	SETS	NOTES
390 DeadLift	5	175 - 215	1	P/w-2 Neck
390 DeadLift	3	230 - 255	1	P/w-2 Neck
390 DeadLift	3	305 - 310	1	Coach Watch
390 DeadLift	4	310 - 320	5	Rest 2:30
270 Close Grip Bench	5	120 - 150	1	4 Board
270 Close Grip Bench	5	215 - 225	4	4 Board
Glute Bar Lift	5	65% - 85%	3	
Pair w/				
SNGL LG ISO Deadlift	10S		3	
Dead lift trade off				
210 Power Snatch	5	95 - 115	1	
Pair w/				
210 Power Snatch	3	125 - 135	1	
Pair w/				
210 Power Snatch	1	165 - 170	1	
210 Power Snatch	2:2:2	145 - 160	4	0:0:0:10
				Box
75 DB Shoulder Press	FFFF	50 - 25	4	
Pair w/				
150 TRI PUSH DOWN	FFFF	100 - 55	4	
Gh Hang				Relax Mouth
Leg Traction				Relax Mouth

BLOCK THREE (5-DAY): Above 80% Concentric Phase Hyperlinks

Day 1	Exercise Hyperlink	Day 3	Exercise Hyperlink	Day 5	Exercise Hyperlink
Box 1	Front squat	Box 1	Back Squat	Box 1	Deadlift
Box 2	Front squat Drop Box Jumps Hip Flex Band Pulls	Box 2	Back Squat USSR Plyo Box Speed Adduction	Box 2	Deadlift Close Grip Bench
Box 3	STEP UP GH HYPR Incline Speed Adduction	Box 3	SL Leg Press Assist Nordic Ham Curl 90 90 Glute Iso Hold	Box 3	Glute Bar Lift Single Leg Iso Deadlift
Box 4	RDL ANT TIB BAND 90 90 Glute Iso Hold	Box 4	ANT TIB BAND PRTNR BND ABS 90 90 Band Twist	Box 4	Power Snatch
Box 5		Box 5		Box 5	
Box 6	Closed Lunge V Band Twist SWB Up TW Band	Box 6		Box 6	DB Shoulder Press Tricep Push Down
Box 7		Box 7		Box 7	
Box 8	GH HANG Rollers Glutes and Hams Traction	Box 8	GH HANG Rollers Quads and Back Laying Wall Shakes	Box 8	GH HANG Leg Traction

BLOCK THREE (5-DAY): ABOVE 80% CONCENTRIC PHASE (UPPER BODY)

Tuesday

100%	Tuesday	REPS	LOAD	SETS	NOTES
300	Power Clean	5,3	150 - 200	1,1	Pre-Set Wup
300	no Rest BB				
300	Power Clean	3	235 - 240	1	Pwr-2 Neck
300	no Rest BB				
300	Power Clean	1,1	265 - 270	3	Pwr-2 Neck
300	Power Clean	1,1	255 - 265	3	0:0:0:15
300	2:15/30 Rest BB				Rest 3:00
300	Power Clean	1,1,1	240 - 250	3	0:0:0:10
300	30 Rest BB				Rest 2:30
300	BENCH PRESS	5	135 - 165	1	Rest 1:30
300	BENCH PRESS	3	175 - 195	1	Rest 1:30
300	BENCH PRESS	3	- 240	1	Coach Watch
300	BENCH PRESS	T	240 - 255	4	3x - Tendo
300	2:15/30 Rest BB				0:0:0:10
	90 90 Band Twist	8		4	
300	Bench Press	15	195 - 210	1	oc-D-2
90	DB INCLINE BENCH	8	70 - 70	3	
225	Lat Pull Down	8	170 - 180	3	+ Shrug
	30 Rest BB				+ Shrug
38	DB Side Lat Raise	8	30 - 30	3	
60	DB Tri Floor Press	6	45 - 50	3	
120	Bar Curl	6	90 - 95	3	
	30 Rest BB				
38	DB Rear Delt	12	25 - 25	3	
	Delt BO OH Reb Drop	6		3	
	30 Rest BB				
	Bam Bam	6	75 - 90	3	
	GH HANG	120s		1	Relax Mouth
	Pair w/ Rollers Glutes & Hams	120s		1	
	Pair w/ Shoulder Traction	300		1	

Thursday

100%	Thursday	REPS	LOAD	SETS	NOTES
210	Power Snatch	5,3	105 - 140	1,1	Pre-Set Wup
210	no Rest BB				Rest 1:30
210	Power Snatch	3	165 - 170	1	Pwr-2 Neck
210	no Rest BB				Rest 1:30
210	Power Snatch	1,1	185 - 190	3	Pwr-2 Neck
210	Power Snatch	1,1	170 - 175	3	0:0:0:20
210	1:30 Rest BB				Rest 2:30
210	Power Snatch	1,1,1	170 - 175	3	0:0:0:20
210	30 Rest BB				Rest 2:30
300	BENCH PRESS	5,3	150 - 200	1,1	
300	no Rest BB				Rest 1:30
300	BENCH PRESS	3	235 - 240	1	Rest 1:30
300	no Rest BB				
300	BENCH PRESS	1	- 285	2	Coach Watch
300	BENCH PRESS	1	265 - 270	3	0:0:0:20
300	2:15/30 Rest BB				Rest 2:30
300	BENCH PRESS	1,1	255 - 265	3	0:0:0:15
	Pair w/				Pair/E. Set
150	Bench Throw	3	70 - 75	5	0:0:0:3
195	Push Press	3	170 - 180	5	Increase Wgt
120	Ez Bar Curl	8	85 - 90	5	Rest 1:30
	30 Rest BB				
180	Gripper	8	125 - 135	5	
	Rear DELT	T		3	
	30 Rest BB				
105	DB BO Row	T	80 - 85	3	
	30 Rest BB				
	Gopher U Abs	8		3	25 Pounds
	GH HANG	120s		1	Relax Mouth
	Pair w/ Rollers Quads & Back	120s		1	
	Pair w/ LAYING WALL SHAKES	120s		1	Relax Mouth

BLOCK THREE (5-DAY): ABOVE 80%
CONCENTRIC PHASE HYPERLINKS

Day 2	Exercise Hyperlink	Day 4	Exercise Hyperlink
Box 1	Power Clean	Box 1	Power Snatch
Box 2	Power Clean	Box 2	Power Snatch
Box 3	Bench Press	Box 3	Bench Press
Box 4	Bench Press 90 90 Band Twist Bench Press	Box 4	Bench Press Bench Throw
Box 5	DB Incline Bench Lat Pull Down DB Side Lateral Raise	Box 5	Push Press EZ Bar Curl Gripper
Box 6	DB Tri Floor Press Bar Curl DB Rear Delt	Box 6	DB Rear Delt DB Bent Over Row Gopher U ABS
Box 7	Delt BO OH Rebound Drops Bam Bam	Box 7	
Box 8	GH HANG Rollers Glutes and Hams Shoulder Traction	Box 8	GH HANG Rollers Quads and Back Laying Wall Shakes

4.13: ABOVE 80 PERCENT SIX-DAY PROGRAM

The table below shows how to take what you learned about the three-day model and convert it to a six-day training platform. In the table, day one loading parameters are in white, day two loading parameters are in light gray, and day three loading parameters are in dark gray.

TABLE 4.23: ABOVE 80 PERCENT THREE-DAY VERSUS SIX-DAY MODEL							
TRAINING WEEK:		**DAY 1**	**DAY 2**	**DAY 3**	**DAY 4**	**DAY 5**	**DAY 6**
THREE-DAY MODEL	FOCUS	TOTAL BODY	OFF	TOTAL BODY	OFF	TOTAL BODY	OFF
	LOAD	82–87%		90–97%		75–80%	
	MEANS APPLIED	TRIPHASIC		DYNAMIC		TRIPHASIC	
SIX-DAY MODEL	FOCUS	LOWER BODY	UPPER BODY	LOWER BODY	UPPER BODY	LOWER BODY	UPPER BODY
	LOAD	82–87%	82–87%	90–97%	90–97%	75–80%	75–80%
	MEANS APPLIED	TRIPHASIC		DYNAMIC		TRIPHASIC	

Two other important aspects of training that can't be forgotten are speed work and conditioning. Table 4.24 shows where in the training week each should be emphasized along with special instructions and example workouts.

Finally, we need to talk about the different exercises, methods, and means I use in a six-day program that I don't use and didn't show you in the three-day program. Click on the hyperlink below for a complete explanation of the six-day training model.

SIX-DAY ABOVE 80 PERCENT TRIPHASIC VIDEO

TABLE 4.24: ABOVE 80 PERCENT SIX-DAY CONDITIONING MODEL

TRAINING DAY	CONDITIONING GOAL	SPECIAL INSTRUCTIONS	EXAMPLE WORKOUT
DAY 1	**Short Sprints** (High Quality Speed)	• Sprints under 10 seconds • Full recovery; rest 90–120 seconds	• Alactic High Quality Workout • Flying 60s • 16 Week Short Sprint Workouts • Cone Agility
DAY 2	**Long Sprints *or* Short Sprints w/ Reduced Rest** (Speed Conditioning)	• Sprints over 15 seconds or • Sprints under 10, recovery under 20 seconds	• High Quality Lactic Anaerobic Power Training Builder • Metabolic Injury Prevention Runs
DAY 3	**Short Sprints** (High Quality Speed)	• Sprints under 10 seconds • Full recovery; rest 90–120 seconds	• Alactic High Quality Workout • Flying 60's • 16 Week Short Sprint Workouts • Cone Agility
DAY 4	**Short Sprints** (Anaerobic Conditioning)	• Sprints under 10 seconds • Limited recovery; 45–60 seconds	• Work Capacity Alactic Anaerobic Training Builder • Flying 60's • 16 Week Short Sprint Workouts • Cone Agility
DAY 5	**Longer Sprints *or* Continuous Running** (Oxidative Conditioning)	This day is purely work capacity focused	• Aerobic Work Capacity Training Builder • Game Speed Conditioning • Bike Conditioning • TrashBall
DAY 6	**Longer Sprints *or* Continuous Running** (Oxidative Conditioning)	This day is purely work capacity focused	• Aerobic Work Capacity Training Builder • Game Speed Conditioning • Bike Conditioning • TrashBall

BLOCK ONE (6-DAY): ABOVE 80% ECCENTRIC PHASE (LOWER BODY)

MONDAY 24-May-10 — 100%

Exercise	REPS	LOAD	SETS	NOTES
OH SQ Rack Press	6		2	Eyes Closed
Pair w/				
2-WAY NECK	8		2	
Pair w/				
STR Leg OC Glute Lifts	6		2	
BACK SQUAT (500)	3	275 - 300		Roll I-band
	2	325 - 350		Spine Rolls
	1	400 - 415		Coach Watch
Pair Below	3	415 - 425		6:0:0:0
Pair Below	3	415 - 425		6:0:0:0
Pair Below	3	415 - 425		6:0:0:0
French Contrast	3	415 - 425		6:0:0:0
Hurdle Hop	4		3	Height
SQ Jump Weighted	4		3	0:2:0:0
			3	reps .9-1.1 Rest 4:00
Acc Band Jump Pause	4		3	
4 way neck	8		2	No Rest
Pair w/				
Wrist Flexion	6		3	No Rest
Pair w/				
ANT TIB BND	10		3	
DB Walking Lunge (200)	6	130 - 140	3	Bands
Pair w/				Pause
Cuban PRSS INC F8	6		3	No Rest
Ankle Band Work	10		3	Band Medium
Glute Bar Lift (500)	6	375 - 400	3	0:2:0:0
Hip FLX BND Pulls	6		3	No Rest
Pair w/				
Iso Ball Grion Sqeeze	10S		3	No Rest
Hip Traction	300S		1	Belly Breath
Pair w/				No Rest
Partner Leg Walks				No Rest
Pair w/				
GH HANG	60S		1	Relax Mouth

WENDESDAY 26-May-10 — 100%

Exercise	REPS	LOAD	SETS	NOTES
Triangle Terror	6		2	
Pair w/				
2-WAY NECK	8		2	
Pair w/				
Piston Squat Band	6		2	Bands
BACK SQUAT (500)	3	275 - 300		Roll I-band
	2	325 - 350		Spine Rolls
	1	400 - 415		Coach Watch
	1	450 - 465		Rest 1:00
	1	450 - 465		Rest 1:00
	1	450 - 465		Rest 1:00
	1	450 - 465		Rest 1:00
p	1	450 - 465		Rest 1:00
ALT INC Power Step Up	4		4	Alternating
Pair w/				Rest 30
USSR Plyo Box	4		4	Pause
Pair w/				Rest 30
Power Step up	4		4	Rest HR 110
DB Step up (100)	6	65 - 70	3	Band Medium
Pair w/				No Rest
Laying External Rot	6		3	5:0:5:0
Pair w/				No Rest
DB SL Calf Raise (100)	10	65 - 70	3	Push Toe
GH HYPR Incline	8		3	No Rest
Pair w/				
Hip FLX BND Pulls LAT	6		3	No Rest
Ankle Band Work	10S		3	No Rest
90 90 Grion ISO Hold	10S			
Squat Iso Hold	300S		1	
Hip Traction	180s		1	belly Breath
GH HANG	120S		1	Relax Mouth
				Relax Mouth

FRIDAY 28-May-10 — 100%

Exercise	REPS	LOAD	SETS	NOTES
3 - WY Ham PRSS	9		2	Eyes Closed
Pair w/				
2-WAY NECK	8		2	
Pair w/				
BAL SNGL LG SQ	6		2	Air Max
FRONT SQUAT (400)	3	220 - 240		Roll I-band
	2	260 - 280		Spine Rolls
	1	320 - 330		Coach Watch
	3	310 - 320		6:0:0:0
	3	310 - 320		6:0:0:0
	3	310 - 320		6:0:0:0
French Contrast	3	310 - 320		6:0:0:0
Hurdle Hop	3		4	Distance
Pair w/				
USSR Plyo Box	3		4	Rest
Pair w/				
Acc Band Jump Pause	3		4	Rest HR 110
Iso Ball Grion Sqeeze	10S		3	
LAT SUP F8	6		3	
Pair w/				
Ankle Band Work	10		3	
RDL Shrug (500)	6	325 - 350	3	3:2:0:0
Hip FLXor ISO Pull	6		1	Toes
SNGL LG ISO Deadlift	10S		3	
GH HANG	120S		1	
Pair w/				
Partner Leg Walks	120S		1	
Pair w/				
Hip Traction	300S		1	Belly Breath

BLOCK ONE (6-DAY): ABOVE 80% ECCENTRIC PHASE
HYPERLINKS

Day 1	Exercise Hyperlink	Day 3	Exercise Hyperlink	Day 5	Exercise Hyperlink
Box 1	OH SQ Rack Press 2 way Neck STR Leg OC Glute lifts	Box 1	Triangle Terror 2 way Neck Piston Squat Band	Box 1	3-way Ham Press 2 way Neck Balance Single Leg Squat
Box 2	Back Squat Back Squat Eccentric	Box 2	Back Squat	Box 2	FRONT SQUAT Eccentric Front Squat
Box 3	Hurdle Hop SQ Jump Weighted ACC Band Jump Pause	Box 3	Alt Inc Power Step Up USSR Plyo Box Power Step up	Box 3	Hurdle Hop USSR Plyo Box ACC Band Jump Pause
Box 4	4 Way Neck Wrist Flexion ANT TIB BND	Box 4	DB Step Up External Rotation Supine DB SL Calf Raise	Box 4	Iso Ball Grion Sqeeze LAT SUP F8 Ankle Band Work
Box 5	DB Walking Lunge Cuban PRSS INC F8 Ankle Band Work	Box 5	GH HYPR Incline Hip FLX BND Pulls LAT 90 90 Groin ISO Hold	Box 5	RDL Shrug Hip Flexor Isometric Pull SNGL LG ISO Deadlift
Box 6	Glute Bar Lifts Hip Flex Band Pulls Iso Ball Grion Sqeeze	Box 6	Squat ISO Hold Hip Traction	Box 6	GH HANG Partner Leg Walks Hip Traction
Box 7	Hip Traction Partner Leg Walks GH HANG	Box 7	GH HANG	Box 7	
Box 8		Box 8		Box 8	

BLOCK ONE (6-DAY): ABOVE 80% ECCENTRIC PHASE (UPPER BODY)

Tuesday — 24-May-11

100%	Exercise	REPS	LOAD	SETS	NOTES
300	BENCH PRESS	5	135 - 165	1	Plw-2 Neck
	Pair w/				
300	BENCH PRESS	3	175 - 195	1	Plw-2 Neck
	Pair w/				
300	BENCH PRESS	1	235 - 240	1	Plw-2 Neck
300	BENCH PRESS	1,1,1,1	180 - 195	4	Chain
	Rack Band Push Up				0:1:0:10
	Pair w/				
	Infraspinatus	3		4	
	Pair w/				
		10		4	
90	DB INCLINE BENCH	9,7,5	65 - 70	3	Increase Wgt
	Pair w/				LS Failure
225	Lat Pull Down	12,x,6	145 - 180	3	
	Pair w/				
30	OH LAT Raise	12	20 - 20	3	
	Pair w/				
240	Dips	x	170 - 190	3	
	Pair w/				
180	Chin up	x	125 - 145	3	
	Pair w/				
	ANT TIB BND	15		3	
64	JM DB Press	10	40 - 45	3	
	Pair w/				
120	BAR CURL	12,x,6	80 - 95	3	
	Pair w/				
	Bam Bam	12		3	
180	Gripper	12	125 - 135	2	LS Failure
	Pair w/				
	Pike SWB Abs	12		2	
	Pair w/				
	SWB Down TW	8		2	
	Chest Rev Grip Iso	180s	60% -	1	
	Pair w/				
	Shr Sho Bi Cav Iso	180s	60% -	1	

Thursday — 26-May-11

100%	Exercise	REPS	LOAD	SETS	NOTES
300	BENCH PRESS	5	135 - 165	1	Plw-2 Neck
	Pair w/				
300	BENCH PRESS	3	175 - 195	1	Plw-2 Neck
	Pair w/				
300	BENCH PRESS	1	235 - 240	1	Plw-2 Neck
300	BENCH PRESS	1,1	255 - 265	4	0:0:0:20
	Med Ball Chest Pass	3		4	one arm
	Pair w/				
	OH SUP F8	10		4	
53	DB Incline Fly	9,7,5	35 - 40	3	Increase Wgt
165	Dynamic Lat Pull	8	115 - 125	3	
	Pair w/				
62	DB Curl to Arnold	8	45 - 50	3	
240	Close Grip Bench	3	220 - 230	3	3 Board
	Pair w/				
60	Incline Hammer Curls	12,x,6	40 - 50	3	Increase Wgt
100	DB SL Calf Raise	15	60 - 65	3	
150	Rev Grip Tri Push	9,7,5	105 - 120	3	Increase Wgt
	Pair w/				
45	Concentration Curl	6	35 - 35	3	LS OC FAIL
	Pair w/				
	Round House	12		3	
	Wrist Flexion	12		3	
	Pair w/				
	Gopher U Abs	12		3	
	Pair w/				
	SWB Up TW	8		3	Each Side
	Chest Rev Grip Iso	180s	60% -	1	
	Pair w/				
	Shr Sho Bi Cav Iso	180s		1	

Saturday — 29-May-10

100%	Exercise	REPS	LOAD	SETS	NOTES
300	BENCH PRESS	5	135 - 165	1	Plw-2 Neck
	Pair w/				
300	BENCH PRESS	3	175 - 195	1	Plw-2 Neck
	Pair w/				
300	BENCH PRESS	1	235 - 240	1	Plw-2 Neck
300	BENCH PRESS	4	240 - 250	4	
	Med Ball Chest Pass	3		4	one arm
	Pair w/				
90	OH SUP F8	10		4	
	DB INCLINE BENCH	10	60 - 65	3	
	Pair w/				
	1 Arm Lat Pull Down	10	75 - 80	3	
	Pair w/				
62	DB Curl to Arnold	8	45 - 50	3	
60	DB Tri Floor Press	12	40 - 40	3	
	Pair w/				
120	Ez Bar Curl	12	80 - 85	3	
	Pair w/				
100	DB SL Calf Raise	15	60 - 65	3	
240	Dips	12	155 - 170	3	
	Pair w/				
105	Drag Curl	6	85 - 85	3	LS OC FAIL
	Pair w/				
	Spider Flips	12		3	
	Wrist Flexion	12		3	
	Pair w/				
	Gopher U Abs	12		3	
	Pair w/				
	SWB Up TW	8		3	Each Side
	Chest Rev Grip Iso	180s		1	
	Pair w/				
	Shr Sho Bi Cav Iso	180s		1	

BLOCK ONE (6-DAY): ABOVE 80% ECCENTRIC PHASE HYPERLINKS

Day 2	Exercise Hyperlink	Day 4	Exercise Hyperlink	Day 6	Exercise Hyperlink
Box 1	Bench Press P/w-2 Neck	Box 1	Bench Press P/w-2 Neck	Box 1	Bench Press P/w-2 Neck
Box 2	Chain Bench Rack Band Push Up Infraspinatus	Box 2	Bench Press MB Chest Pass SA OH SUP F8	Box 2	Bench Press MB Chest Pass SA OH SUP F8
Box 3	DB INCLINE BENCH Lat Pull Down OH LAT Raise	Box 3	Dumbbell Incline Fly Dynamic Lat Pull DB Curl to Arnold	Box 3	DB incline bench 1 Arm Lat Pull Down DB Curl to Arnold
Box 4	Dips Chin Up ANT TIB BND	Box 4	Close Grip Bench Incline Hammer Curl DB SL Calf Raise	Box 4	DB Tri FLoor Press Ez Bar Curl DB SL Calf Raise
Box 5	JM Dumbbell Press Bar Curl Bam Bams	Box 5	Tri push down Concentration Curl Round House	Box 5	Dips Drag Curl Spider Flips
Box 6	Gripper Pike Swiss Ball Abs SWB Down TW	Box 6	Wrist Flexion Gopher U Abs SWB Up TW	Box 6	Wrist Flexion Gopher U Abs SWB Up TW
Box 7	Chest Reverse Grip ISO Shr Sho Bi Cav Iso	Box 7	Chest Reverse Grip ISO Shr Sho Bi Cav Iso	Box 7	Chest Reverse Grip ISO Shr Sho Bi Cav Iso
Box 8		Box 8		Box 8	

BLOCK TWO (6-DAY): ABOVE 80% ISOMETRIC PHASE (LOWER BODY)

MONDAY — 14-Jun-10

Exercise	REPS	LOAD	SETS	NOTES
OH SQ Rack Press	6		2	Eyes Closed
Pair w/				
2-WAY NECK	8		2	
Pair w/				
STR Leg OC Glute Lifts	6		2	
BACK SQUAT (500)	3	275 - 300	2	Roll I-band
	2	325 - 350	2	Spine Rolls
	2	400 - 415	2	CW TEST
Pair Below	2	365 - 390	2	0:3:0:0
Pair Below	2	365 - 390	2	0:3:0:0
Pair Below	2	365 - 390	2	0:3:0:0
complete Block below				
After each Set	2	365 - 390	2	0:3:0:0
Hurdle Hop	4		3	Height
Pair w/				0:2:0:0
SQ Jump Weighted	4		3	Pause
Acc Band Jump	4		3	Rest 4:00
4 way neck	8		2	No Rest
Pair w/				
Wrist Flexion	6		3	No Rest
Pair w/				
ANT TIB BND	10		3	
DB Walking Lunge (200)	6	130 - 140	3	Bands
Pair w/				Pause
Cuban PRSS INC F8	6		3	No Rest
Pair w/				
Ankle Band Work	10		3	Band Medium
Glute Bar Lift (500)	6	375 - 400	3	0:2:0:0
Pair w/				No Rest
Hip FLX BND Pulls	6		3	No Rest
Pair w/				
Iso Ball Grion Sqeeze	10S		3	No Rest
Hip Traction	300S		1	Belly Breath
Pair w/				
Partner Leg Walks				No Rest
Pair w/				
GH HANG	60S		1	Relax Mouth

WENDESDAY — 16-Jun-10

Exercise	REPS	LOAD	SETS	NOTES
Triangle Terror	6		2	
Pair w/				
2-WAY NECK	8		2	
Pair w/				
Piston Squat Band	6		2	Bands
BACK SQUAT (500)	3	275 - 300	2	Roll I-band
	2	325 - 350	2	Spine Rolls
	1	400 - 415	1	
Speed 95% Drop off	1	435 - 465	1	1:45 Rest
	1	435 - 465	1	1:45 Rest
	1	435 - 465	1	1:45 Rest
	1	435 - 465	1	1:45 Rest
	1	435 - 465	1	1:45 Rest
	1	435 - 465	1	1:45 Rest
ALT INC Power Step Up	4		4	Alternating
Pair w/				Rest 30
USSR Plyo Box	4		4	Pause
				Rest 30
Power Step up	4		4	Rest HR 110
DB Step up (100)	6	65 - 70	3	Band Medium
				No Rest
Laying External Rot	6		3	5:0:5:0
				No Rest
DB SL Calf Raise (100)	10	65 - 70	3	Push Toe
GH HYPR Incline	8		3	
Pair w/				No Rest
Hip FLX BND Pulls LAT	6		3	
Pair w/				No Rest
90 90 Grion ISO Hold	10S		3	
Squat Iso Hold	300S		1	
Hip Traction	180s		1	belly Breath
GH HANG	120S		1	Relax Mouth

FRIDAY — 18-Jun-10

Exercise	REPS	LOAD	SETS	NOTES
3 - WY Ham PRSS	9		2	
Pair w/				
2-WAY NECK	8		2	
Pair w/				
BAL SNGL LG SQ	6		2	Af Max
FRONT SQUAT (400)	3	220 - 240	3	Roll I-band
	2	260 - 280	2	Spine Rolls
	1	320 - 330	1	Coach Watch
	3	310 - 320	3	0:3:0:0
	3	310 - 320	3	0:3:0:0
	3	310 - 320	3	0:3:0:0
French Contrast	3	310 - 320	3	0:3:0:0
Hurdle Hop	3	310 - 320	4	Distance
USSR Plyo Box	3		4	
Acc Band Jump Pause	3		4	
Iso Ball Grion Sqeeze	10S		3	
Pair w/				
LAT SUP F8	6		3	
Pair w/				
Ankle Band Work	10		3	Band Medium
RDL Shrug (500)	6	325 - 350	3	3:2:0:0
Pair w/				Toes
Hip FLXor ISO Pull	6		3	
SNGL LG ISO Deadlift	10S		3	
BENCH PRESS (300)	FFFF	195 - 105	4	
DB Shoulder Press (75)	FFF	55 - 30	3	OC
Rev Grip Tri Push (150)	FFF	105 - 60	3	
GH HANG	120S		1	Relax Mouth
Partner Leg Walks	120S		1	
Pair w/				
Hip Traction	300S		1	Relax Mouth

BLOCK TWO (6-DAY): ABOVE 80% ISOMETRIC PHASE
HYPERLINKS

Day 1	Exercise Hyperlink	Day 3	Exercise Hyperlink	Day 5	Exercise Hyperlink
Box 1	OH SQ Rack Press 2 way Neck STR Leg OC Glute lifts	Box 1	Triangle Terror 2 way Neck Piston Squat Band	Box 1	3-way Ham Press 2 way Neck Balance Single Leg Squat
Box 2	Back Squat Back Squat Isometric	Box 2	Back Squat	Box 2	FRONT SQUAT Isometric Front Squat
Box 3	Hurdle Hop SQ Jump Weighted ACC Band Jump Pause	Box 3	Alt Inc Power Step Up USSR Plyo Box Power Step up	Box 3	Hurdle Hop USSR Plyo Box ACC Band Jump Pause
Box 4	4 Way Neck Wrist Flexion ANT TIB BND	Box 4	DB Step Up External Rotation Supine DB SL Calf Raise	Box 4	Iso Ball Grion Sqeeze LAT SUP F8 Ankle Band Work
Box 5	DB Walking Lunge Cuban PRSS INC F8 Ankle Band Work	Box 5	GH HYPR Incline Hip FLX BND Pulls LAT 90 90 Groin ISO Hold	Box 5	RDL Shrug Hip Flexor Isometric Pull SNGL LG ISO Deadlift
Box 6	Glute Bar Lifts Hip Flex Band Pulls Iso Ball Grion Sqeeze	Box 6	Squat ISO Hold Hip Traction	Box 6	BENCH PRESS DB Shoulder Press Chest Rev Grip Iso
Box 7	Hip Traction Partner Leg Walks GH HANG	Box 7	GH HANG	Box 7	GH HANG Partner Leg Walks Hip Traction
Box 8		Box 8		Box 8	

BLOCK TWO (6-DAY): ABOVE 80% ISOMETRIC PHASE (UPPER BODY)

Tuesday — 29-Jun-10

100%	Exercise	REPS	LOAD	SETS	NOTES
300	BENCH PRESS	5	135 - 165	1	Pfw-2 Neck
	Pair w/				
300	BENCH PRESS	3	175 - 195	1	Pfw-2 Neck
	Pair w/				
300	BENCH PRESS	1	235 - 240	1	Pfw-2 Neck
300	BENCH PRESS	3	265 - 280	4	
	Rack Band Push Up	4		4	
	Delt BO Lat Reb Drop	10		4	
90	DB INCLINE BENCH	15	60 - 65	3	OC
	Pair w/				
105	1 Arm Lat Pull Down	12,9,6	70 - 85	3	
	Pair w/				
	Incline Rear Delt	12		3	
240	Dips	x	170 - 190	3	
	Pair w/				
180	Chin up	x	125 - 145	3	
	Pair w/				
64	ANT TIB BND	15		3	
	JM DB Press	10	40 - 45	3	OC
	Pair w/				
120	BAR CURL	12,9,6	80 - 95	3	
	Pair w/				
	Bam Bam	12		3	
180	Gripper	12	125 - 135	2	LS Failure
	Pair w/				
	Pike SWB Abs	12		2	
	Pair w/				
	SWB Down TW	8		2	
	Chest Rev Grip Iso	180s	60% -	1	
	Pair w/				
	Shr Sho Bi Cav Iso	180s	60% -	1	

Thursday — 1-Jul-10

100%	Exercise	REPS	LOAD	SETS	NOTES
300	BENCH PRESS	5	135 - 165	1	Pfw-2 Neck
	Pair w/				
300	BENCH PRESS	3	175 - 195	1	Pfw-2 Neck
	Pair w/				
300	BENCH PRESS	1	235 - 240	1	Pfw-2 Neck
300	BENCH PRESS	1,1	255 - 265	4	0:0:0:20
	Med Ball Chest Pass	3		4	one arm
	Pair w/				
	Delt BO OH Reb Drop	10		4	
53	DB Incline Fly	15	35 - 35	3	OC
	Pair w/				
165	Dynamic Lat Pull	8	115 - 125	3	
	Pair w/				
62	DB Curl to Arnold	8	45 - 50	3	
240	Close Grip Bench	3	220 - 230	3	3 Board
60	Incline Hammer Curls	12,9,6	40 - 50	3	Increase Wgt
	Pair w/				
100	DB SL Calf Raise	15	60 - 65	3	
150	Rev Grip Tri Push	9,7,5	105 - 120	3	Increase Wgt
	Pair w/				
45	Concentration Curl	6	35 - 35	3	LS OC FAIL
	Pair w/				
	Round House	12		3	
	Wrist Flexion	12		3	
	Pair w/				
	Gopher U Abs	12		3	
	Pair w/				
	SWB Up TW	8		3	Each Side
	Chest Rev Grip Iso	180s	60% -	1	
	Pair w/				
	Shr Sho Bi Cav Iso	180s		1	

Saturday

100%	Exercise	REPS	LOAD	SETS	NOTES
300	BENCH PRESS	5	135 - 165	1	Pfw-2 Neck
	Pair w/				
300	BENCH PRESS	3	175 - 195	1	Pfw-2 Neck
	Pair w/				
300	BENCH PRESS	1	235 - 240	1	Pfw-2 Neck
300	BENCH PRESS	4	240 - 250	4	
	Med Ball Chest Pass	3		4	one arm
	Pair w/				
90	OH SUP F8	10		4	
	DB INCLINE BENCH	10	60 - 65	3	
	Pair w/				
	1 Arm Lat Pull Down	10	75 - 80	3	
	Pair w/				
62	DB Curl to Arnold	8	45 - 50	3	
60	DB Tri Floor Press	12	40 - 40	3	
120	Ez Bar Curl	12	80 - 85	3	
100	DB SL Calf Raise	15	60 - 65	3	
240	Dips	12	155 - 170	3	
	Pair w/				
105	Drag Curl	6	85 - 85	3	LS OC FAIL
	Pair w/				
	Spider Flips	12		3	
	Wrist Flexion	12		3	
	Pair w/				
	Gopher U Abs	12		3	
	Pair w/				
	SWB Up TW	8		3	Each Side
	Chest Rev Grip Iso	180s		1	
	Shr Sho Bi Cav Iso	180s		1	

BLOCK TWO (6-DAY): ABOVE 80% ISOMETRIC PHASE
HYPERLINKS

Day 2	Exercise Hyperlink	Day 4	Exercise Hyperlink	Day 6	Exercise Hyperlink
Box 1	Bench Press P/w-2 Neck	Box 1	Bench Press P/w-2 Neck	Box 1	Bench Press P/w-2 Neck
Box 2	Bench Press Rack band push up Delt Lateral Rebound Drop	Box 2	Bench Press MB Chest Pass SA Delt Lateral Rebound Drop	Box 2	Bench Press MB Chest Pass SA OH SUP F8
Box 3	DB Incline OC 1 Arm Lat Pull Down DB Rear Delt	Box 3	Dumbbell Incline Fly Dynamic Lat Pull DB Curl to Arnold	Box 3	DB incline bench 1 Arm Lat Pull Down DB Curl to Arnold
Box 4	Dips Chin Up ANT TIB BND	Box 4	Close Grip Bench Incline Hammer Curl DB SL Calf Raise	Box 4	DB Tri FLoor Press Ez Bar Curl DB SL Calf Raise
Box 5	JM Dumbbell Press Bar Curl Bam Bams	Box 5	Tri push down Concentration Curl Round House	Box 5	Dips Drag Curl Spider Flips
Box 6	Gripper Pike Swiss Ball Abs SWB Down TW	Box 6	Wrist Flexion Gopher U Abs SWB Up TW	Box 6	Wrist Flexion Gopher U Abs SWB Up TW
Box 7	Chest Reverse Grip ISO Shr Sho Bi Cav Iso	Box 7	Chest Reverse Grip ISO Shr Sho Bi Cav Iso	Box 7	Chest Reverse Grip ISO Shr Sho Bi Cav Iso
Box 8		Box 8		Box 8	

BLOCK THREE (6-DAY): ABOVE 80% CONCENTRIC PHASE (LOWER BODY)

MONDAY — 28-Jun-10 (100%)

Exercise	REPS	LOAD	SETS	NOTES
OH SQ Rack Press	6		2	Eyes Closed
Pair w/				
2-WAY NECK	8		2	
Pair w/				
STDING Glute Kicks	6		2	
BACK SQUAT (500)	3	275 - 300		Roll I-band
	2	325 - 350		Spine Rolls
Test	1	400 - 415		Coach Watch
Pair Below	3	415 - 425		0:3:0:0
Pair Below	3	415 - 425		0:3:0:0
Pair Below	3	415 - 425		0:3:0:0
French Contrast	3	415 - 425		0:3:0:0
Hurdle Hop	4		4	Distance
Squat Jump (250)	4	200 - 205	4	0:0:0:0
Acc Band Jump	4		4	Rest 5:00
4 way neck	8		2	no Rest
Pair w/				
Wrist Flexion	6		3	no Rest
Pair w/				
ANT TIB BND	10		3	Band Medium
Walking Drop Lunge Jump	4		3	Bands
Pair w/			3	Speed/Jump / Toes
Cuban PRSS INC F8	6		3	
Ankle Band Work	10		3	Band Medium
Glute Bar Lift (500)	6	375 - 400	3	0:0:0:0
Hip FLX BND Pulls	6		3	No Rest
Pair w/				
Iso Ball Grion Sqeeze	10S		3	
Hip Traction	300S		1	Belly Breath
Pair w/				No Rest
Partner Leg Walks				No Rest
Pair w/				
GH HANG	60S		1	Relax Mouth

WENDESDAY — 30-Jun-10 (100%)

Exercise	REPS	LOAD	SETS	NOTES
Triangle Terror	6		2	
Pair w/				
2-WAY NECK	8		2	
Pair w/				
Piston Squat Band	6		2	Bands
BACK SQUAT (500)	3	275 - 300		Roll I-band
	2	325 - 350		Spine Rolls
	1	400 - 415		Coach Watch
Speed 95% Drop off	1	450 - 465		
	1	450 - 465		
	1	450 - 465		
	1	450 - 465		
	1	450 - 465		
Split SQ Drop Jump	4		4	
USSR Plyo Box	4		4	Rest 30 / Bands
Squat Jump (250)	4	170 - 175	4	Rest 30 / Rest 2:00
Power Step up	4		3	Bands Speed/Jump
Pair w/			3	5:0:5:0
Laying External Rot	6		3	Rest 30
Pair w/				
DB SL Calf Raise (100)	10	65 - 70	3	Knee Bend
Nordic HAM Curls	8		3	Assist
Pair w/				Rest 30
Hip FLX BND Pulls LAT	6		3	Rest 30
Pair w/				
90 90 Grion ISO Hold	10S		3	Rest 1:00
Squat Iso Hold	300S		1	be tuff
Band Stretch 1	30s		1	
GH HANG	120S		1	Relax Mouth
Pair w/				
Hip Traction	120S		1	
Pair w/				
LAYING WALL SHAKES	120S		1	Relax Mouth

FRIDAY — 2-Jul-10 (100%)

Exercise	REPS	LOAD	SETS	NOTES
3 - WY Ham PRSS	9		2	
Pair w/			2	no rest
2-WAY NECK	8		2	
Pair w/				no rest
BAL SNGL LG SQ	6		2	Air Max
Hurdle Hop	4		3	
Pair w/			3	Rest 30
USSR Plyo Box	4		3	
Pair w/				Rest 30
Acc Band Jump	4		3	
Single Leg Squat (225)	12	145 - 160	3	
Pair w/			3	Rest 30
SL Reverse Hyper (150)	7	105 - 115	3	
Pair w/				Rest 30
Cuban PRSS INC F8	6		3	.....
Cross Over STEP Up	4		3	Bands
SWB LG Curl SNGL Leg	8		3	Rest 30
Thors Hammer	8		3	.....
BENCH PRESS (300)	FFFF	195 - 105	4	Rest 45
Pair w/				
DB Shoulder Press (75)	FFF	55 - 30	3	OC
Pair w/				Rest 45
TRI PUSH DOWN (150)	FFF	105 - 60	3	Rest 45
Nordic HAM Curls	6		2	
Pair w/				
Hip FLX or ISO Pull	6		2	
Iso Ball Grion Sqeeze	10S		3	
Hindu Squat Iso	180s		1	
Glute Ham Back Cav Iso	180s		1	
GH HANG	120S		1	Relax Mouth
Pair w/				
Partner Leg Walks	120S		1	
Pair w/				
LAYING RELAXATION	120S		1	Relax Mouth

BLOCK THREE (6-DAY): ABOVE 80% CONCENTRIC PHASE HYPERLINKS

Day 1	Exercise Hyperlink	Day 3	Exercise Hyperlink	Day 5	Exercise Hyperlink
Box 1	OH SQ Rack Press 2 way Neck Standing Glute Kicks	Box 1	Triangle Terror 2 way Neck Piston Squat Band	Box 1	3-way Ham Press 2 way Neck Balance Single Leg Squat
Box 2	Back Squat Back Squat Isometric	Box 2	Back Squat	Box 2	Hurdle Hop USSR Plyo Box ACC Band Jump
Box 3	Hurdle Hop Squat Jump ACC Band Jump	Box 3	Split SQ Drop Jump USSR Plyo Box Squat Jump	Box 3	Single leg squat SL Reverse Hyper Cuban PRSS INC F8
Box 4	4 Way Neck Wrist Flexion ANT TIB BND	Box 4	Power Step Up External Rotation Supine DB SL Calf Raise	Box 4	Crossover Step Up SWB LG Curl SNGL Leg Thors Hammer
Box 5	Walking Drop Lunge Jump Cuban PRSS INC F8 Ankle Band Work	Box 5	Nordic HAM Curls Hip FLX BND Pulls LAT 90 90 Groin ISO Hold	Box 5	BENCH PRESS DB Shoulder Press TRI PUSH DOWN
Box 6	Glute Bar Lifts Hip Flex Band Pulls Iso Ball Grion Sqeeze	Box 6	Squat ISO Hold	Box 6	Nordic HAM Curls Hip FLXor ISO Pull Iso Ball Grion Sqeeze
Box 7	Hip Traction Partner Leg Walks GH HANG	Box 7	GH HANG Hip Traction LAYING WALL SHAKES	Box 7	H-sq Shi Bi Trap Glute Ham Back Cav Iso
Box 8		Box 8		Box 8	GH HANG Partner Leg Walks Laying Relaxation

BLOCK THREE (6-DAY): ABOVE 80% CONCENTRIC PHASE (UPPER BODY)

Tuesday — 22-Jun-10

%100		REPS	LOAD	SETS	NOTES
300	BENCH PRESS	5	135 - 165	1	P/w-2 Neck
	Pair w/				
300	BENCH PRESS	3	175 - 195	1	P/w-2 Neck
	Pair w/				
300	BENCH PRESS	1	235 - 240	1	P/w-2 Neck
300	BENCH PRESS	20	195 - 210	4	oc-d/oc-a
	Pair w/				oc+2
	Reactive Bench Toss	4		4	Rebound
	Pair w/				
	Det BO Lat Reb Drop	10		4	
90	DB INCLINE BENCH	15	60 - 65	3	oc+2
105	DB BO Row	8	55 - 65	3	Reactive
	Pair w/				
	Ext/Flex Shoulder Shock	12		3	
240	Dips	x	170 - 190	3	
	Pair w/				
180	Chin up	x	125 - 145	3	
	Pair w/				
	ANT TIB BND	15		3	
64	JM DB Press	10	40 - 45	3	oc+2
	Pair w/				
	Bicep shock curls	6		3	
	Pair w/				
	Plate Flips	12		3	
	Wrist Flexion	12		2	LS Failure
	Pike SWB Abs	12		2	
	SWB Down TW	8		2	
	Chest Rev Grip Iso	180s	60%	1	
	Pair w/				
	Shr Sho Bi Cav Iso	180s	60%	1	

Thursday — 24-Jun-10

%100		REPS	LOAD	SETS	NOTES
300	BENCH PRESS	5	135 - 165	1	P/w-2 Neck
	Pair w/				
300	BENCH PRESS	3	175 - 195	1	P/w-2 Neck
	Pair w/				
300	BENCH PRESS	1	235 - 240	1	P/w-2 Neck
300	BENCH PRESS	12	225 - 235	4	oc-d/oc-a
	Pair w/				oc+2
	Reactive Bench Toss	3		4	Rebound
	Pair w/				
	Det BO OH Reb Drop	10		4	
90	DB INCLINE BENCH	15	60 - 65	3	oc+2
165	Dynamic Lat Pull	8	115 - 125	3	
	Pair w/				
	EXT Rot Part Shock	8		3	
240	Close Grip Bench	3	220 - 230	3	3 Board
	Pair w/				
60	Incline Hammer Curls	12,*,*	40 - 50	3	Increase Wgt
	Pair w/				
	FRT Raise Drops	6		3	
150	Rev Grip Tri Push	9,7.5	105 - 120	3	Increase Wgt
	Pair w/				
45	Concentration Curl	6	35 - 35	3	LS OC FAIL
	Pair w/				
	Wrist Extension	12		3	
	Plate Hold	30S		3	
	Gopher U Abs	12		3	
	Pair w/				
	SWB Up TW	8		3	Each Side
	Chest Rev Grip Iso	180s	60%	1	
	Pair w/				
	Shr Sho Bi Cav Iso	180s		1	

Saturday

%100		REPS	LOAD	SETS	NOTES
300	BENCH PRESS	5	135 - 165	1	P/w-2 Neck
	Pair w/				
300	BENCH PRESS	3	175 - 195	1	P/w-2 Neck
	Pair w/				
300	BENCH PRESS	1	235 - 240	1	P/w-2 Neck
300	BENCH PRESS	4	240 - 250	4	
	Pair w/				
	Med Ball Chest Pass	3		4	one arm
	OH SUP F8	10		4	
90	DB INCLINE BENCH	10	60 - 65	3	
	1 Arm Lat Pull Down	10	75 - 80	3	
	Pair w/				
62	DB Curl to Arnold	8	45 - 50	3	
60	DB Tri Floor Press	12	40 - 40	3	
	Pair w/				
120	Ez Bar Curl	12	80 - 85	3	
	Pair w/				
100	DB SL Calf Raise	15	60 - 65	3	
240	Dips	12	155 - 170	3	
	Pair w/				
105	Drag Curl	6	85 - 85	3	LS OC FAIL
	Spider Flips	12		3	
	Wrist Flexion	12		3	
	Gopher U Abs	12		3	
	Pair w/				
	SWB Up TW	8		3	Each Side
	Chest Rev Grip Iso	180s		1	
	Pair w/				
	Shr Sho Bi Cav Iso	180s		1	

BLOCK THREE (6-DAY): ABOVE 80% CONCENTRIC PHASE HYPERLINKS

Day 2	Exercise Hyperlink	Day 4	Exercise Hyperlink	Day 6	Exercise Hyperlink
Box 1	Bench Press P/w-2 Neck	Box 1	Bench Press P/w-2 Neck	Box 1	Bench Press P/w-2 Neck
Box 2	Bench Press 2POC Reactive Bench Toss Delt Lat Rebound Drop	Box 2	Bench Press 2POC Reactive Bench Toss Delt Lat Rebound Drop	Box 2	Bench Press Med Ball Chest Pass OH SUP F8
Box 3	DB Incline OC DB BO Row Reactive Ext/Flx Shoulder Shock	Box 3	DB Incline OC Dynamic Lat Pull EXT Rot Part Shock	Box 3	DB INCLINE BENCH 1 Arm Lat Pull Down DB Curl to Press
Box 4	Dips Chin Up ANT TIB BND	Box 4	Board Close Grip Bench Press Incline Hammer Curls FRT Raise Drops	Box 4	DB Tri Floor Press Ez Bar Curl DB SL Calf Raise
Box 5	JM DB Press Bicep Curl Shock Plate Flips	Box 5	Tri push down Concentration Curl Wrist Extension	Box 5	Dips Drag Curl Spider Flips
Box 6	Wrist Flexion Pike Swiss Ball Abs SWB Up TW	Box 6	Plate Hold Gopher U Abs SWB Up TW	Box 6	Wrist Flexion Gopher U Abs SWB Up TW
Box 7	Chest Reverse Grip ISO Shr Sho Bi Cav Iso	Box 7	Chest Reverse Grip ISO Shr Sho Bi Cav Iso	Box 7	Chest Reverse Grip ISO Shr Sho Bi Cav Iso
Box 8		Box 8		Box 8	

4.14: ABOVE 80 PERCENT TWO-DAY IN-SEASON PROGRAM

Last but not least, the table below shows how to take what you learned about the three-day model and convert it to a two-day in-season program. In the table, day one loading parameters are in white, day two loading parameters are in light gray, and day three loading parameters are in dark gray. Remember, whenever athletes are in-season, all their volume work comes from practice. Additional volume in the weight room or by conditioning will likely lead to an overtrained, underperforming athlete.

TABLE 4.25: ABOVE 80 PERCENT THREE-DAY VERSUS TWO-DAY IN-SEASON MODEL

TRAINING WEEK:		DAY 1	DAY 2	DAY 3	DAY 4	DAY 5	DAY 6
THREE-DAY MODEL	FOCUS	TOTAL BODY	OFF	TOTAL BODY	OFF	TOTAL BODY	OFF
	LOAD	82–87%		90–97%		75–80%	
	MEANS APPLIED	TRIPHASIC		DYNAMIC		TRIPHASIC	
TWO-DAY MODEL	FOCUS	TOTAL BODY	OFF	LOWER BODY	OFF	OFF	OFF
	LOAD	82–87%		90–97%			
	MEANS APPLIED	TRIPHASIC		DYNAMIC			

For those of you looking for a conditioning table, you won't find it. Remember, during the season, all the athletes' volume and conditioning comes from practice. If a coach takes an athlete and has him run or condition outside of his structured practice, he will overtrain in-season. Both the central and peripheral mechanisms will become overworked and the athlete's performance level will drop off.

Finally, we need to talk about the different exercises, methods, and means I use in a two-day in-season program that I don't use and didn't show you in the three-day program. Click on the hyperlink below for a complete explanation of the two-day in-season training model.

TWO-DAY IN-SEASON ABOVE 80 PERCENT TRIPHASIC VIDEO

BLOCK ONE (2-DAY IN-SEASON): ABOVE 80% ECCENTRIC PHASE

MONDAY (100%)

Exercise	REPS	LOAD	SETS	NOTES
Stding SQ Drop P.Jump	C1T		2	2½ Tendo
Pair w/				0:2:0:6
Cuban PRSS INC F8	5		2	PNr-2 Neck
Pair w/				
ANT TIB BND	10		2	Each Leg
500 Back Squat	2	415 - 440	3	5:0:0:0
Pair w/				Spotter Help
Hip Flex Iso Prone	4		3	0:5:0:0
Pair w/				Bench
1 Arm LAT Pull	8		3	Rest 1:30
105 DB BENCH	6	70 - 75	3	5:0:0:0
Pair w/				Bands
GH HYPR Incline	5		3	0:5:0:0
Pair w/				
30 OH LAT Raise	10	20 - 20	3	+Shrug
64 JM DB Press	6	50 - 50	2	3:0:0:0
105 Drag Curl	6	80 - 85	2	
Pair w/				
90 90 Grion ISO Hold	15S		2	
H-Sq Sh Bi Trap	180s		1	
Chest Rev Grip ISO	180s		1	
Pair w/				
575 Hex Deadlift	30s	-	1	135 or 185
	8	70% - 75%	2	
Core Workout 5				
GH HANG	120S		1	
Pair w/				
Rollers Glutes & Hams	120S		1	
Pair w/				
LAYING RELAXATION	120S		1	

WENDESDAY (100%)

Exercise	REPS	LOAD	SETS	NOTES
Stding SQ Drop Jump	C1T		2	2½ Tendo
Pair w/				0:0:0:6
Tea Cup Stuff	5		2	
Pair w/				
Calf Raises	8		2	
750 Leg Press	3	695 - 710	3	
Pair w/				
Iso Ball Grion Squeeze	4		3	0:5:0:0
Pair w/				
165 Dynamic Lat Pull	8	125 - 130	3	Rest 1:30
300 BENCH PRESS	3	280 - 285	3	
Ball BND LG Curls	6		3	
Pair w/				
38 DB Rear Delt	10	25 - 25	3	
45 DB Tri Pro Sup	10	30 - 35	2	
60 DB Curl to Press	6	45 - 50	2	
Pair w/				
90 90 Glute ISO Hold	15S		2	
Glute Ham Back Cav Iso	180s		1	
H-Sq Sh Bi Trap	120S		1	
Pair w/				Toes
Pair w/				
Core Workout 1		8	70% - 75%	2	Box 36
GH HANG	120S		1	Relax Mouth
Pair w/				
Rollers Quads & Back	120S		1	
Pair w/				
LAYING WALL SHAKES	120S		1	Relax Mouth

BLOCK ONE (2-DAY): ABOVE 80% ECCENTRIC PHASE HYPERLINKS

Day 1	Exercise Hyperlink	Day 2	Exercise Hyperlink
Box 1	Stding SQ Drop P Jump Cuban Press INC F8 ANT TIB BND	Box 1	Sting SQ Drop Jump Tea Cup Stuff Calf Raises
Box 2	Back Squat Eccentric Hip Flex Iso Prone 1 Arm LAT Pull	Box 2	Leg Press Iso Ball Groin Squeeze Dynamic Lat Pull
Box 3	DB Bench GH HYPER Incline OH LAT Raise	Box 3	BENCH PRESS Ball BND LG Curl DB Rear Delt
Box 4	JM DB Press Drag Curl 90 90 Groin ISO Hold	Box 4	DB Tri Pro Sup DB Curl to Press 90 90 Glute ISO Hold
Box 5	H-sq Shi Bi Trap Chest Rev Grip Iso Hex Deadlift	Box 5	Glute Ham Back Cav Iso H-sq Shi Bi Trap
Box 6		Box 6	
Box 7		Box 7	
Box 8	GH Hang Rollers Glutes & Hams Laying Relaxation	Box 8	GH Hang Rollers Quads & Back LAYING WALL SHAKES

BLOCK TWO (2-DAY IN-SEASON): ABOVE 80% ISOMETRIC PHASE

WENDESDAY

100%	WENDESDAY	REPS	LOAD	SETS	NOTES
	Vertimax 2 Band Pause	C1T		2	2x - Tendo
	Pair w/				Set Drop off
	Tea Cup Stuff	5		2	
	Pair w/				
	Calf Raises	8		2	
750	Leg Press	3	695 - 710	3	
	Pair w/				
	Iso Ball Grion Sqeeze	4		3	
165	Dynamic Lat Pull	8	125 - 130	3	Rest 1:30
300	BENCH PRESS	3	280 - 285	3	
	Pair w/				
	Ball BND LG Curls	6		3	
	Pair w/				
38	DB Rear Delt	10	25 - 25	3	
45	DB Tri Pro Sup	10	30 - 35	2	
60	DB Curl to Press	6	45 - 50	2	
	Pair w/				
	90 90 Glute ISO Hold	15S		2	
	Glute Ham Back Cav Iso	180s		1	
	Pair w/				
	H-Sq Sh Bi Trap	120S		1	
	Pair w/				
	Coreworkout 6				
		8	70% - 75%	2	
	GH HANG	120S		1	Relax Mouth
	Pair w/				
	Rollers Quads & Back	120S		1	
	Pair w/				
	LAYING WALL SHAKES	120S		1	Relax Mouth

MONDAY

100%	MONDAY	REPS	LOAD	SETS	NOTES
	Squat Jump Pause	C1T		2	2x - Tendo
	Cuban PRSS INC F8	5		2	Set Drop off / PN-2 Neck
	Glute Bar Lifts	5		2	Blue Pad
500	Back Squat	2	415 - 440	3	0:4:0:0 / Box
	Hip Flex Iso Prone	4		3	0:5:0:0 / Bench
105	1 Arm LAT Pull	8		3	Rest 1:30
	DB BENCH	6	70 - 75	3	0:4:0:0 / Bands
	GH HYPR Incline	5		3	0:5:0:0
30	OH LAT Raise	10	20 - 20	3	+ Shrug
60	DB Tri Floor Press	6	45 - 50	2	0:2:0:0
	Dual Action Bicep Curls	6		2	
	Pair w/				
	90 90 Grion ISO Hold	15S		2	
	H-Sq Sh Bi Trap	180s		1	
	Pair w/				
	Chest Rev Grip Iso	180s		1	
	Core Workout 3				
		8	70% - 75%	2	
	GH HANG	120S		1	
	Rollers Glutes & Hams	120S		1	
	Pair w/				
	LAYING RELAXATION	120S		1	

BLOCK TWO (2-DAY): ABOVE 80% ISOMETRIC
PHASE HYPERLINKS

Day 1	Exercise Hyperlink	Day 2	Exercise Hyperlink
Box 1	Squat Jump Pause Cuban Press INC F8 Glute Bar Lifts	Box 1	Squat Jump Pause Tea Cup Stuff Calf Raises
Box 2	Back Squat Isometric Hip Flex Iso Prone 1 Arm LAT Pull	Box 2	Leg Press Iso Ball Groin Squeeze Dynamic Lat Pull
Box 3	DB Bench Isometric GH HYPER Incline OH LAT Raise	Box 3	BENCH PRESS Ball BND LG Curl DB Rear Delt
Box 4	DB Tri Floor Press Dual Action Bicep Curls 90 90 Groin ISO Hold	Box 4	DB Tri Pro Sup DB Curl to Press 90 90 Glute ISO Hold
Box 5	H-sq Shi Bi Trap Chest Rev Grip Iso	Box 5	Glute Ham Back Cav Iso H-sq Shi Bi Trap
Box 6		Box 6	
Box 7		Box 7	
Box 8	GH Hang Rollers Glutes and Hams Laying Relaxation	Box 8	GH Hang Rollers Quads & Back LAYING WALL SHAKES

BLOCK THREE (2-DAY IN-SEASON): ABOVE 80% CONCENTRIC PHASE

MONDAY

100%		REPS	LOAD	SETS	NOTES
250	Squat Jump	C1T	140 - 150	2	2x - Tendo
	Cuban PRSS INC F8	5		2	Set Drop off / Pw-2 Neck
	Ankle Band Work	8		2	Each Side
500	Back Squat	2	415 - 440	3	Reactive
	Pair w/				
	Russian Switch Lunge	4		3	0:5:0:0 / Bench
	Pair w/				
75	1 Arm Lat Pull Supine	8	55 - 60	3	Rest 1:30
300	BENCH PRESS	2	250 - 265	3	Reactive
	GH HYPR Incline	5		3	Reactive
	Pair w/				
30	OH LAT Raise	10	20 - 20	3	+ Shrug
60	DB Tri Ext	6	45 - 50	2	
	Pair w/				
	Bicep shock curls	6		2	
	Pair w/				
	90 90 Grion ISO Hold	15S			
	H-Sq Sh Bi Trap	180s		1	
	Pair w/				
	Chest Rev Grip Iso	180s		1	
	Pair w/				
	Coreworkout 8	8	70% - 75%	2	
	GH HANG	120S		1	
	Pair w/				
	Rollers Glutes & Hams	120S		1	
	Pair w/				
	LAYING RELAXATION	120S		1	

WENDESDAY

100%		REPS	LOAD	SETS	NOTES
	Vertimax DS 2 Band	C1T		2	2x - Tendo
	Tea Cup Stuff	5		2	Set Drop off
	Pair w/				
	Calf Raises	8		2	
500	Back Squat	3	465 - 475	3	Reactive / Sport SQ
	Pair w/				
	Iso Ball Grion Sqeeze	4		3	0:5:0:0
	Pair w/				
165	Dynamic Lat Pull	8	125 - 130	3	Rest 1:30
300	BENCH PRESS	1	255 - 265	4	Reactive
	Pair w/				
	Ball LG Curl	6		3	Reactive
	Pair w/				
	Delt Lat Rebound Drop	10		3	
45	DB Tri Pro Sup	10	30 - 35	2	
	Pair w/				
60	DB Curl to Press	6	45 - 50	2	
	Pair w/				
	90 90 Glute ISO Hold	15S		2	
	Glute Ham Back Cav Iso	180s		1	
	H-Sq Sh Bi Trap	120s		1	
	Coreworkout 5	8	70% - 75%	2	
	GH HANG	120S		1	Relax Mouth
	Pair w/				
	Rollers Quads & Back	120S		1	
	Pair w/				
	LAYING WALL SHAKES	120S		1	Relax Mouth

BLOCK THREE (2-DAY): ABOVE 80%
CONCENTRIC PHASE HYPERLINKS

Day 1	Exercise Hyperlink	Day 2	Exercise Hyperlink
Box 1	Squat Jump Cuban Press INC F8 Ankle Band Work	Box 1	Squat Jump Tea Cup Stuff Calf Raises
Box 2	Back Squat Russian Switch Lunge 1 Arm LAT Pull	Box 2	Back Squat Iso Ball Groin Squeeze Dynamic Lat Pull
Box 3	BENCH PRESS GH HYPER Incline OH LAT Raise	Box 3	BENCH PRESS Ball LG Curl Delt Lateral Rebound Drop
Box 4	DB Tri Ext Bicep Shock Curls 90 90 Groin ISO Hold	Box 4	DB Tri Pro Sup DB Curl to Press 90 90 Glute ISO Hold
Box 5	H-sq Shi Bi Trap Chest Rev Grip Iso	Box 5	Glute Ham Back Cav Iso H-sq Shi Bi Trap
Box 6		Box 6	
Box 7		Box 7	
Box 8	GH Hang Rollers Glutes and Hams Laying Relaxation	Box 8	GH Hang Rollers Quads & Back LAYING WALL SHAKES

SECTION 5

HIGH FORCE AT HIGH VELOCITY
(55-80 Percent)

5.1: TRAINING BETWEEN 55 AND 80 PERCENT

The moment I tell someone that I refer to my speed-strength phase as a "high force at high velocity" phase, I'm met with a blank stare. That stare, I've come to find, is a sign that the person is trying to reconcile in their mind how an athlete can produce a high force at high velocities. You see, most people have come to view these two variables—force and velocity—as inverse dependent rather than independent variables. They think that an increase in one must mean the decrease in another. You will recall from the last section that this is the classic parametric relationship often associated with F*m* and V*m* on the hyperbolic curve. This curve has come to embody a relationship between force and velocity that has led strength coaches to believe the only way to train force (strength) is to train with heavy loads all the time! I sit here today telling you that this is blatantly wrong. Force and velocity are not dependent on one another. Quite to the contrary, they can both be produced at high levels by an athlete. And not surprisingly, the athletes who can produce both variables at high levels are always the ones who everyone *depends* on to come through in the clutch. They are the elite.

Based on the hyperbolic curve, many people view my definition as a paradox, a statement that is seemingly contradictory to common sense or preconceived notions. To be honest, they aren't completely wrong. Like most things in training, there isn't any single definition that is right *all the time*. The idea that force and velocity are dependent variables is correct when held in the context with which it was originally intended. The hyperbolic curve was originally created from the research of A.V. Hill and looked at isolated muscle tissue from cadavers.[32] The researchers isolated the calf muscle, hooked it up to a car battery (this might be a slight exaggeration, but I doubt it), and stimulated it to perform isotonic contractions. Isotonic contractions simply mean that the tension remains unchanged as the muscle's length changes. Lifting an object at a constant speed is an example of isotonic contractions. Hill and his colleagues found that as they increased

---

[32] Hill AV (1953) The mechanics of active muscle. *Proceedings of the Royal society* B141.

the wattage applied to the muscle, the rate of muscle shortening (velocity) decreased. The hyperbolic curve was born.

Now, I don't know about you, but I have a hard time finding a lot of transferability from a cadaver hooked up to a car battery performing a contraction at a constant rate of speed (isotonic) to an explosive, dynamic, elite athlete. However, the question remained from this early research as to whether this curve, obtained under strict isotonic conditions, can be used to predict the behavior of the contractile component under dynamic conditions. Based on the research, it is highly questionable whether the velocity of shortening at each point along the hyperbolic curve is a function of only the force at that instant or influenced by other factors such as the preceding rate of force development or additional energy contributions from other components.[33]

So what does the hyperbolic curve supposedly tell us?

It claims four things:

1) Velocity of movement is inversely proportional to load—kind of.
2) It is impossible to exert a high force with fast movements—kind of.
3) The highest velocities are attained at light loads—true!
4) The intermediate values of force and velocity depend on maximal isometric force—true!

As you can see, the hyperbolic curve is correct half of the time. I should quantify that by saying that it is correct half the time when talking about its relationship to sport performance. If we were applying the hyperbolic curve to its original context—a steady isotonic contraction—all four points would be correct.[34] However, when looking at explosive, dynamic movement, its application falls short. You see, the curve failed to include one *huge* variable that is pertinent to sport performance—the series elastic component of dynamic contraction. When you *include* the

---

[33] Jewell BR, Winkie DR (1958) An analysis of the mechanical components in frog's striated muscle. *Journal of Physiology* 143:515–40.

[34] Huxley AF (1957) Muscle structure and theories of contraction. *Progress Biophysiology* 7:255–318.

extra energy supplied by the stretch shortening cycle (SSC) during full speed dynamic movements, points one and two from above are incorrect. When lifting moderate loads (55–80 percent), the addition of a powerful SSC makes it possible to develop high levels of force at high velocities.

According to the hyperbolic curve, the highest power outputs would occur somewhere around 50 percent of the athlete's 1RM (figure 5.1). Because power is the product of force and velocity (P = F x V), you simply find the highest values associated with the highest power output along the contraction curve. Why do you think everyone prescribes loads of 45–55 percent on their dynamic effort days? It's because that is what is prescribed by the parametric relationship that force and velocity play, according to the hyperbolic curve.

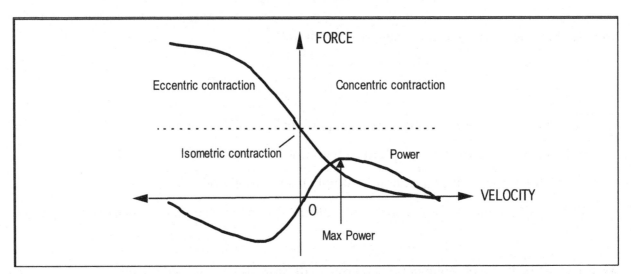

Figure 5.1: An idealized force-velocity curve with a power curve overlaid based on the work of A.V. Hill. This doesn't take into account the contribution of the stretch shortening cycle. Graph from *Supertraining*; used with permission.

This is a classic example of taking research and prescribing it to a population that it was never intended for—athletes. You have to recognize that the force-velocity curve as you know it is a romanticized view of how the body works. It ignores the impact of the SSC as well as neural inhibition, motor unit recruitment, and the stretch reflex. Sure, this way is simpler to understand and program for, but it won't maximize the power producing abilities of your athletes. It will lead you down a path that will result in using loads below that which will create the greatest adaptations at high velocities.

The work of A.V. Hill and his colleagues, such as B. Katz, D.R. Wilki, and L. MacPherson from the 1940s and 50s, and their concept of a parametric relation between force and velocity stood for over fifty years. By no means should the work of these men be minimized. They laid the groundwork for our current understanding of the human body. Modern day researchers, however, have taken a closer look at the hyperbolic curve and its implications for power development in maximal dynamic contractions. The work by Dr. Paavo Komi in 2000 showed that for *in vivo* muscle contractions (meaning live tissue), the hyperbolic curve actually shows a parabolic shape. Instead of bowing inward, the line bows outward (figure 5.2).[35] The implications of this are that it is possible to produce high forces at high velocities.

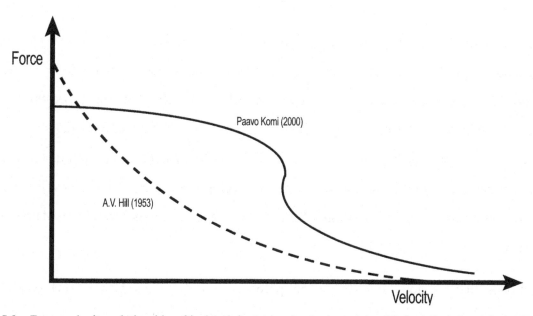

Figure 5.2: Force-velocity relationship of isolated, isotonic muscle contraction (dashed line) from the work of Dr. Hill verses the relationship of *in vivo* human muscles (solid line) as seen in the work of Dr. Komi. The graph shows that the addition of the SSC enables muscle tissue to generate high levels of force during high-velocity movements.

---

[35] Komi PV (2000) Stretch-shortening cycle: a powerful model to study normal and fatigued muscle. *Journal of Biomechanics* 33:1197–1206.

In his experiment, Dr. Komi placed a fiber optic cable into the Achilles tendon of his subjects with a 19-gauge needle. The things people do in the name of science...wow! After that fun little event, the subjects performed various jumps of different kinds with the cable still implanted to measure the forces being produced by the soleus (through the Achilles tendon). The results showed that when taking into account the effect of the stretch shortening cycle and Golgi tendon inhibition, the hyperbolic curve wasn't completely hyperbolic. At levels of high force production, velocity of movement could be greatly enhanced during dynamic actions through the addition of kinetic energy from the SSC.

It should be noted that at lower forces, Hill's hyperbolic curve still applies. As Dr. Hatfield explained, loads that are light (below 55 percent of an athlete's 1RM) don't pose enough resistance (force) to generate high power outputs. Velocity will continue to increase as these loads decrease. However, it increases at the expense of force and power development.

During his study, Dr. Hatfield not only found the specific loading percentage that optimized an athlete's power production, but also the range of training loads that seemed to help develop total body power, the optimal training zone for establishing an efficient, high threshold nervous system. He refers to these percentages as the *training zone*.[36] Dr. Hatfield demonstrated that training within 55 percent to 80 percent of an athlete's 1RM was optimal for retaining the highest power outputs and teaching an athlete's body to develop high rates of force development. The best explanation of this zone is to think of it as an inverted "U", which can be explained by two rational points:

1) Loads that are too light (below 55 percent of an athlete's 1RM) don't pose enough resistance (force) to generate high power outputs even though the velocity of the bar remains high.

2) Loads that are heavy (above 80 percent of an athlete's 1RM) decrease the terminal velocity of movement and decrease power output.

---

[36] Hatfield F (1989) *Power: A scientific approach.* New York: McGraw-Hill Publishing.

In both cases, the rationale for staying within the *training zone* lies with the amount of time a muscle can spend under maximal tension with a given training load. A load that is very light can be moved fast. However, it is impossible to recruit the large, power producing, high threshold motor units that produce high power outputs. This goes back to motor unit recruitment, which we discussed in section three. A load that is too heavy, on the other hand, *does* provide time for a muscle to recruit its high threshold motor units. The motor units are fatigued, however, before the completion of the movement, resulting in decreased velocity of the bar and a lower power output.

5.2: LOADING PARAMETERS

Just as in the previous section, we will use the three-day model of the 55–80 percent training block to explain the loading parameters and sequencing of exercises, as well as the specialized training methods used to maximize the parameters of this phase. At the end of this section, there will be two-day, four-day, five-day, and six-day in-season models built out and labeled so that you can immediately implement them with your athletes. The principles and foundations of each program are identical, so understanding a three-day model (Monday, Wednesday, Friday) will teach you all you need to know when reviewing and building similar models of differing training week lengths.

When training with loads of 55–80 percent, equal emphasis is placed on both the force (**F**) and velocity (**V**) portions of the power equation. Using loads at 55–80 percent of one's 1RM, the power output remains high because, as stated previously, the percentages are within Dr. Hatfield's *training zone*. This range maximizes the contribution of the SSC to the rapid production of force when using moderately heavy loads and ensures that an athlete can continue to produce *high force at high velocities*.

Even though the loads are lighter than the above 80 percent blocks, emphasis is still placed on quality of movement and repetition as opposed to quantity. When training for power, this must always be your goal. Remembering that the power suffers after the third repetition of an exercise, the only sensible answer is to end the set and save energy for a high quality second set.

Table 5.1 shows the loading scheme (sets/reps/percentages) for my 55–80 percent block. Notice that even though the loads have decreased by 10–15 percent, the rep range has only increased by one to two reps per set. This is a common mistake that most coaches make. They assume that just because an athlete can do more reps with less weight, they should. Wrong! Emphasis must always be placed on quality, high level neural work. Practice doesn't make perfect. Perfect practice makes perfect!

TABLE 5.1

7 1-RM	MAXIMUM REPS POSSIBLE	MONDAY LOADING (MEDIUM INTENSITY)			WEDNESDAY LOADING (HIGH INTENSITY)			FRIDAY LOADING (HIGH VOLUME)		
		HIGH QUALITY REPS (STRENGTH)	SETS (OFF-SEASON)	SETS (IN-SEASON)	HIGH QUALITY REPS (STRENGTH)	SETS (OFF-SEASON)	SETS (IN-SEASON)	HIGH QUALITY REPS (VOLUME)	SETS (OFF-SEASON)	SETS (IN-SEASON)
80%	5 - 6				1 - 2	4 - 5	2 - 3			
77.5%	6 - 7				1 - 3	4 - 5	2 - 3			
75%	7 - 8				1 - 3	4 - 5	3 - 4			
72.5%	8 - 9				2 - 3	4 - 5	3 - 4			
70%	9 - 10	2 - 3	4 - 6	3 - 4						
67.5%	11 - 12	2 - 3	4 - 6	3 - 5						
65%	13 - 14	3	4 - 6	3 - 5						
62.5%	14 - 15	3	4 - 6	3 - 5				5 - 8	4 - 6	
60%	15 - 16							5 - 8	4 - 6	IN-SEASON VOLUME COMES FROM PRACTICE
57.5%	17 - 18							5 - 8	4 - 6	
55%	19 - 20							5 - 8	4 - 6	

This table displays my three-day loading variables of 55–80 percent undulated mesocycle. The column on the far left displays the percentage load of the athlete's 1RM with the maximum number of repetitions possible listed in the column to the right. The reps and sets within each training day indicate the number of each that can be performed while maintaining a high quality of work for the athlete. A few things to notice —the rep ranges stay the same regardless of whether the athlete is in-season or in off-season training, the number of sets used for in-season training are fewer than with off-season training because of the high work demands and added stress of practices and games during the season, and all the volume work comes from practices and games (see Friday/Sets (In-Season). Don't train volume in-season. You'll overtrain your athletes.

Figure 5.3 depicts my 55–80 percent three-day undulated model. This is what I also refer to as my *high force at high velocity phase.*

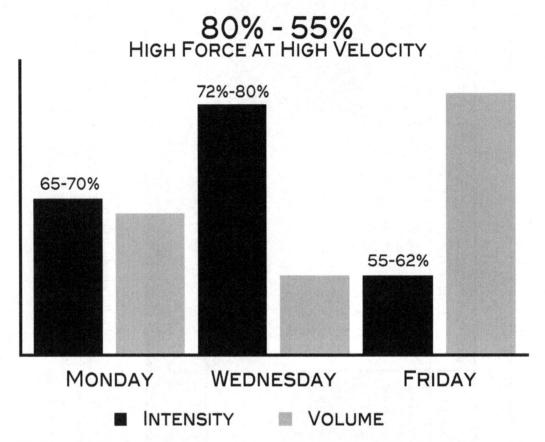

Figure 5.3: Graph depicting the training loads associated with the three-day 55–80 percent training model.

The above figure is the same one that I used to show you the above 80 percent high load at low velocity phase of my undulating model. However, there is one major difference—all the percentages are now 55–80 percent. Again, this is based off the work of Dr. Hatfield melded with my own theories about isolating specific components of the nervous system for further specificity of training parameters.

It is important that you get over the idea that in order to keep an athlete strong or make him more powerful, he must lift heavy loads. He doesn't! You can lift loads below 80 percent at higher velocities while still applying high amounts of force through the enhanced SSC and see improved strength in athletes while increasing their power output.

Let's take a quick run through of the loading parameters. They are very similar to the above 80 percent *high force at low velocity phase*. Rep ranges stay fairly constant. Monday is your medium heavy day using loads that equal 70 percent of your athlete's 1RM. I know that an athlete could likely lift this load ten times. However, I will only have him perform sets of two or three reps focusing on moving the weight at a high velocity. Again, the point here is to train the athlete to be powerful. Teach his neuromuscular system to use the kinetic energy benefits of the SSC with a high rate of force development in the concentric phase. After three reps, the athlete's ability to maintain a high rate of force development (RFD) is severely limited by energy substrate depletion as well as neuromuscular fatigue.

Wednesday is the heavy day of the week, using a load that equals 80 percent of the athlete's 1RM. I use the term "heavy" as a relative term. The load isn't going to be interpreted by the athlete's body as heavy, so the goal must be to attack the weight—moving it at high velocities and accentuating the SSC. Now, I know in the previous phase we performed sets of three at 80 percent. However, here we're only going to perform singles. The difference is this single rep will have a much higher eccentric/concentric velocity.

Friday, day three, is again correlated with lighter loads and increased volume. Here I typically use 65 percent of the athlete's 1RM for two to four reps. However, sometimes I will decrease that to 55 percent, depending on the methods I'm using. Again, I can't stress enough the importance of quality reps over quantity even on a volume day. Any training performed with suboptimal focus —that is to say with a low rate of force development and diminished velocities—will send mixed neural signaling patterns and inhibit the adaptability of the athlete to other training stressors within the block. The loading variables table from the previous page explains loads that should *not* be used on a given training day. This is shown by the shaded areas and their associated loads.

5.3: 55 TO 80 TRAINING BLOCK

Now that you understand the loading scheme and undulation used within the 55–80 percent training week, let's take a closer look at the actual block that makes up this mesocycle. This will be short and sweet because unlike the previous phase, which consisted of three separate blocks, this phase consists of only one. The chart below shows the loading variables used on each day in the training week. Just as before, the length of the block can be shortened or extended to fit different peaking schedules. Typically, my athletes perform this block for three to four weeks. This has proven to be optimal. However, there are times when the block can be as short as two or as long as five weeks.

TABLE 5.2: BLOCK 4 LOADING VARIABLES (55–80%)				
BLOCK	DAY	LOAD	REPS	SETS
BLOCK 4 3–4 WEEKS	MONDAY (MEDIUM INTENSITY)	62–70%	2–3	4–6
	WEDNESDAY (HIGH INTENSITY)	72–80%	1–3	4–5
	FRIDAY (HIGH VOLUME)	75–80%	5–8	4–6

Taking into account the range of loading variables that can be used within each training day of the undulated week, coaches can develop progressive loading schemes to constantly spur gains week after week for their athletes. Below is a table outlining the typical progression that I've found to work the best with my athletes. If an athlete's training block length is shorter than four weeks, adjust by starting with higher loads in the progression. For example, if an athlete only has two weeks to train in the 55–80 percent phase, use loading parameters from weeks three and four (Table 5.3). If the block length is extended, maintain the same progression (Table 5.3) and have the athlete repeat week four loading on the fifth week.

TABLE 5.3: PROGRESSIVE LOADING SCHEME FOR 55–80%			
WEEK	MONDAY LOADING (MEDIUM INTENSITY)	WEDNESDAY LOADING (HIGH INTENSITY)	FRIDAY LOADING (LOW INTENSITY)
1	62.5% 3 REPS, 4–6 SETS	72.5% 1–3 REPS, 4–5 SETS	55% 5–6 REPS, 4–6 SETS
2	65% 2–3 REPS, 4–6 SETS	75% 1–3 REPS, 4–5 SETS	57.5% 5–6 REPS, 4–6 SETS
3	67.5% 2-3 REPS, 4–6 SETS	77.5% 1–3 REPS, 4–5 SETS	60% 5–6 REPS, 4–6SETS
4	70% 2–3 REPS, 4–6 SETS	80% 1–3REPS, 4–5 SETS	62.5% 5–6 REPS, 4–6 SETS

5.4: SPECIALIZED METHODS OF APPLYING TRAINING MEANS

Just as the parameters of each mesocycle are specialized, it is important that the methods used to develop them should be specifically molded as well to promote maximal adaptation of the athlete. The ability of these methods to promote positive adaptation through increased RFD and power development is unparalleled. For this specific mesocycle, the 55–80 percent phase, there is one method in particular that develops RFD and reactive ability better than any other when using moderate loads at high velocities. This method is known as biometric training. Biometrics is the science of measuring and analyzing biological data. It is the process by which an athlete's physical traits are measured and recorded by an electronic device as a means of confirming or identifying a specific characteristic. In this case, the characteristic we are measuring is fatigue.

The original biometric method and still the gold standard in application is the Tendo unit. I love these. They are amazing. They measure the bar speed of every repetition, giving a coach feedback on the force, velocity, and power output of the bar and allow the coach to see the state of fatigue of an athlete from set to set, one workout to the next. I've been very fortunate at the University of Minnesota to have a budget that allowed me to buy several when they first came out a decade ago. Over the past several years, I have experimented with trying to find a simple, inexpensive way to simulate the biometric measure of the Tendo unit that would allow anyone to take advantage of this potent training method. After years of trial and error, I came up with the 'timed set drop-off' method. These are relatively easy for a coach to implement, inexpensive to perform (requiring only a stopwatch), and work just as well as the Tendo unit.

TIMED DROP-OFFS

One easily manipulated variable for developing an athlete's requisite physical qualities is time. Not only does it correspond well with energy system development, but it is also highly practical to implement in any coach's program. The concept is simple—keep time constant or vary it such that athletes either perform more work in that time frame or more work. I will give two examples of how I use this variable to form the biometric training methods that I use with my athletes in the 55–80 percent training block.

Depending on the time of the year and the athlete, we'll use time as our determinant of when a set is completed. For example, I might have our men's hockey team take a prescribed weight based on an athlete's maximum and give him a certain amount of reps. So hypothetically, let's say that we take 60–70 percent of an athlete's 1RM bench press and have him do six reps. Obviously, this is very light for only six reps. The parameters you choose to use vary based on the desired qualities you're looking to develop. In this case, we're trying to develop a high level of speed-strength by increasing the athletes RFD. After the athlete unracks the barbell, the coach will begin a stopwatch precisely when the first movement downward begins. The coach then stops the watch exactly after the last rep is locked out. Record the time on the athlete's sheet.

Before you begin this method, it's important to know what you'll use as your drop-off or cutoff point. I tend to use 3–7 percent drop-offs when using hand-timed biometric measures because there is a greater range of variability by the timer. If I'm using a more precise biometric means to measure fatigue such as a Tendo unit, I will use a lower percentage as my cutoff point (more on that in a minute). After years of trial and error, I've found that these guidelines work the best in ensuring fatigue but not overtraining of my athletes. The drop-off percentage used is dictated by the amount of recovery time the athlete has before returning to similar forms of stress. That is, if athletes do a bench work out, how long do they rest until they bench again? Table 5.4 explains the guidelines that work best.

TABLE 5.4: HAND-TIMED BIOMETRIC PARAMETERS			
DROP-OFF	REST PERIOD	WORKOUT (STRESS A)	NEXT RETURN TO STRESS A
3%	24 HRS		TUESDAY
4–5%	48 HRS	MONDAY	WEDNESDAY
6–7%	72 HRS		THURSDAY

When using a stopwatch to hand-time an athlete's biometric response, it can be slightly complex. What works best is to print out a sheet listing various times on the far left-hand column. To the right of them is the drop-off that would indicate that a exercise needs to be stopped. For example, if our athlete's best bench was 135 pounds for six reps in four seconds and the workout had a parameter of a five percent drop-off, the athlete would continue to perform sets until his time increased to 4.20 seconds, at which point the exercise is terminated.

Time Drop Off Charts 5% Drop Off

Best			Drop off	Best			Drop off	Best			Drop off
1.5			1.575	3.5			3.675	5.5			5.775
1.55			1.6275	3.55			3.7275	5.55			5.8275
1.6			1.68	3.6			3.78	5.6			5.88
1.65			1.7325	3.65			3.8325	5.65			5.9325
1.7			1.785	3.7			3.885	5.7			5.985
1.75			1.8375	3.75			3.9375	5.75			6.0375
1.8			1.89	3.8			3.99	5.8			6.09
1.85			1.9425	3.85			4.0425	5.85			6.1425
1.9			1.995	3.9			4.095	5.9			6.195
1.95			2.0475	3.95			4.1475	5.95			6.2475
2			2.1	4			4.2	6			6.3
2.05			2.1525	4.05			4.2525	6.05			6.3525
2.1			2.205	4.1			4.305	6.1			6.405
2.15			2.2575	4.15			4.3575	6.15			6.4575
2.2			2.31	4.2			4.41	6.2			6.51
2.25			2.3625	4.25			4.4625	6.25			6.5625
2.3			2.415	4.3			4.515	6.3			6.615
2.35			2.4675	4.35			4.5675	6.35			6.6675
2.4			2.52	4.4			4.62	6.4			6.72
2.45			2.5725	4.45			4.6725	6.45			6.7725
2.5			2.625	4.5			4.725	6.5			6.825
2.55			2.6775	4.55			4.7775	6.55			6.8775
2.6			2.73	4.6			4.83	6.6			6.93
2.65			2.7825	4.65			4.8825	6.65			6.9825
2.7			2.835	4.7			4.935	6.7			7.035
2.75			2.8875	4.75			4.9875	6.75			7.0875
2.8			2.94	4.8			5.04	6.8			7.14
2.85			2.9925	4.85			5.0925	6.85			7.1925
2.9			3.045	4.9			5.145	6.9			7.245
2.95			3.0975	4.95			5.1975	6.95			7.2975
3			3.15	5			5.25	7			7.35
3.05			3.2025	5.05			5.3025	7.05			7.4025
3.1			3.255	5.1			5.355	7.1			7.455
3.15			3.3075	5.15			5.4075	7.15			7.5075
3.2			3.36	5.2			5.46	7.2			7.56
3.25			3.4125	5.25			5.5125	7.25			7.6125
3.3			3.465	5.3			5.565	7.3			7.665
3.35			3.5175	5.35			5.6175	7.35			7.7175
3.4			3.57	5.4			5.67	7.4			7.77
3.45			3.6225	5.45			5.7225	7.45			7.8225

Figure 5.4: An example of a biometric drop-off chart. The left-hand column shows the athlete's best time on a given exercise. The right-hand column tells the coach the time at which the athlete will terminate performing sets due to fatigue. The two middle columns are check boxes to allow a coach to mark and track multiple athletes' work sets at one time. You can find additional drop-off charts on xlathlete.com.

A few things to keep in mind—the drop-off is based on the athlete's best set. It isn't uncommon to see an athlete get better times three to four sets into the exercise due to the potentiation effect. Also, to be consistent, have the same coach time the same athletes. Lastly, after the athletes perform a work set in whatever time frame, have them go perform some non-intensive assistance exercises. They may do some light shoulder prehabilitation, groin work, or whatever. It shouldn't detract from the main movement, but still keep them moving until they return for the next set (about two to four minutes later). This serves a dual purpose of shortening the total lift time by supersetting prehabilitation exercises with main movements and keeping the nervous system engaged. Studies have found that mild stimulation of the nervous system after intensive work bouts leads to increased performance in subsequent work bouts.[37] One particular study found that having the athlete perform simple math problems between work bouts increased performance. Researchers theorized that it kept the neural synaptic pathways in the brain active and primed for additional work.[38] In laymen's terms, it appears that this mild stimulation is equivalent to keeping the engine running on the car instead of turning it off.

The best movements to use with biometric training are going to be, as always, the big lifts—back squats, hex bar deadlifts (it's easier to move the hex bar quickly than the straight bar), and bench presses. This form of biometrics is simply one way in which a coach can use the athlete's readiness to gauge how much they will do that day to ensure that optimal fatigue is applied and maximal gains achieved. There are limitations to this, mainly how hard athletes push themselves. It isn't uncommon, however, to see athletes pushing each other to get better times. It creates an environment of competitiveness with immediate feedback. I have never seen athletes compete so hard in a weight room as when I use biometric training, trying to beat their time so that they're the last guy still performing work sets.

---

[37] Filipovic A, Kleinöder H, Dörmann U, Mester J (2011) Electromyostimulation—A systematic review of the influence of training regimens and stimulation parameters on effectiveness in electromyostimulation training of selected strength parameters. *Journal of Strength & Conditioning Research* 25(11):3218–38.

[38] Burns K (2011) Applied exercise physiology lecture. *The University of Minnesota*, 11/18.

Bear in mind that with an increase in speed, athletes are liable to adjust their technique accordingly. If you start seeing obvious changes in technique (i.e., cutting reps short) or something dangerous (low back rounding in a back squat), end the set. Give them one more chance to get their technique back to an acceptable range. Ultimately, decide if this will work for your team/athletes and then understand what types of adaptations you want to make. Don't just throw it in a program because it seems easy to implement and might be fun. It can be a useful method insofar as the coach implementing it doesn't have his/her head in the sand.

✓ Coach's Corner

BIOMETRIC TENDO UNIT TRAINING
BY: CAL DIETZ

One of the unique advantages that a Tendo unit provides is that it gives athletes feedback on bar speed or velocity of power output so that they realize how hard they can train. The unique thing about a Tendo is that it will give feedback such that the athlete knows how hard he/she is training , or if they can push themselves harder. It will also give them a facilitated motor pattern. I truly believe that by seeing that feedback number and pushing themselves, athletes learn how to apply force into the ground. The Tendo unit is such a unique tool for this. Please be aware that the technique could get out of control based upon the amount of effort the athletes are pushing into the bar and the floor. So please be aware and don't let technique get out of control when using these methods.

How did you come across the drop-off methods for your biometric training?
Much of my biometric method and the amount of the percentage drop-off that is used came from the necessity of training large large groups of athletes with varying abilities. For example, I have fifth year seniors with high work capacities who can train through the roof, and first year freshman who have never trained before. This was a realization that I dealt with as a college strength coach. I needed to be able to control and regulate the sets, reps, and volumes to provide optimal training for my athletes. In talking with great track coaches like Phil Lundin and college strength coaches like Todd Hamer, it's obvious that in this type of training the quality and speed must remain high. This has been confirmed by many conversations with sport biomechanist Dr. Michael Yessis.

Quality and speed are king in sports. This has always been my guideline for training at least 90 percent of the time. We all know that you have to build work capacity in the human so that you can have greater speed quality development at a later date, but the guidelines should be for speed. That's how the biometric methods came to be. I, or any other strength coach, didn't develop this specifically. You see it in many training methodologies throughout history such as in track and field and swimming programs. One of the track coaches I talked to asked me a question: "How many sets and reps should I do to make sure that I get optimal training without overtraining? How do I know how to do the correct amount?"

The answer—you take a percentage drop-off. For example, if an athlete's best effort on any particular distance is four seconds, have the athlete continue to run that particular distance until 4.12 seconds or slower. That would be the slowest point and the training point at which you would stop the athlete. In this scenario, we're using time as the plyometric measure for the amount of training that can be completed.

The other possibility is if you're doing another three percent drop-off in high quality work. You could take a flying thirty meters and reduce it by one meter. So you would take the best thirty-meter effort the athlete has. If it was two seconds, you would reduce the distance the athlete runs and have him continue to do 29-meter flying runs until he ran two seconds or slower. You can always manipulate the rest, but in most cases, you would want the rest to be maximal because you're training for maximal effort, which is something we can get into later. The concept from various coaches developed into my time set controls biometric training. Essentially, you're doing the same thing as the track coach did to regulate training, but you would do it in the weight room. You can take a set weight with an exercise, and if you do five reps in four seconds, you will keep doing five repetitions until you do the same weight in 4.12 seconds. At that point, your regulation of sets becomes dictated by time.

I found this method to be optimal with submaximal days. For example, in the undulated periodization model, you would complete this on day one using the three training methods. There are other ways to manipulate the time sets, but I have found this to be optimal for measuring the time it would take an experienced coach with a stopwatch in timing the sets. Please keep in mind that technique is also a variable. If the athlete's technique changes over the sets, stop the amount of sets you're doing because the change in technique often increases the time. The athlete won't have consistent metrics and you won't be able to continue measuring what he's doing effectively and correctly. As with everything in maximal effort training—even with the submaximal loads—you would most likely focus on technique.

How did you come up with various drop-off percentages?
The drop-off percentages that I use in my programming with more advanced athletes basically came from simple concepts from testing an athlete in the vertical at the beginning of a workout. Train the athlete for that particular day. Stop when the vertical goes back up and the athlete isn't fatigued and still supercompensating with the jump squat height. In the beginning, I used some other device for measuring the percentage of the drop-offs that the athlete performed and how soon they recovered. Then I used those methods to provide myself with the frequency (how often) the athlete should train again.

For example, I had a professional athlete who had camp in four weeks. He hadn't worked upper body all summer and had come to me for help. He was a fighter in the NHL and informed me that he must get his bench to over ten reps with 225 pounds. On day one, we tested him, and he could only do two reps. He had been to a higher level prior to that, but at this point in time and over the summer, he had never trained upper body. As a result, we went with a 1–2 percent drop-off and benched every day for four weeks. By the end of his training with me at four and a half weeks, we rep tested him and he went to thirteen reps with 225 pounds. Understand that this athlete had been close to that level before but needed to train the motor skill to get better and do it as often as he could. Some days we only got six to eight reps in a certain weight. On other days, we did as many as sixteen singles at a certain percentage above or below 225 pounds. Again, we could keep training every day because we regulated the amount of drop-off and the quality of the drop-off that he performed each day, so he didn't overtrain and was able to heal for 24 hours.

TABLE 5.5: TENDO UNIT BIOMETRIC PARAMETERS			
DROP-OFF	REST PERIOD	WORKOUT (STRESS A)	NEXT RETURN TO STRESS A
1–2%	24 HRS		TUESDAY
2–4%	48 HRS	MONDAY	WEDNESDAY
5–6%	72 HRS		THURSDAY

Example

One of the most amazing results I've seen from a plyometric method was an elite, professional athlete with large work capacity potential perform his training sets for roughly four sets of squats at a body weight of 205 pounds. He was using 295 pounds and would do one repetition, rest 15 seconds, and do another repetition. With our drop-off percentage guidelines, he achieved 3–4 percent. He was able in one set to perform 31 repetitions and not drop-off more than three percent of his bar speed during that set. That particular day, the athlete did over seventy repetitions of the back squat at 295 pounds at a very high velocity. Essentially, some could say it was a jump squat because he was coming off the ground at the top due to acceleration. He was accelerating all the way through the bar. If he had done eighty repetitions, we would have overtrained him. If he had done fifty repetitions, he would have been undertrained for that particular workout and the demands we imposed on him.

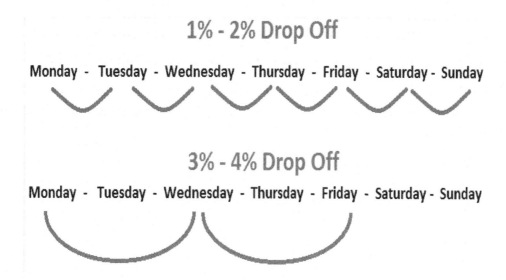

Figure 5.5: Example of the different biometric drop-off percentages used with Tendo unit measures.

How do you use biometric training on max effort days?

One of the great things about the max effort training is that it gives the athletes a huge amount of feedback in their ability to push against a lot of force. In my undulated weekly model, it would go on the max effort day, which would be day two loading methods. I often use Tendo training for maximal velocity training in regards to regulating max effort days. Essentially, what you're doing with the Tendo is measuring the bar speed. This will give you an understanding of how many sets an athlete should do on a particular day. I often only do singles or clusters with this particular method, so please be aware that anything more than a single with maximal loads probably isn't optimal. For example, I had an athlete regulate in regards to a three percent drop-off. This particular professional athlete weighed 205 pounds and back squatted 295 pounds for 72 singles over four sets on one day. He came in two days later. We tested him and he was able to repeat things that he did two days prior during the workout in regards to bar speed and vertical jump height. We know this athlete's work capacity ability at this point and training age. He was able to handle a 2–3 percent drop-off on training in every other day frequency. In one of the sets, this particular athlete did 32 reps in a row before he reached a three percent drop-off.

The max effort biometric training is inspired by the Bulgarians. They hit maximal effort on a particular day to find out where the athlete was and then reduced the weight by five to ten kilos and hit singles until either technique failed or the weight couldn't be lifted any more in that particular workout. This isn't confirmed through Bulgarian coaches—only through people who have talked to many Bulgarian coaches over the years. It seems to be a very effective method for training maximal effort. The biggest key for maximal effort is being able to find the drop-off point on a percentage base in regards to how much the athlete should reduce bar speed and when the next time his training will take place.

Sources

Kulakov (1969) Cybernetics and sports. *Soviet Sports Review,* September: 4-3.

Ogol'tsow (1989) Biological principles in the body's adaptation to training loads. *Soviet Sport Review*, March: 24-1.

Loginov, A., Shmonon, B., Penza, H., & Belinsky, V. (1977) Automated control system motor types. Source unknown.

5.5: MONDAY, MEDIUM INTENSITY (SUBMAXIMAL EFFORT)

LOADING

Below is a section from the loading table, showing exclusively the loading variables applied on Monday (Table 5.6). Just as before, shaded sections indicate that these are loads that wouldn't be used at this point of the training week.

TABLE 5.6: MONDAY LOADING (MEDIUM INTENSITY)				
7 1-RM	MAXIMUM REPS POSSIBLE	HIGH QUALITY REPS (STRENGTH)	SETS (OFF-SEASON)	SETS (IN-SEASON)
80%	5–6			
77.5%	6–7			
75%	7–8			
72.5%	8–9			
70%	9–10	2–3	4–6	3–4
67.5%	11–12	2–3	4–6	3–5
65%	13–14	3	4–6	3–5
62.5%	14–15	3	4–6	3–5
60%	15–16			
57.5%	17–18			
55%	19–20			

WORKOUTS

On the next page you will find Monday's workout for the three-day, 55–80 percent block. The column on the left is the actual workout, using our "imaginary" athlete to calculate the loads used on each exercise. The column on the right, labeled "Coaching Points," gives further explanation about exercise sequencing and important coaching queues to use with your athletes. The coaching points are labeled with the respective workout box that they apply to. At the end of this section, you will find workouts for each block of a four-day, five-day, six-day, and two-day in-season model.

BLOCK FOUR, MONDAY

100%	MONDAY	21-Jun-10			
		REPS	LOAD	SETS	NOTES
	OH SQ Rack Press	6		2	Eyes Closed
	Pair w/				
	2-WAY NECK	8		2	
	Pair w/				
	STDING Glute Kicks	6		2	
500	BACK SQUAT	3	275 - 300		Roll I-band
		2	325 - 350		Spine Rolls
	Test	2	400 - 415		CW TEST
	Pair Below	3	350 - 365		0:0:0:0
	Pair Below	3	350 - 365		0:0:0:0
	Pair Below	3	350 - 365		0:0:0:0
	French Contrast	3	350 - 365		0:0:0:0
	Hurdle Hop	4		4	Distance
	Pair w/				
250	Squat Jump	4	200 - 205	4	0:0:0:0
	Pair w/				
	Acc Band Jump	4		4	Rest 5:00
	4 way neck	8		2	
	Pair w/				no Rest
	Wrist Flexion	6		3	
	Pair w/				no Rest
	ANT TIB BND	10		3	Band Medium
	Walking Band Lunge Jump	4		3	Bands
	Pair w/				Speed/Jump
105	DB BENCH	9,7,5	75 - 85	3	Toes
	Pair w/				
225	Lat Pull Down	8	170 - 180	3	
500	Glute Bar Lift	6	375 - 400	3	0:0:0:0
	Pair w/				No Rest
	Hip FLX BND Pulls	6		3	
	Pair w/				No Rest
75	DB Shoulder Press	10S	45 -	3	OC
150	Rev Grip Tri Push	8	115 - 120	3	
	Pair w/				No Rest
	Bicep shock curls	10S		3	
	Pair w/				No Rest
	Bam Bam	10		3	

COACHING POINTS AND EXERCISE TUTORIAL

Box 1

-In the first cluster of exercises, these may often be skipped if a very intense dynamic warm up has been completed that involves a number of disciplines from various sciences to activate the body to train.

Over head rack squat; Manual 4-way neck; Standing Glute Kicks

Box 2-4

-Back squat: Notice the first three sets are warm up sets and the third set is one that the coach watches to test the fatigue level of the athletes.

-The four work sets at submaximal loads in the back squat are paired with the following six exercises. The first three are used to complete the French contrast method and the last three are used as active rests during the course of training. In this case, the French contrast was used to address various aspects of the particular sport training with these methods.

-Notice that the hurdle hop is for a distance during this program. In the prior programs, the hurdle hops were for height. I feel that distance is a better correlation in sports performance when jumping hurdles, so I save the distance part of this for the latter stages of training.

Back Squat; Hurdle Hop; Squat Jump; Accelerated Band Jump; 4 way neck; Wrist Flexion; Anterior Tib BND

Box 5

-Walking band lunge jumps are done at high speeds, extremely quickly. The athlete is coached to jump in the air and drive through his big toe.

Walking Band Lunge Jumps; DB Bench; Lat Pull Down

Box 6

-The dumbbell OC shoulder press is used very effectively in this case and doesn't stress the triceps but only isolates the shoulder girdle.

Glute Bar Lift; Hip Flex Band Pulls; DB Shoulder Press

Box 7

-The bicep shock curl is a reactive exercises for the upper arm; the athlete turns the palms down and away after releasing the bar, and supinates the hand fully when catching it.

Reverse Grip Tricep Push Down; Bicep Curl Shock; Bam Bams

√ COACH'S CORNER

BAND TRAINING
BY: CAL DIETZ & JONATHON JANZ
EDITED BY: BEN PETERSON

The use of elastic bands in training has occurred for quite some time, increasing in popularity with each passing year. Initially utilized by "old time Strongmen" in the form of chest expanders, elastic resistance has long been a convenient (though sometimes dubious) means of training the muscles. More recently, elastic resistance has taken the form of bands, which are either used on their own or in unison with free weights and/or machines. These loops of durable rubber have many different uses in the weight room.

Studies have suggested support for the use of bands in training, primarily with regards to improvements in peak force and peak power during exercises, which combine bands and traditional weight training exercises (such as back squats; 2). For example, a back squat load of 85 percent of an athlete's maximum, combined with resistance bands attached to the barbell has been shown to significantly increase the athlete's peak force and peak power output during the exercise (2). This increase in force and power during training may, over time, induce favorable adaptations in the athlete to a greater extent than weight training without bands (1). In some cases, the addition of bands in training has increased strength and power levels two to three times greater than training that doesn't include bands (1).

There are several different ways of utilizing bands in training. One method is to use them as a means of assisting exercises or other activities. This type of use helps to introduce bands to athletes unfamiliar with them. For example, an athlete may choose to use a band to aid with stretching, known as band stretching. The band essentially replaces the need to have a partner to help with stretching. Athletes may also use bands to assist with exercises such as the band pull-up or chin-up. By taking advantage of the band's elasticity, the athlete is able to more easily complete the exercise and perform more repetitions than without the band.

By far the most common use of bands is in the form of resistance for exercise. Whether they are used alone such as in the Bulgarian band squat or in combination with weighted implements (barbells and/or dumbbells), bands can supplement nearly any exercise and add greater stress and variety. Increased stress and novel stimuli help to encourage adaptation and challenge athletes to develop a higher level of force and power output in such activity.

The elastic resistance provided by bands alone is often enough to make several exercises much more difficult. The piston squat becomes decidedly more intense with the addition of a band as does the split squat. For these normally body weight exercises, resistance is increased with the use of the band. The addition of the band also compels the athlete to exert more force throughout the entire range of motion (accommodating resistance; 3). In the piston squat, for example, the band is lax when the athlete is sitting upon the bench. The most difficult part of this exercise is the initial liftoff phase from the bench and body weight alone is more than adequate for resistance. As the athlete stands up, the exercise becomes easier as the active muscles move into a range of motion of increased mechanical advantage. During this part of the exercise, the athlete's own body weight is significantly easier to move. To make this phase more difficult, the band begins to stretch and provide increased resistance. Thus, the athlete receives a greater amount of stress throughout the entire range of motion for this exercise with the addition of a band. This scenario may be duplicated with many other body weight exercises such as push-ups and sit-ups. Once an athlete has adapted to a particular body weight exercise, one may add additional resistance in the form of a band in order to increase the degree of difficulty.

Body weight exercises aren't the only activities that can be made more difficult with the addition of bands. One can attach bands to a weighted barbell and perform back squats, bench presses, and a host of other exercises. As mentioned before, the addition of bands to an exercise forces the athlete to exert a greater amount of effort throughout the entire range of motion. This is true for weighted exercises as well. For example, a maximum back squat of 500 pounds represents the amount of weight an athlete can successfully lift from a full squat to an erect position. The limiting factor for success in this lift is the highly difficult range of motion near the bottom of the squat. Once this is negotiated, the rest of the range of motion is considerably easier. This essentially means that the athlete can lift 500 pounds from the bottom of a squat. As we know from experience, however, athletes can squat considerably more weight in shorter ranges of motion (such as the half squat or quarter squat). As a result, coaches will often prescribe half rack squats with significantly more weight than the athlete's maximum full squat in order to properly stress the athlete within that range of motion. While this is certainly an acceptable practice, it may be easier and more efficient to attach bands to the barbell for use during full squats. The bands will be lax at the bottom of the squat, where the load on the bar is enough to fully stress the athlete, but increase in tension as the athlete stands up (which more adequately trains the stronger portion of the lift). Bands can be added to numerous exercises including dumbbell exercises. If a coach seeks a method of making an exercise more difficult or simply wants to add more variety to a program, band training may be an excellent option.

References

1. Anderson CE, Sforzo GA, Sigg JA (2008) The effects of combining elastic and free weight resistance on strength and power in athletes. *Journal of Strength and Conditioning Research* 22(2):567–74.
2. Wallace BJ, Winchester JB, McGuigan MR (2006) Effects of elastic bands on force and power characteristics during the back squat exercise. *Journal of Strength and Conditioning Research* 20(2):268–72.
3. Zatsiorsky V (1995) *Science and Practice of Strength Training*. Second Edition. Champaign, IL: Human Kinetics Publishers.

5.6: WEDNESDAY, HIGH INTENSITY (MAXIMAL EFFORT)

LOADING

Below is a section from the loading table, showing exclusively the loading variables applied on Monday (Table 5.7). Just as before, shaded sections indicate that these are loads that wouldn't be used at this point of the training week.

TABLE 5.7: WEDNESDAY LOADING (HIGH INTENSITY)				
7 1RM	MAXIMUM REPS POSSIBLE	HIGH QUALITY REPS (STRENGTH)	SETS (OFF-SEASON)	SETS (IN-SEASON)
80%	5–6	1–2	4–5	2–3
77.5%	6–7	1–3	4–5	2–3
75%	7–8	1–3	4–5	3–4
72.5%	8–9	2–3	4–5	3–4
70%	9–10			
67.5%	11–12			
65%	13–14			
62.5%	14–15			
60%	15–16			
57.5%	17–18			
55%	19–20			

WORKOUTS

On the next page you will find Monday's workout for the three-day, 55–80 percent block. The column on the left is the actual workout, using our "imaginary" athlete to calculate the loads used on each exercise. The column on the right, labeled "Coaching Points," gives further explanation about exercise sequencing and important coaching queues to use with your athletes. The coaching points are labeled with the respective workout box that they apply to.

BLOCK FOUR, WEDNESDAY

100%	WENDESDAY	23-Jun-10	REPS	LOAD	SETS	NOTES
	Triangle Terror		6		2	
	Pair w/					
	2-WAY NECK		8		2	
	Pair w/					
	Piston Squat Band		6		2	Bands
500	BACK SQUAT		3	275 - 300		Roll I-band
			2	325 - 350		Spine Rolls
			1	400 - 415		
	Speed 95% Drop off		1	390 - 400		1:15 Rest
			1	390 - 400		1:15 Rest
			1	390 - 400		1:15 Rest
			1	390 - 400		1:15 Rest
			1	390 - 400		1:15 Rest
			1	390 - 400		1:15 Rest
			1	390 - 400		1:15 Rest
	Split SQ Drop Jump		4		4	
	Pair w/					Rest 30
	USSR Plyo Box		4		4	Bands
	Pair w/					Rest 30
250	Squat Jump		4	170 - 175	4	Rest 2:00
	Power Step up		4		3	Bands
	Pair w/					Speed/Jump
	Laying External Rot		6		3	5:0:5:0
	Pair w/					Rest 30
100	DB SL Calf Raise		10	65 - 70	3	Knee Bend
	Nordic HAM Curls		8		3	Assist
	Pair w/					Rest 30
90	DB INCLINE BENCH		9,7,5	65 - 70	3	
	Pair w/					Rest 30
105	DB BO Row		8	80 - 85	3	Rest 1:00
200	DB RDL InLine		6	150 - 160	3	
	Pair w/					
	Hip FLX BND Pulls		6		3	
	Pair w/					
75	DB Shoulder Press		10S	45 -	3	
150	Rev Grip Tri Push		8	115 - 120	3	
	Pair w/					
	Bicep shock curls		10S		3	
	Pair w/					
	Bam Bam		10		3	

COACHING POINTS AND EXERCISE TUTORIAL

BOX 1
-The first box can be skipped if an intense dynamic warm up has been completed.
Over head rack squat; Manual 4-way neck; Standing Glute Kicks

BOX 2
-More advanced athletes will use 8 percent of the drop-off during this time, which will be the indicator of how many sets must be completed.
Back Squat

BOX 3
-The next cluster of exercises are split squat jumps, Russian plyos, and loaded squat jumping, which is just a combination of plyometrics post-maximal effort squat.
Split Squat Drop Jump; USSR Plyo Box Bands; Squat Jump

BOX 4
-The power step up is performed with bands attached around the athlete's waist; the athlete should drive the foot through the box forcefully. The coach holding the band should not hold so tight as to reduce the speed of the movement
-For the DB SL calf raise, cue the athletes to push through the big toe
Power Step Up; Laying Eccentric External Rotation; DB SL Calf Raise

BOX 5
-Adjust the band tensin with the nordic hamstring curl; athletes generally should use between a light and mini band
Nordic Ham Curls Assisted; DB Incline Bench; DB BO Row

BOX 6
-The hip flexor band pull is an explosive exercise for the anterior hip musculature
DB RDL InLine; Hip Flexor Band Pulls; DB Shoulder Press

BOX 7
-The bicep shock curl is an explosive exercise for the upper arm; the athlete should turn the palms down and away after releasing the bar. When bring the hands up, the athlete should fully supinate the hand and catch the bar. This is done as fast and explosively as possible.
Reverse Grip Triceps Push-Down; Bicep Curl Shock; Bam Bams

✓ Coach's Corner

PROPER BREATHING FOR SPORTS RECOVERY
By: Cal Dietz & Daniel Raimondi
Edited By: Ben Peterson

An often overlooked component of many programs is restoration and recovery. Coaches attempt to manipulate variables in their workouts, changing intensities, volume, and exercises in order to cause adaptation. However, a training program is most effective if the athlete is able to recover from and adapt to the previous stress/workout. There are numerous techniques used to aid in restoration—recovery baths, contrast showers, proper nutrition, stretching, massage, and recovery rollers. This article will cover a technique seldom employed and even less commonly programmed—breathing.

Slow, deep, breathing has been shown to induce a calming effect on the body, decreasing everything from blood pressure to stress. Deep voluntary belly breathing also has been shown to shift the nervous system from sympathetic dominance to parasympathetic dominance (Jerath et al. 2006). What does this mean for your athletes? It means faster recovery by starting the digestive process sooner, creating stronger and faster athletes while responding better to future stress.

The neural response to training is well documented with an excitatory effect occurring in response to a stressor. Therefore, the key to recovery is being able to switch as soon as possible from the catabolic state brought on by training into a more anabolic state (Chen et al. 2011). The faster an athlete can go from an excited state to a calm one, the more capable he will be recovering from the workout.

So what exactly constitutes good belly breathing? Well, it's basically as simple as it sounds—deep breathing into the naval. Take a deep breath into your belly through the nose and exhale slowly through the mouth. Another useful tip is to take longer to exhale than to inhale. So an example of a good, deep breath might be a four-second inhale held for seven seconds with eight seconds taken to exhale (Weil). Repeat this process three to four times, letting your body calm itself, relax, and adjust to the new breathing pattern.

The last piece of this breathing puzzle is simply how to program it into your workout. Most coaches are raising an eyebrow. With time restrictions, most agree that the focus of the workout should be the workout. I'd contend that taking five to ten minutes at the end of the training session to include something as simple as deep, belly breathing can have huge impacts on future training sessions. One could also combine this type of breathing with a stretch (think yoga). An example might be a simple bar hang with slow, relaxing, rhythmic breaths. Another variation would be to perform a glute ham hang. To do this, have the athlete lie face down on a glute ham machine, hang over the edge, and let the body completely relax.

This will not only readjust the breathing pattern but also help to decompress the spine. Every breath out should feel the body relax more and more, such that the spine feels longer and the athlete feels zero tension.

References

Chen JL, Yeh DP, Lee JP, Chen CY, Huang CY, Lee SD, Chen CC, Kuo TBJ, Kao CL, Kuo CH (2011) Parasympathetic Nervous Activity Mirrors Recovery Status in Weightlifting Performance After Training. *Journal of Strength and Conditioning Research* 25(0/00):1–7.

Jerath R, Edry JW, Barnes VA, Jerath V (2006) Physiology of Long Pranayamic Breathing: Neural Respiratory Elements May Provide a Mechanism that Explains How Slow, Deep, Breathing Shifts the Autonomic Nervous System. *Journal of Medical Hypotheses* 67(3):566–71.

Weil Andrew. Breathing: Three Exercises. Retrieved from http://www.drweil.com/.

5.7: FRIDAY, LOW INTENSITY (HIGH VOLUME)

LOADING

Friday is very similar to Monday with the exception that you replace the moderate intensity level with extra volume. The last training day of the week is always the most difficult in terms of trying to generate intensity, focus, and excitement from the athlete. They have worked hard all week—training, doing homework, going to class, hanging out with their friends, going to other activities like piano lessons or club sports. All that "stress" adds up fast. To try and keep the training level as high as possible, I have found that it works best to expand the list of methods used to keep the athlete's attention. Training means used on Friday include but aren't limited to bodybuilding methods, Strongman training, dinosaur training, and CrossFit methods.

These methods are applied by using the loading variables listed in the table 5.8. Any shaded area signifies that it's a load that shouldn't be used on the low intensity/high volume day.

7 1RM	MAXIMUM REPS POSSIBLE	HIGH QUALITY REPS (STRENGTH)	SETS (OFF-SEASON)	SETS (IN-SEASON)
TABLE 5.8: FRIDAY LOADING VARIABLES (HIGH VOLUME)				
77.5%	6–7			
75%	7–8			
72.5%	8–9			
70%	9–10			
67.5%	11–12			
65%	13–14			
62.5%	14–15	5–8	4–6	IN-SEASON VOLUME COMES FROM PRACTICE
60%	15–16	5–8	4–6	
57.5%	17–18	5–8	4–6	
55%	19–20	5–8	4–6	

WORKOUTS

On the next page you will find Friday's workout for the three-day, 55–80 percent block. Coaching points with their respective hyperlinks to the exercises are in the right-hand column. At the end of this section, you will find workouts for each block of a four-day, five-day, six-day, and two-day in-season model.

BLOCK FOUR, FRIDAY

100%	FRIDAY	25-Jun-10			
		REPS	LOAD	SETS	NOTES
	3 - WY Ham PRSS	9		2	Eyes Closed
	Pair w/				no rest
	2-WAY NECK	8		2	
	Pair w/				no rest
	BAL SNGL LG SQ	6		2	Air Max
	Hurdle Hop	4		3	
	Pair w/				Rest 30
	USSR Plyo Box	4		3	
	Pair w/				Rest 30
	Acc Band Jump	4		3	
225	Single Leg Squat	12	145 - 160	3	
	Pair w/				Rest 30
150	SL Reverse Hyper	7	105 - 115	3	
	Pair w/				Rest 30
	Cuban PRSS INC F8	6		3	
	Cross Over STEP Up	4		3	Bands
	Pair w/				Rest 30
	SWB LG Curl SNGL Leg	8		3	
	Pair w/				Rest 30
	Thors Hammer	8		3	
300	BENCH PRESS	FFFF	195 - 105	4	Rest 45
	Pair w/				
75	DB Shoulder Press	FFF	55 - 30	3	OC
	Pair w/				Rest 45
150	TRI PUSH DOWN	FFF	105 - 60	3	Rest 45
	Nordic HAM Curls	6		2	
	Pair w/				
	Hip FLXor ISO Pull	6		2	
	Pair w/				
	Iso Ball Grion Sqeeze	10S		3	
	Hindu Squat Iso	180s		1	
	Glute Ham Back Cav Iso	180s		1	
	GH HANG	120S		1	Relax Mouth
	Pair w/				
	Partner Leg Walks	120S		1	
	Pair w/				
	LAYING RELAXATION	120S		1	Relax Mouth

COACHING POINTS AND EXERCISE TUTORIAL

**On day three, I will often address some more plyometrics even in a fatigued state but still try to keep the quality high, however with an understanding that this block in particular could be my tenth to twelfth week into training.

Box 1
3 Way Hamstring Press; Manual 4-way neck; Balance Single Leg Squat

Box 2
Hurdle Hop; Russian Plyo Box; Accelerated Band Jump

Box 3
-With this high volume day, I have selected exercises that will increase work capacity and paired them together with the single leg squat and the single leg reverse hyper.
Single Leg Squat; Reverse Hyper; Cuban Press Incline Figure 8

Box 4
Cross Over Step Up; Single Leg Ball Curl SL; Thors Hammer

Box 5
-The bench press, dumbbell shoulder press, oscillatory movement, and triceps push-down are all done to failure (signified by the FFF). The latter part of the week is the only time that I do sets to failure in my undulated model.
Bench Press; DB Shoulder Press; Tri push down

Box 6
Nordic Hamstring Curl; Hip Flexor Isometric Pull; Isometric Ball Groin Squeeze

Box 7
-Once into training, I've found little value in long duration isometrics and have found the only place they can be inserted into a program to address the qualities that may increase for these types of movements are in the latter part of the week during fatigued states to increase work capacity quality.
Isometric Hindu Squat Trap Shoulder Bicep Hold; Isometric Glute Ham Back Iso

Box 8
Glute Ham Hang; Partner Leg Walks; Laying Relaxation

√ COACH'S CORNER

COACHING THE SQUAT FOR TALLER ATHLETES
BY: CAL DIETZ AND TOMMY MILLER
EDITED BY: BEN PETERSON

When teaching young athletes to squat, coaches need to remember that squatting isn't a "cookie cutter" exercise. Not everyone's squatting form is going to look the same. This is especially true of taller athletes or athletes with long thighs (femurs). When training taller athletes, a coach must recognize the inherent biomechanical disadvantage that a taller athlete experiences when squatting compared to the efforts of shorter athletes. This must be accounted for.

When an athlete performs a squat, there is a great amount of torque about the knee and hip joints. When an athlete has a long thigh (femur), there is considerably more torque about the knee joint when compared to shorter athletes. To counteract that increased amount of torque, it has been said that the athlete should incline the trunk (or bend farther forward) in order to bring the center of gravity closer to the knee joint, thus reducing torque. However, to safely incline the trunk, an athlete must position the bar further down his back, which will put more stress upon the hip joints and hip extensors while lessening the stress on the knee joints.

In theory, this may seem like a good idea. In practice, however, an athlete who doesn't possess a strong enough back to lift the weight in such a manner may set himself up for injury. The stress applied to the back when the torso is more inclined is much greater than that which is applied to a straighter or more upright torso. So if this is the case with your athlete, what is the solution? In order to safely squat an athlete with long thighs, the coach must tell the athlete to spread out his feet. This will not actually shorten the length of the thigh but will help the athlete keep his center of gravity closer to the knee joint while performing a safe and effective squat. Being able to squat correctly will allow the athlete to increase the torque about the hip joint and less about the knee joint, thus shifting the stress to the glutes and hip extensors.

If an athlete uses a wide stance when squatting, special attention must be paid to the feet as well as how the knees move during the exercise. As a result of a utilizing a wide squatting stance, an athlete will tend to place more weight on the medial side of his foot, which may cause the knees to move inward. Coaches need to be aware of this and must correct this error when it appears (by encouraging the athlete to keep his knees in line with his legs). Squatting with a wide stance will help provide a biomechanical advantage for taller athletes by reducing torque about the knee joints. The wider stance allows the athlete to obtain a lower squatting depth than a more traditional, narrower stance.

5.8: 55–80 PERCENT THREE-DAY PROGRAM OVERVIEW

TABLE 5.9: UNDULATING BLOCK MODEL

TRAINING WEEK:		DAY 1	DAY 2	DAY 3	DAY 4	DAY 5	DAY 6
THREE-DAY MODEL	FOCUS	TOTAL BODY	OFF	TOTAL BODY	OFF	TOTAL BODY	OFF
	LOAD	62–70%		72–80%		55–62%	
	MEANS APPLIED	BIOMETRIC		DYNAMIC/ BIOMETRIC		VOLUME	

TABLE 5.10: 55–80 PERCENT THREE-DAY CONDITIONING MODEL

TRAINING DAY	CONDITIONING GOAL	SPECIAL INSTRUCTIONS	EXAMPLE WORKOUT
DAY 1	**Long Sprints** *or* **Short Sprints with Reduced Rest** (Speed Conditioning)	• Sprints over 15 seconds or • Sprints under 10, recovery under 20 seconds.	• High Quality Lactic Anaerobic Power Training Builder • Metabolic Injury Prevention Runs
DAY 2	**Short Sprints** (High Quality Speed)	• Sprints under 10 seconds • Full recovery; rest 90–120 seconds.	• Alactic High Quality Workout • Flying 60's • 16 Week Short Sprint Workouts • Cone Agility
DAY 3	**Longer Sprints** *or* **Continuous Running** (Oxidative Conditioning)	This day is purely work capacity focused	• Aerobic Work Capacity Training Builder • Game Speed Conditioning • Bike Conditioning • TrashBall

BLOCK FOUR (3-DAY): HIGH FORCE AT HIGH VELOCITY (55-80%)

MONDAY — 21-Jun-10 (100% / 500)

Exercise	REPS	LOAD	SETS	NOTES
OH SQ Rack Press	6		2	Eyes Closed
Pair w/				
2-WAY NECK	8		2	
Pair w/				
STDNG Glute Kicks	6		2	
BACK SQUAT	3	275 - 300		Roll I-band
	2	325 - 350		Spine Rolls
Test	2	400 - 415		CW TEST
Pair Below	3	350 - 365		0:0:0:0
Pair Below	3	350 - 365		0:0:0:0
Pair Below	3	350 - 365		0:0:0:0
French Contrast	3	350 - 365		0:0:0:0
Hurdle Hop	4		4	Distance
Pair w/				
Squat Jump 250	4	200 - 205	4	0:0:0:0
Pair w/				
Acc Band Jump	4		4	Rest 5:00
4 way neck	8		2	no Rest
Pair w/				
Wrist Flexion	6		3	no Rest
Pair w/				
ANT TIB BND	10		3	Band Medium
Vaulting Band Lngs-Jump	4		3	Speed/Jump
Pair w/				
DB BENCH 105	9,7,5	75 - 85	3	Toes
Lat Pull Down 225	8	170 - 180	3	
Glute Bar Lift 500	6	375 - 400	3	0:0:0:0
Hip FLX BND Pulls	6		3	No Rest
Pair w/				
DB Shoulder Press 75	10S	45 -	3	No Rest
Rev Grip Tri Push 150	8	115 - 120	3	OC
Pair w/				
Bicep shock curls	10S		3	No Rest
Pair w/				
Bam Bam	10		3	No Rest

WENDESDAY — 23-Jun-10 (100% / 500)

Exercise	REPS	LOAD	SETS	NOTES
Triangle Terror	6		2	
Pair w/				
2-WAY NECK	8		2	
Pair w/				
Piston Squat Band	6		2	Bands
BACK SQUAT	3	275 - 300		Roll I-band
	2	325 - 350		Spine Rolls
	1	400 - 415		
Speed 35% Drop off	1	390 - 400		1:15 Rest
	1	390 - 400		1:15 Rest
	1	390 - 400		1:15 Rest
	1	390 - 400		1:15 Rest
	1	390 - 400		1:15 Rest
	1	390 - 400		1:15 Rest
Split SQ Drop Jump	4		4	
Pair w/				
USSR Plyo Box	4		4	Rest 30 / Bands
Squat Jump 250	4	170 - 175	4	Rest 2:00
Power Step up	4		3	Bands Speed/Jump
Laying External Rot	6		3	5:0:5:0
DB SL Calf Raise 100	10	65 - 70	3	Rest 30
Nordic HAM Curls	8		2	Assist
Pair w/				
DB INCLINE BENCH 90	9,7,5	65 - 70	3	Rest 30
Pair w/				
DB BO Row 105	8	80 - 85	3	Rest 30
DB RDL InLine 200	6	150 - 160	3	Rest 1:00
Hip FLX BND Pulls	6		3	
Pair w/				
DB Shoulder Press 75	10S	45 -	3	
Rev Grip Tri Push 150	8	115 - 120	3	
Pair w/				
Bicep shock curls	10S		3	
Pair w/				
Bam Bam	10		3	

FRIDAY — 25-Jun-10 (100%)

Exercise	REPS	LOAD	SETS	NOTES
3 - WY Ham PRSS	9		2	no Gain
Pair w/				
2-WAY NECK	8		2	no rest
Pair w/				
BAL SNGL LG SQ	6		2	Air Max
Hurdle Hop	4		3	Rest 30
Pair w/				
USSR Plyo Box	4		3	Rest 30
Pair w/				
Acc Band Jump	4		3	
Single Leg Squat 225	12	145 - 160	3	Rest 30
Pair w/				
SL Reverse Hyper 150	7	105 - 115	3	Rest 30
Pair w/				
Cuban PRSS INC F8	6		3	Rest 30
Cross Over STEP Up	4		3	Bands
SvB LG Curl SNGL Leg	8		3	Rest 30
Thors Hammer	8		3	-...??
BENCH PRESS 300	FFFF	195 - 105	4	Rest 45
DB Shoulder Press 75	FFF	55 - 30	3	OC
TRI PUSH DOWN 150	FFF	105 - 60	3	Rest 45
Nordic HAM Curls	6		2	Rest 45
Pair w/				
Hip FLXor ISO Pull	6		2	
Iso Ball Groin Sqeeze	10S		3	
Hindu Squat Iso	180s		1	
Glute Ham Back Cav Iso	180s		1	
GH HANG	120S		1	Relax Mouth
Pair w/				
Partner Leg Walks	120S		1	
Pair w/				
LAYING RELAXATION	120S		1	Relax Mouth

5.9: 55–80 PERCENT FOUR-DAY PROGRAM

Below, you will find how to take the three-day model and extrapolate it to a four-day model. In table 5.11, day one loading parameters are in white, day two loading parameters are in light gray, and day three loading parameters are in dark gray. Notice that in the four-day model there isn't a dark gray day. In this mesocycle, day three loading parameters (signified by the color blue) are the "volume" days of the week. In a four-day model, there aren't enough training days to give each focus its own volume day. Instead of sacrificing a high intensity day of training, extra volume work is placed at the end of training days two and five of the week.

TABLE 5.11: 55–80 PERCENT THREE-DAY VERSUS FOUR-DAY MODEL							
TRAINING WEEK:		DAY 1	DAY 2	DAY 3	DAY 4	DAY 5	DAY 6
THREE-DAY MODEL	FOCUS	TOTAL BODY	OFF	TOTAL BODY	OFF	TOTAL BODY	OFF
	LOAD	62–70%		72–80%		55–62%	
	MEANS APPLIED	BIOMETRIC		DYNAMIC/ BIOMETRIC		VOLUME	
FOUR-DAY MODEL	FOCUS	LOWER BODY	UPPER BODY	OFF	LOWER BODY	UPPER BODY	OFF
	LOAD	62–70%	62–70%		72–80%	72–80%	
	MEANS APPLIED	BIOMETRIC			DYNAMIC/ BIOMETRIC		

Another important aspect of training that can't be forgotten is speed work and conditioning. Table 5.12 shows where in the training week each should be emphasized along with an example workout.

TABLE 5.12: 55–80 PERCENT FOUR-DAY CONDITIONING MODEL

TRAINING DAY	CONDITIONING GOAL	SPECIAL INSTRUCTIONS	EXAMPLE WORKOUT
DAY 1	**Short Sprints** (High Quality Speed)	• Sprints under 10 seconds • Full recovery; rest 90–120 seconds.	• Alactic High Quality Workout • Flying 60's • 16 Week Short Sprint Workouts • Cone Agility
DAY 2	**Long Sprints *or* Short Sprints with Reduced Rest** (Speed Conditioning)	• Sprints over 15 seconds or • Sprints under 10, recovery under 20 seconds.	• High Quality Lactic Anaerobic Power Training Builder • Metabolic Injury Prevention Runs
DAY 3	**Short Sprint** (High Quality Speed)	• Sprints under 10 seconds • Full recovery; rest 90–120 seconds.	• Alactic High Quality Workout • Flying 60's • 16 Week Short Sprint Workouts • Cone Agility
DAY 4	**Longer Sprints *or* Continuous Running** (Oxidative Conditioning)	This day is purely work capacity focused	• Aerobic Work Capacity Training Builder • Game Speed Conditioning • Bike Conditioning • TrashBall

Finally, we need to talk about the different exercises, methods, and means that I use in a four-day program that I don't use and didn't show you in the three-day program. The following hyperlink will take you to a video that explains the four-day program in detail.

FOUR-DAY 55–80 PERCENT VIDEO

QUICK TRAINING NOTES

Day one
- The back squat at submaximal effort is paired with power step-ups and cycle kicks, which are highly reactive. This is a contrast method based upon this particular sport's individual needs. Isometrics were still used in early season to build this particular team's work capacity levels.

Day two
- The bench press is paired with various exercises that are important to the particular sport trained.
- This program is essentially an upper body day with any four-day split.
- Days one and two of this particular program are submaximal days.

Day three
- The lat pull and press is a unique exercise. It is done with an eccentric component in this particular lift and is highly effective for swimming.
- The sport back squat, which is mentioned earlier in this book, is paired with an accelerated band jump, which in the acceleration sport would be done to deep squat levels and in other sports such as distance running or swimming would be done to higher levels.

Day four
- This is another upper body day with clustered training used to address maximal effort and is paired with a clap push-up. Often the clap push-up is done with bands around the arm pits hanging from the racks. It's done at a high speed and a high velocity.

BLOCK FOUR (4-DAY): HIGH FORCE AT HIGH VELOCITY (55-80%)

Day one

100%	Exercise	REPS	LOAD	SETS	NOTES
500	Back Squat	5	225 - 275	1	
	Pair w/				
500	Back Squat	3	295 - 325	1	P/v-2 Neck
	Pair w/				
500	Back Squat	1	390 - 400	1	Each Leg
500	Back Squat	4	365 - 375	4	
	Pair w/				
	Power Step up	6		4	
	Cycle Kicks	8		4	Reactive
	90 90 Groin ISO Hold	10S		3	
	3 - WY HAM Touch	6		3	0:5:0:0
	Pair w/				
200	Walking Lunge	6	150 - 160	3	
	Hip Flex Ecc Prone	6		4	3:0:0:0
	Pair w/				
	BO DB Push Back	8		4	
	Pair w/				
	Supine Glt Ham Bk Iso	60S	180s 60%: -	1	
	Glute Ham Back Cav Iso	60S		1	
		5	65% - 70%	1	
		4	75% - 75%	3	
	3:00 Core Test				
	SWB Down TW	8		2	
	GH HANG	120S		1	
	Pair w/				
	Rollers Glutes & Hams	120S		1	
	Pair w/				
	LAYING RELAXATION	120S		1	

Day 2

100%	Exercise	REPS	LOAD	SETS	NOTES
300	BENCH PRESS	5	135 - 165	1	P/ Gripper
	Pair w/				
300	BENCH PRESS	3	175 - 195	1	P/ Gripper
	Pair w/				
300	BENCH PRESS	1	235 - 240	1	P/ Gripper
300	BENCH PRESS	4	220 - 225	4	
	Pair w/				
38	DB Rear Delt	9	25 - 30	4	0:4:0:0
	Pair w/				
	Leg Press Calf Raise	10		4	Rest 1:30
53	DB Incline Fly	8	40 - 40	3	5:0:0:0
	Pair w/				
105	DB BO Row	6	85 - 85	3	3:0:0:0
	Pair w/				
	Side DELT Raise	10		3	
90	JM DB Press	8	65 - 70	4	
	Pair w/				
120	Bar Curl	8	85 - 95	4	
	Pair w/				
	Chest Rev Grip Iso	180s		1	
	Supine Glt Ham Bk Iso	180s	120s 40%: -	1	
	Pair w/				
		5	65% - 70%	1	
	Pair w/				
		1	80% - 80%	1	
	Pair w/				
		8	70% - 75%	4	
	3:00 Core Test				
	SWB Down TW	8		2	
	GH HANG	120S		1	Relax Mouth
	Pair w/				
	Rollers Quads & Back	120S		1	
	Pair w/				
	LAYING WALL SHAKES	120S		1	Relax Mouth

Day 3

100%	Exercise	REPS	LOAD	SETS	NOTES
500	Glute Bar Lift	8	350 - 375	2	
	Pair w/				
	Lat Pull And Press	5		2	0:0:5:0
	Pair w/				
	3 - WY HAM Touch	9		2	Each Leg
500	Back Squat	5	225 - 275	1	
500	Back Squat	3	295 - 325	1	
	Pair w/				
500	Back Squat	1	390 - 400	1	
500	Back Squat	3	375 - 400	3	Sport Squat
	Acc Band Jump	5		4	Speed
	Pair w/				
	KA bent over rows	8		4	
	90 90 Groin ISO Hold	10S		3	3:0:0:0
	Pair w/				
	Ball LG Curl	5		3	Speed
	Pair w/				
200	Walking Lunge	6	150 - 160	3	Jump
		180s	60%: -	1	
	Glute Ham Back Cav Iso	60S		1	
	Pair w/				
	Supine Glt Ham Bk Iso	60S		1	
		5	65% - 70%	1	
		4	75% - 75%	3	
	Core workout 1	8		3	
	SWB Down TW	8		2	
	GH HANG	120S		1	
	Pair w/				
	Rollers Glutes & Hams	120S		1	
	Pair w/				
	LAYING RELAXATION	120S		1	

Day 4

100%	Exercise	REPS	LOAD	SETS	NOTES
300	BENCH PRESS	5	135 - 165	1	
	Pair w/				
300	BENCH PRESS	3	175 - 195	1	
	Pair w/				
300	BENCH PRESS	1	235 - 240	1	0:0:0:20
300	BENCH PRESS	1,1	250 - 255	4	
	Pair w/				
	Clap Push Up	5		4	
	Rear DELT	8		4	Rest 1:30
120	DB BENCH	9,7,5	85 - 95	3	5:0:0:0
105	DB BO Row	6	85 - 85	3	3:0:0:0
210	DB Shrug	10	135 - 145	3	
90	JM DB Press	8	65 - 70	4	
60	Incline Hammer Curls	8	40 - 45	4	
	Pair w/				
	Chest Rev Grip Iso	60S		1	
	Supine Glt Ham Bk Iso	60S	120s 40%: -	1	
	Pair w/				
		5	65% - 70%	1	
		1	80% - 80%	3	
		3	90% - 95%	4	
	Coreworkout 2	8		3	
	SWB Down TW	8		2	
	GH HANG	120S		1	Relax Mouth
	Pair w/				
	Rollers Quads & Back	120S		1	
	Pair w/				
	LAYING WALL SHAKES	120S		1	Relax Mouth

280

BLOCK FOUR (4-DAY): High Force at High Velocity
Hyperlinks

Day 1	Exercise Hyperlink	Day 2	Exercise Hyperlink	Day 3	Exercise Hyperlink	Day 4	Exercise Hyperlink
Box 1	Back Squat	Box 1	Bench Press	Box 1	Glute Bar Lift Lat Pull and Press 3- Way Ham Touch	Box 1	Bench Press
Box 2	Back Squat Power Step up Cycle Kicks	Box 2	Bench Press DB Rear Delt Leg Press Calf Raise	Box 2	Back Squat	Box 2	Bench Press Clap Push Up DB Rear Delt
Box 3	90 90 Groin ISO Hold 3- Way Ham Touch DB Walking Lunge	Box 3	DB Incline Fly DB Bent Over Row Side DELT Raise	Box 3	Sport back Squat Accelerated Band Jump KA Bent Over Rows	Box 3	DB Bench DB Bent Over Row DB Shrug
Box 4	Hip Flex Ecc Prone Dumbbell Push Backs	Box 4	JM DB Press Bar Curl Chest Reverse Grip Iso	Box 4	90 90 Groin ISO Hold Ball LG curl DB Walking Lunge	Box 4	JM DB Press Incline Hammer Curls Chest Reverse Grip Iso
Box 5	Supine Glute Ham Back Iso	Box 5	Supine Glute Ham Back Iso	Box 5	Glute Ham Back Cav Iso Supine Glute Ham Back Iso	Box 5	Supine Glute Ham Back Iso
Box 6	Glute Ham Back Cav Iso	Box 6		Box 6		Box 6	
Box 7	3:00 Core Test SWB Down TW	Box 7	3:00 Core Test SWB Down TW	Box 7	SWB Down TW	Box 7	SWB Down TW
Box 8	GH HANG Rollers Glutes and Hams Laying Relaxation	Box 8	GH HANG Rollers Quads and Back Laying Wall Shakes	Box 8	GH HANG Rollers Glutes and Hams Laying Relaxation	Box 8	GH HANG Rollers Quads and Back Laying Wall Shakes

5.10: 55-80 PERCENT FIVE-DAY PROGRAM

Table 5.13 shows how to take what you learned about the three-day model and convert it to a five-day training platform. In the table, day one loading parameters are in white, day two loading parameters are in light gray, and day three loading parameters are in dark gray.

TABLE 5.13: 55-80 PERCENT THREE-DAY VERSUS FIVE-DAY MODEL							
TRAINING WEEK:		DAY 1	DAY 2	DAY 3	DAY 4	DAY 5	DAY 6
THREE-DAY MODEL	FOCUS	TOTAL BODY	OFF	TOTAL BODY	OFF	TOTAL BODY	OFF
	LOAD	62-70%		72-80%		55-62%	
	MEANS APPLIED	BIOMETRIC		DYNAMIC		VOLUME	
FIVE-DAY MODEL	FOCUS	LOWER BODY	UPPER BODY	LOWER BODY	UPPER BODY	TOTAL BODY	OFF
	LOAD	62-70%	62-70%	72-80%	72-80%	55-62%	
	MEANS APPLIED	BIOMETRIC		DYNAMIC		VOLUME	

Another important aspect of training that can't be forgotten is speed work and conditioning. Table 5.14 shows where in the training week each should be emphasized along with an example workout.

TABLE 5.14: 55–80 PERCENT FIVE-DAY CONDITIONING MODEL

TRAINING DAY	CONDITIONING GOAL	SPECIAL INSTRUCTIONS	EXAMPLE WORKOUT
DAY 1	**Short Sprints** (High Quality Speed)	• Sprints under 10 seconds • Full recovery; rest 90–120 seconds.	• Alactic High Quality Workout • Flying 60's • 16 Week Short Sprint Workouts • Cone Agility
DAY 2	**Long Sprints** *or* **Short Sprints w/ Reduced Rest** (Speed Conditioning)	• Sprints over 15 seconds or • Sprints under 10, recovery under 20 seconds.	• High Quality Lactic Anaerobic Power Training Builder • Metabolic Injury Prevention Runs
DAY 3	**Short Sprints** (High Quality Speed)	• Sprints under 10 seconds • Full recovery; rest 90–120 seconds.	• Alactic High Quality Workout • Flying 60's • 16 Week Short Sprint Workouts • Cone Agility
DAY 4	**Short Sprints** (Anaerobic Conditioning)	• Sprints under 10 seconds • Limited recovery; 45–60 seconds	• Work Capacity Alactic Anaerobic Training Builder • Flying 60's • 16 Week Short Sprint Workouts • Cone Agility
DAY 5	**Longer Sprints** *or* **Continuous Running** (Oxidative Conditioning)	This day is purely work capacity focused	• Aerobic Work Capacity Training Builder • Game Speed Conditioning • Bike Conditioning • TrashBall

Finally, we need to talk about the different exercises, methods, and means that I use in a five-day program that I don't use and didn't show you in the three-day program. The following hyperlink will take you to a video that explains the five-day program.

FIVE-DAY 55–80 PERCENT VIDEO

QUICK TRAINING NOTES

Day one

- The hex deadlift is done with a time control drop-off point using the biometric methods mentioned in this book. The athlete will perform the weight listed for six repetitions. We will take a percentage of the drop-off, and he will perform that particular weight in 3.1 seconds six times. When he can't reach that time or the bar travels more slowly, his sets drop at that point. We have had athletes do ten, eleven, and twelve sets with this particular method. The athlete will pair these exercises below for particular rest periods of up to 3.5–5 minutes doing these prehabilitation exercises between the main sets.
- The single leg press is highly reactive and is a must watch on the video to see how to perform the exercise.

Day two

- Loading is a set drop-off using Tendo units on the bench press. Between these sets of bench presses, I had the athletes rotate between vibration devices held on the flexors or chest muscles and then iced them between sets to stimulate the nervous system.
- The vibration devices are set at high frequency.
- The sets are completed to failure.
- Isometrics were used during this particular time to keep increasing work capacity levels for the last six weeks of summer training.

Day three

- Maximal loading lower body.
- This is a maximal effort day at submaximal levels used to train the athletes for strength qualities.
- We do the sports back squat in a particular time for four reps. We will time the reps and then use a drop-off percentage of their best time. For example, if the athlete completed four reps within five seconds, the drop-off is 5.15 for this particular loading method.
- The athlete will also complete five more exercises within the rest cycle, which will include some contrasting with the single leg bench hops and the split squat.
- By adding plyometrics, one must realize that the drop-off percentages may need to go a little higher because of the greater stress in a similarly specific area of the back squat.

Day Four

- Maximal loading upper body
- At this point, we're completing with the bench press Tendo testing for percent drop-off with set drop-off percentages based upon the current level of the athlete's readiness.
- These are often paired with exercises for stimulation or prehabilitation.

Day Five

- Keep in mind this particular lift is a work capacity lift with high volume and low intensities.

- Notice that the bench press, the dumbbell bench press, and the triceps push-down are essentially my day three upper body loading model, which would usually take place on a Saturday. I pushed it into Friday so that it quickly addresses upper body work capacity.
- Many people ask, "Because you've done your max effort on Thursday, can you do work capacity on Friday?" I've never found this to be a problem. Essentially, you've taken care of the maximal, high quality work on Thursday and you might be fatigued to train work capacity. A fatigued state won't be very detrimental unless it's within athletes of the highest quality and level.

BLOCK FOUR (5-DAY): HIGH FORCE AT HIGH VELOCITY (LOWER BODY)

MONDAY — 12-Jul-11 / 19-Jul-11

100%	Exercise	REPS	LOAD	SETS	NOTES
	Hurdle Hop S.L.	4		3	Speed
	Pair w/				Height
	Split SQ Drop Jump	4	PH3 PH4	3	Box/Speed
	Pair w/				Each leg
	Acc. Split jump	3		3	Each Leg
575	Hex Deadlift	5	260 - 315	1	PN=2 Neck
	Pair w/				Quad/20
575	Hex Deadlift	3	340 - 375	3	PN=2 Neck
	Pair w/				Back Rolls
575	Hex Deadlift	1	450 - 460	1	PN=2 Neck
575	Hex Deadlift	6	375 - 345	tc	TC
	Pair w/				Set Drop off
	Speed Abduction	5		3	Rest 30
	Pair w/				
	2-WAY NECK	8		3	Rest 30
	Cuban PRSS	6		3	Each Leg
	Pair w/				Rest 30
	Speed Adduction	6		3	Rest 30
100	Ankle Band Work	10		3	
375	SL Leg Press	6	245 - 265	3	Reactive
125	DB Straight Leg DL	6	80 - 90	3	3 way
	Pair w/				
100	DB SL Calf Raise	10	65 - 70	3	0:0:0.0
500	Glute Bar Lift	6	325 - 350	3	
	Pair w/				
	Hip FLX BND Pulls LAT	6		3	
	Pair w/				
	Iso Ball Groin Sqeeze	10S			
	Cross Swing Abs	5		3	
	Core Training 4				
	Hip Traction	30s	40%	1	Each Leg
	GH HANG	120S		1	Relax Mouth
	Pair w/				
	Rollers Glutes & Hams	120S		1	
	LAYING RELAXATION	120S		1	Relax Mouth

WENDESDAY — 14-Jul-11 / 21-Jul-11

100%	Exercise	REPS	LOAD	SETS	NOTES
500	Sport Back Squat	5	225 - 275	1	PN=2 Neck
	Pair w/				I-band Rolls
500	Sport Back Squat	3	295 - 325	1	PN=2 Neck
	Pair w/				Back Rolls
500	Sport Back Squat	3	390 - 400	1	PN=2 Neck
500	Sport Back Squat	4	350 -	TC	TC
	Pair w/				Set Drop off
	SNGL LG BCH Hop	4		4	Alternating
	Pair w/				
	Split SQ Drop	3		4	Each Leg
	Hip FLXor ISO Pull	6S		4	Each Leg
	Pair w/				Alternating
	Speed Adduction	6		4	
	Pair w/				
	Ankle Band Work	8		2	Each Side
	Walking Band Lungs Jump	5		2	Bands
	Pair w/				Jump
	USSR Plyo Box	3		2	Speed
	Pair w/				
100	DB SL Calf Raise	4	95 - 95	2	Knee Bend
	Nordic HAM Curls	6		2	
	Pair w/				
	Power Step up	4		2	Alternating
	Pair w/				
	90 90 Groin ISO Hold	15S		2	
500	Glute Bar Lift	6	375 - 400	2	
	Pair w/				
	Manual Clam Glutes	5		2	
	Pair w/				
	Depth Drop	5		2	Box 36
	Hindu Squat Iso	180s		1	
	Pair w/				
	Glute Ham Back Cav Iso	180s		1	
	GH HANG	120S		1	Relax Mouth
	Pair w/				
	Rollers Quads & Back	120S		1	
	Pair w/				
	LAYING WALL SHAKES	120S		1	Relax Mouth

FRIDAY — 16-Jul-11 / 23-Jul-11

100%	Exercise	REPS	LOAD	SETS	NOTES
	3 - WY Ham PRSS	9		2	Spe Speed
	Pair w/				
	2-WAY NECK	8		2	
	Pair w/				Ar Max
	BAL SNGL LG SQ	6		2	
	Hurdle Hop S.L.	4		3	
	Pair w/				
	Acc Vertmax 1 Band	3		3	
	Pair w/				
250	Squat Jump	5	125 - 150	3	
225	Single Leg Squat	12	145 - 160	3	
150	SL Reverse Hyper	7	105 - 115	3	
	Pair w/				
	Cuban PRSS INC F8	6		3	
	LAT BND Lunge	4		2	
	Pair w/				
	SwB LG Curl SNGL Leg	8		2	
	Pair w/				
	Thors Hammer	8		2	
	Messie FRT SQ s	8		2	
	Pair w/				
	LAT SUP F8	6		2	
	Pair w/				
	Ankle Band Work	10		2	
200	DB RDL InLine	6	150 - 160	2	
	Pair w/				
	Hip FLXor ISO Pull	10S		2	
	Pair w/				
	Iso Ball Groin Sqeeze	15S		2	
300	BENCH PRESS	FFFF	195 - 105	4	
75	DB Shoulder Press	FFF	55 - 30	3	OC
	TRI PUSH DOWN	FFF	70% - 40%	3	
	GH HANG	120S		1	Relax Mouth
	Pair w/				
	Partner Leg Walks	120S		1	
	Pair w/				
	LAYING RELAXATION	120S		1	Relax Mouth

BLOCK FOUR (5-DAY): HIGH FORCE AT HIGH VELOCITY
HYPERLINKS

Day 1	Exercise Hyperlink	Day 3	Exercise Hyperlink	Day 5	Exercise Hyperlink
Box 1	Hurdle Hop Single Leg Split SQ Drop Jump Acc Split Jump	Box 1	Sport back Squat	Box 1	3 Way Ham Press Balance Single Leg Squat
Box 2	Hex Deadlift	Box 2	Sport back Squat Single Leg Bench Hops Split SQ Drop	Box 2	Hurdle Hop Single Leg Squat Jump
Box 3	Hex Deadlift Speed Abduction	Box 3	Hip Flexor Iso Pull Speed Adduction Ankle Band Work	Box 3	Single Leg Squat Cuban Press INC F8
Box 4	Cuban Press Speed Adduction Ankle Band Work	Box 4	Walking Band Lunge Jump USSR Plyo Box DB Single Leg Calf Raise	Box 4	Lateral Band Lunge SWB Leg Curl Single Leg Thors Hammer
Box 5	SL Leg Press DB Straight Leg DL DB Single Leg Calf Raise	Box 5	Nordic Ham Curls Power Step up 90 90 Groin ISO Hold	Box 5	Messier Front Squat Figure 8 Lateral Supine Ankle Band Work
Box 6	Glute Bar Lift Hip FLX BND Pulls LAT Iso Ball Groin Squeeze	Box 6	Glute Bar Lift Manual Clam Glutes Depth Drop	Box 6	DB RDL Inline Hip Flexor Iso Pull Iso Ball Groin Squeeze
Box 7	Cross Swing Abs Hip Traction	Box 7	Glute Ham Back Cav Iso	Box 7	Bench Press DB Shoulder Press Tricep Push Down
Box 8	GH HANG Rollers Glutes and Hams Laying Relaxation	Box 8	GH HANG Rollers Quads and Back Laying Wall Shakes	Box 8	GH HANG Partner Leg Walks Laying Relaxation

BLOCK FOUR (5-DAY): HIGH FORCE AT HIGH VELOCITY (UPPER BODY)

Tuesday 7-Jul-08

%100	Exercise	REPS	LOAD	SETS	NOTES
300	BENCH PRESS	5	135 - 165	1	
	Pair w/				
300	BENCH PRESS	3	175 - 195	1	
	Pair w/				
300	BENCH PRESS	1	235 - 240	1	
300	BENCH PRESS	C1T	165 - 180	3	3% - Tendo
	Pair w/				Set Drop off
	Med Ball Chest Pass	4		4	Alt-Vib-Ice
	Pair w/				
	Det BO OH Reb Drop	10		4	
90	DB INCLINE BENCH	12	65 - 70	3	oc-2
	Pair w/				
105	DB BO Row	12	70 - 75	3	Reactive
	Pair w/				
30	OH LAT Raise	12	20 - 20	3	+ Shrug
64	JM DB Press	6	50 - 50	2	
	Pair w/				
	Bicep shock curls	10		2	
	ANT TIB BND	15		2	
150	Rev Grip Tri Push	10	100 - 105	3	
	Pair w/				
105	Revs Curl	12,x,x	70 - 85	3	
	Pair w/				
	Spider Flips	12		3	Each Arm
360	Shrug	FFF	250 - 145	3	
	Closed Lunge V BND TW	10		2	
	Pair w/				
180	Gripper	12	135 - 145	2	LS Failure
	Chest Rev Grip Iso	180s		1	
	Pair w/				
	Shr Sho Bi Cav Iso	180s		1	
	Pair w/				
	ISO SPLIT	30s	40% -	1	Each Leg
	GH HANG	120s		1	Relax Mouth
	Pair w/				
	Rollers Glutes & Hams	120S		1	

Thursday 9-Jul-08

%100	Exercise	REPS	LOAD	SETS	NOTES
300	BENCH PRESS	5	135 - 165	1	
	Pair w/				
300	BENCH PRESS	3	175 - 195	1	
	Pair w/				
300	BENCH PRESS	1	235 - 240	1	
300	BENCH PRESS	C1T	210 - 225	4	4% - Tendo
	Pair w/				Set Drop off
	Push up Drops	3		4	Alt-Vib-Ice
	Pair w/				
	Det BO Lat Reb Drop	10		4	Each Leg
90	DB INCLINE BENCH	9,7,5	65 - 70	3	
	Pair w/				
165	Dynamic Lat Pull	8	125 - 130	3	
	Pair w/				
75	DB Shoulder Press	20	45 - 50	3	OC
240	Close Grip Bench	3	215 - 220	3	3 Board
60	Incline Hammer Curls	8	40 - 45	3	
100	DB SL Calf Raise	15	60 - 65	3	Knee Bend
60	DB Tri Floor Press	10	40 - 40	3	
105	Drag Curl	6	85 - 85	3	
	Pair w/				
	Round House	12		3	
	Wrist Flexion	12		2	
	Pair w/				
	Gopher U Abs	12		2	
	Pair w/				
	SWB Up TW	8		2	
	Chest Rev Grip Iso	180s		1	
	Pair w/				
	Shr Sho Bi Cav Iso	180s		1	
	GH HANG	120S		1	Relax Mouth
	Pair w/				
	Rollers Quads & Back	120S		1	
	LAYING WALL SHAKES	120S		1	Relax Mouth

BLOCK FOUR (5-DAY): HIGH FORCE AT HIGH VELOCITY HYPERLINKS

Day 2	Exercise Hyperlink	Day 4	Exercise Hyperlink
Box 1	Bench Press	Box 1	Bench Press
Box 2	Bench Press Med Ball Chest Pass Delt BO OH Rebound Drops	Box 2	Bench Press Push Up Drops Delt Lateral Rebound Drop
Box 3	DB Incline Bench DB Bent Over Row OH LAT Raise	Box 3	DB Incline Bench Dynamic Lat Pull DB Shoulder Press
Box 4	JM DB Press Bicep Shock Curls ANT TIB BAND	Box 4	Close Grip Bench Incline Hammer Curls DB Single Leg Calf Raise
Box 5	Reverse Grip Tri Pushdown Reverse Curl Spider Flips	Box 5	DB Tri Floor Press Drag Curl Round House
Box 6	Shoulder Shrug Closed Lunge V Band Twist Gripper	Box 6	Gopher U ABS SWB Up TW
Box 7	Chest Reverse Grip Iso Shr Sho Bi Cav Iso Iso Split	Box 7	Chest Reverse Grip Iso Shr Sho Bi Cav Iso GH HANG
Box 8	GH HANG Rollers Glutes and Hams	Box 8	Rollers Quads and Back Laying Wall Shakes

5.11: 55-80 PERCENT SIX-DAY PROGRAM

Table 5.15 shows how to take what you learned about the three-day model and convert it to a six-day training platform. In the table, day one loading parameters are in white, day two loading parameters are in light gray, and day three loading parameters are in dark gray.

TABLE 5.15: 55-80 PERCENT THREE-DAY VERSUS SIX-DAY MODEL							
TRAINING WEEK:		**DAY 1**	**DAY 2**	**DAY 3**	**DAY 4**	**DAY 5**	**DAY 6**
THREE-DAY MODEL	FOCUS	TOTAL BODY	OFF	TOTAL BODY	OFF	TOTAL BODY	OFF
	LOAD	62-70%		72-80%		55-62%	
	MEANS APPLIED	BIOMETRIC		DYNAMIC/ BIOMETRIC		VOLUME	
SIX-DAY MODEL	FOCUS	LOWER BODY	UPPER BODY	LOWER BODY	UPPER BODY	LOWER BODY	UPPER BODY
	LOAD	62-70%	82-87%	72-80%	90-97%	55-62%	75-80%
	MEANS APPLIED	BIOMETRIC		DYNAMIC/BIOMETRIC		VOLUME	

Another important aspect of training that can't be forgotten is speed work and conditioning. Table 5.16 shows where in the training week each should be emphasized along with an example workout. Finally, we need to talk about the different exercises, methods, and means that I use in a six-day program that I don't use and didn't show you in the three-day program. The following hyperlink will take you to a video that explains the six-day program.

SIX-DAY 55-80 PERCENT VIDEO

TRAINING DAY	CONDITIONING GOAL	SPECIAL INSTRUCTIONS	EXAMPLE WORKOUT
DAY 1	**Short Sprints** (High Quality Speed)	• Sprints under 10 seconds • Full recovery; rest 90–120 seconds.	• Alactic High Quality Workout • Flying 60's • 16 Week Short Sprint Workouts • Cone Agility
DAY 2	**Long Sprints _or_ Short Sprints with Reduced Rest** (Speed Conditioning)	• Sprints over 15 seconds or • Sprints under 10, recovery under 20 seconds.	• High Quality Lactic Anaerobic Power Training Builder • Metabolic Injury Prevention Runs
DAY 3	**Short Sprints** (High Quality Speed)	• Sprints under 10 seconds • Full recovery; rest 90–120 seconds.	• Alactic High Quality Workout • Flying 60's • 16 Week Short Sprint Workouts • Cone Agility
DAY 4	**Short Sprints** (Anaerobic Conditioning)	• Sprints under 10 seconds • Limited recovery; 45–60 seconds	• Work Capacity Alactic Anaerobic Training Builder • Flying 60's • 16 Week Short Sprint Workouts • Cone Agility
DAY 5	**Longer Sprints _or_ Continuous Running** (Oxidative Conditioning)	This day is purely work capacity focused	• Aerobic Work Capacity Training Builder • Game Speed Conditioning • Bike Conditioning • Trash Ball
DAY 6	**Longer Sprints _or_ Continuous Running** (Oxidative Conditioning)	This day is purely work capacity focused	• Aerobic Work Capacity Training Builder • Game Speed Conditioning • Bike Conditioning • Trash Ball

TABLE 5.16: 55–80 PERCENT SIX-DAY CONDITIONING MODEL

QUICK TRAINING NOTES

Day one

- Notice that the Olympics lifts are extremely high quality. Speed often causes an excitation of the nervous system and will facilitate practice later in the day.
- This particular contrasting method is used with various loads changing from higher loads to lower loads to facilitate speed.

Day two

- Workout two is upper body in nature, and we use a submaximal loading with bands. Use Tendo units as your drop-off regulation.
- Day two front squats are performed with bands, which requires posterior and upper back strength in regards to holding the right positions.
- The front squat submaximal loading is often paired with reactive plyometrics.
- The glute ham hyper is very highly reactive in the free fall and then held for four seconds at the bottom position. Come back up as fast as possible and then actually push yourself down with your quads into the bottom position.
- The Romanian deadlift is an excellent posterior chain exercise in regards to strength efforts in strength sports.

Day three

- Power snatch down with cluster training and various changing of loads from higher and lower to enhance speed properties of each individual lift. This is the first lift of the particular day and the highest loading levels in this type of cycle.
- The incline bench press is done with clusters and singles for this particular throwing athlete. The incline bench press sets are then followed by a bench press throw at 75 lbs, which is roughly 50 percent of this athlete's max bench press.

Day four

- The max lower body leg day in this loading cycle is at 80 percent with a four percent drop-off the biometrics method. With this particular lift, the sets are four complete sets and the repetitions are a four percent drop-off regulated by the athlete's state of readiness paired with Russian ploy boxes and speed abductions.
- Depending on the type of technique used in throwing, the speed adduction is an effective tool.

Day five

- You will notice that this particular day is extremely light. Sometimes our athletes will do both morning and afternoon lifts prior to a meet so that they can be at the beginning of the season's training of six days a week and compete at a meet Friday night and/or Saturday.

Day six

- This lift is often done after a meet or after a morning training session to increase work capacity potential, which will be backed off on the very next cycle.
- The power snatch is often substituted for the deadlift in case the athlete's back feels tight or fatigued.
- The deadlift is often used with a hex bar to prevent fatiguing the thrower's back.

BLOCK FOUR (6-DAY): HIGH FORCE AT HIGH VELOCITY (UPPER BODY)

Monday

100%	Monday	REPS	LOAD	SETS	NOTES
300	Power Clean	5	135 - 165	1	Pre-Set Wup
					Rest 1:30
300	Power Clean	3	175 - 195	1	Ptv-2 Neck
					Rest 1:30
300	Power Clean	1	- 240	1	Ptv-2 Neck
300	Power Clean	3	195 - 205	3	0:0:0:15
	Pair w/				Rest 3:00
300	Power Clean	3	210 - 225	3	0:0:0:10
	Pair w/				Rest 2:30
300	BENCH PRESS	5	135 - 165	1	
	Pair w/				Rest 1:30
300	BENCH PRESS	3	175 - 195	1	
	Pair w/				Rest 1:30
300	BENCH PRESS	1	- 240	1	Coach Watch
300	BENCH PRESS	C1t	210 - 225	4	3:- Tendo / Bands
	Pair w/				45 Pounds
	INC OH Sit Up	10		5	
	Pair w/				Rest 1:30
300	Bench Press	15	195 - 210	1	
90	DB INCLINE BENCH	9,7,5	65 - 70	3	
	Pair w/				Rest 1:30
225	Lat Pull Down	9,7,5	160 - 180	3	Increase Wgt
	Pair w/				Rest 1:30
38	DB Side Lat Raise	10	25 - 30	3	
60	DB Tri Ext	6	45 - 50	4	0:0:0:0
	Pair w/				Rest 1:30
120	Bar Curl	8,6,4	85 - 95	3	
	Pair w/				Rest 1:30
38	DB Rear Delt	12	25 - 25	4	
	Bam Bam	12	200% - 75%	3	
	GH HANG	120S		1	Relax Mouth
	Pair w/				
	Rollers Glutes & Hams	120S		1	
	Pair w/				
	ISO SPLIT	30s		1	

Wednesday

100%	Wednesday	REPS	LOAD	SETS	NOTES
210	Power Snatch	5	95 - 115	1	Pre-Set Wup
					Rest 1:30
210	Power Snatch	3	125 - 135	1	Ptv-2 Neck
					Rest 1:30
210	Power Snatch	1	- 170	1	Ptv-2 Neck
210	Power Snatch	1,1	170 - 175	3	0:0:0:20
	Pair w/				Rest 2:30
210	Power Snatch	1,1	150 - 160	5	0:0:0:20
	Pair w/				Rest 2:30
240	INCLINE BENCH	5	110 - 130	1	
					Rest 1:30
240	INCLINE BENCH	3	140 - 155	1	
					Rest 1:30
240	INCLINE BENCH	1	- 190	1	Coach Watch
240	INCLINE BENCH	1,1	190 - 200	3	0:0:0:20
	Pair w/				Rest 2:30
240	INCLINE BENCH	1,1	175 - 180	5	0:0:0:15
	Pair w/				Pair/E. Set
150	Bench Throw	3	70 - 75	5	0:0:0:3
195	Push Press	3	145 - 155	4	Increase Wgt
	Pair w/				Rest 1:30
60	DB Curl	8	40 - 45	4	
	Pair w/				Rest 1:30
180	Gripper	10	115 - 125	4	
105	EZ Tri Ext	6	85 - 85	3	Chain
	Pair w/				Rest 1:30
105	1 Arm Lat Pull Down	8	80 - 85	3	
	Pair w/				Rest 1:30
	Gopher U Abs	8		3	25 Pounds
	GH HANG	120S		1	Relax Mouth
	Pair w/				
	Rollers Quads & Back	120S		1	
	Pair w/				
	LAYING WALL SHAKES	120S		1	Relax Mouth

Friday

100%	Friday	REPS	LOAD	SETS	NOTES
300	Power Clean	5	135 - 165	1	Pre-Set Wup
					Rest 1:30
300	Power Clean	3	175 - 195	1	Ptv-2 Neck
					Rest 1:30
300	Power Clean	1	225 - 240	1	Ptv-2 Neck
300	Power Clean	3	165 - 180	4	0:0:0:10
					Rest 2:30
					0:0:0:10
					Rest 2:30
300	BENCH PRESS	5	135 - 165	1	
	Pair w/				
300	BENCH PRESS	3	175 - 195	1	
300	BENCH PRESS	1	235 - 240	1	Coach Watch
300	Bench Press	3	165 - 180	4	
	Pair w/				
	Med Ball Chest Pass	3		5	Speed
					Rest 2:00
					0:4:0:0
					Decrease Wgt
	GH HANG	120S		1	Relax Mouth
	Pair w/				
	Rollers Quads & Back	120S		1	
	Pair w/				
	LAYING WALL SHAKES	120S		1	Relax Mouth

BLOCK FOUR (6-DAY): High Force at High Velocity
Hyperlinks

Day 1	Exercise Hyperlink	Day 3	Exercise Hyperlink	Day 5	Exercise Hyperlink
Box 1	Power Clean	Box 1	Power Clean	Box 1	Power Clean
Box 2	Power Clean	Box 2	Power Clean	Box 2	Power Clean
Box 3	Bench Press	Box 3	Incline Press	Box 3	Bench Press
Box 4	Bench Press INC OH Sit Up Bench Press	Box 4	Incline Press Bench Throw	Box 4	Bench Press Med Ball Chest Pass
Box 5	DB INCLINE BENCH Lat Pull Down DB Side Lateral Raise	Box 5	Push Press DB Curl	Box 5	
Box 6	DB Tri Ext Bar Curl DB Rear Delt	Box 6	EZ tri Ext 1 Arm Lat Pull Down Gopher U Abs	Box 6	
Box 7	 Bam Bam	Box 7		Box 7	
Box 8	GH HANG Rollers Glutes and Hams Laying Wall Shakes	Box 8	GH HANG Rollers Quads and Back Laying Wall Shakes	Box 8	GH HANG Rollers Quads and Back Laying Wall Shakes

BLOCK FOUR (6-DAY): HIGH FORCE AT HIGH VELOCITY (LOWER BODY)

Tuesday (100%)

%	Exercise	REPS	LOAD	SETS	NOTES
400	FRONT SQUAT	5	180 – 220	1	PNv-2 Neck
	Pair w/				
400	FRONT SQUAT	3	235 – 260	1	PNv-2 Neck
	Pair w/				
400	FRONT SQUAT	1	– 320	1	PNv-2 Neck
400	FRONT SQUAT	3	280 – 300	5	Bands
	Pair w/				Rest 1:30
	Drop Box Jump	4		5	Reactive
	Pair w/				
	Hip FLX BND Pulls	8		3	
200	STEP UP	4	160 – 165	4	Reactive
	Pair w/				
500	GH HYPR Incline	6		4	0:4:0:0
	Pair w/				Reactive
	Speed Adduction	10		3	
500	RDL	5	400 – 415	3	0:0:0:0
	Pair w/				+ Shrug
	ANT TIB BND	10		3	
	90 90 Glute ISO Hold	10S		3	
	Closed Lunge V BND TW	10		2	Rest 1:00
	Pair w/				
	SWB TW Band	10		2	
	GH HANG	120S		1	Relax Mouth
	Pair w/				Twist
	Rollers Glutes & Hams	120S		1	

Thursday (100%)

%	Exercise	REPS	LOAD	SETS	NOTES
500	Back Squat	5	225 – 275	1	
	Pair w/				
500	Back Squat	3	295 – 325	1	
500	Back Squat	1	– 400	1	4%-Tendo
500	Back Squat	C1T	390 – 400	4	Rest 2:30
	Pair w/				Speed
	USSR Plyo BX Pause	4		4	
	Pair w/				Each Leg
	Speed Adduction	6		4	
375	SL Leg Press	5	300 – 310	3	Rest 1:00
	Pair w/				Bands
	Assist Nordic Ham Curl	6		3	
	Pair w/				
	90 90 Glute ISO Hold	10S		3	
	ANT TIB BND	10		3	
	Pair w/				
	PRTNR BND Abs	5		3	
	Pair w/				Each Side
	SWB Down TW	10		3	
	GH HANG	120S		1	Relax Mouth
	Pair w/				
	Rollers Quads & Back	120S		1	
	LAYING V/ALL SHAKES	120S		1	Relax Mouth

Saturday (100%)

%	Exercise	REPS	LOAD	SETS	NOTES
390	DeadLift	5	175 – 215	1	PNv-2 Neck
390	DeadLift	3	230 – 255	1	PNv-2 Neck
390	DeadLift	3	– 310	1	Cook Work
390	DeadLift	3	275 – 295	5	Rest 2:30
270	Close Grip Bench	5	120 – 150	1	4 Board
270	Close Grip Bench	8	175 – 190	5	4 Board
	Nordic HAM Curls	6		3	
	Pair w/				Knee Bend
	Calf Raises	12		3	
30	OH LAT Raise	12	– 25	3	
120	BAR CURL	8	90 – 95	3	
210	JM Press	8	160 – 170	3	
	Pair w/				
	Cuban PRSS INC F8	6		3	0:0:0:10 Box
210	Power Snatch	5	95 – 115	1	
	Pair w/				
210	Power Snatch	3	125 – 135	1	
210	Power Snatch	1	80% – 80%		0:0:0:10
210	Power Snatch	2.2	145 – 160	4	Box
					Relax Mouth

BLOCK FOUR (6-DAY): High Force at High Velocity Hyperlinks

Day 2	Exercise Hyperlink	Day 4	Exercise Hyperlink	Day 6	Exercise Hyperlink
Box 1	FRONT SQUAT	Box 1	Back Squat	Box 1	Deadlift
Box 2	Front squat Drop Box Jumps Hip Flex Band Pulls	Box 2	Back Squat USSR Plyo Box Speed Adduction	Box 2	Deadlift Close Grip Bench
Box 3	STEP UP GH HYPR Incline Speed Adduction	Box 3	SL Leg Press Assist Nordic Ham Curl 90 90 Glute Iso Hold	Box 3	Nordic HAM Curls Calf Raises OH LAT Raise
Box 4	RDL ANT TIB BAND 90 90 Glute Iso Hold	Box 4	ANT TIB BAND PRTNR BND ABS SWB Down TW	Box 4	Bar Curl JM Dumbbell Press Cuban Press INC F8
Box 5		Box 5		Box 5	
Box 6	Closed Lunge V Band Tw SWB Up TW Band	Box 6		Box 6	
Box 7		Box 7		Box 7	Power Snatch
Box 8	GH HANG Rollers Glutes and Hams	Box 8	GH HANG Rollers Quads and Back Laying Wall Shakes	Box 8	Power Snatch

5.12: 55-80 PERCENT TWO-DAY IN-SEASON PROGRAM

Last but not least, the table below shows how to take what you learned about the three-day model and convert it to a two-day in-season program. In table 5.17, day one loading parameters are in white, day two loading parameters are in light gray, and day three loading parameters are in dark gray. Remember, whenever athletes are in-season, all their volume work comes from practice. Additional volume in the weight room or through conditioning will likely lead to an overtrained, underperforming athlete.

TABLE 5.17: 55-80% THREE-DAY VERSUS TWO-DAY IN-SEASON MODEL							
TRAINING WEEK:		DAY 1	DAY 2	DAY 3	DAY 4	DAY 5	DAY 6
THREE-DAY MODEL	FOCUS	TOTAL BODY	OFF	TOTAL BODY	OFF	TOTAL BODY	OFF
	LOAD	62–70%		72–80%		55–62%	
	MEANS APPLIED	BIOMETRIC		DYNAMIC/ BIOMETRIC		VOLUME	
TWO-DAY MODEL	FOCUS	TOTAL BODY	OFF	LOWER BODY	OFF	OFF	OFF
	LOAD	82–87%		90–97%			
	MEANS APPLIED	BIOMETRIC		DYNAMIC/ BIOMETRIC			

Remember, *don't do any additional conditioning in-season outside of organized practice*! Finally, we need to talk about the different exercises, methods, and means that I use in a two-day in-season program that I don't use and didn't show you in the three-day program. Click on the hyperlink below for a complete explanation of the two-day in-season training model.

TWO-DAY IN-SEASON 55-80 PERCENT VIDEO

BLOCK FOUR (2-DAY IN-SEASON): HIGH FORCE AT HIGH VELOCITY

MONDAY — 24-Nov-08

100%		REPS	LOAD	SETS	NOTES
250	Squat Jump	C1T	140 - 150	2	2%-Tendo
	Pair w/				Set Drop off
	Cuban PRSS INC F8	5		2	PW-2 Neck
	Pair w/				
	Ankle Band Work	8		2	Each Side
500	Back Squat	3	300 - 325	3	Reactive
	Hip Flex Iso Prone	4		3	Bands / 0:5:0:0
	Pair w/				Bench
75	1 Arm Lat Pull Supine	8	55 - 60	3	Rest 1:30
300	BENCH PRESS	4	220 - 225	3	Reactive
	GH HYPR Incline	5		3	Reactive
	Pair w/				
30	OH LAT Raise	10	20 - 20	3	+ Shrug
60	DB Tri Ext	6	45 - 50	2	
	Pair w/				
	Bicep shock curls	6		2	
	Pair w/				
	90 90 Groin ISO Hold	15S		2	
	H-Sq Sh Bi Trap	180s		1	
	Pair w/				
	Chest Rev Grip Iso	180s		1	
	Core workout 5				
	Pike SWB Abs	8		2	
	GH HANG	120s		1	
	Pair w/				
	Rollers Glutes & Hams	120s		1	
	Pair w/				
	LAYING RELAXATION	120s		1	

WENDESDAY — 26-Nov-08

100%		REPS	LOAD	SETS	NOTES
	Vertimax DS 2 Band	C1T		2	2%-Tendo
	Pair w/				Set Drop off
	Tea Cup Stuff	5		2	
	Pair w/				
	Calf Raises	8		2	
500	Back Squat	3	390 - 400	3	Reactive
	Iso Ball Grion Sqeeze	4		3	0:5:0:0
	Pair w/				
165	Dynamic Lat Pull	8	125 - 130	3	Rest 1:30
300	BENCH PRESS	3	235 - 240	3	Reactive
	Ball LG Curl	6		3	Reactive
	Pair w/				
38	DB Rear Delt	10	25 - 25	3	
45	DB Tri Pro Sup	10	30 - 35	2	
	Pair w/				
60	DB Curl to Press	6	45 - 50	2	
	Pair w/				
	90 90 Glute ISO Hold	15S		2	
	Glute Ham Back Cav Iso	180s			
	H-Sq Sh Bi Trap	120s		1	
	Core workout 9				
	PRTNR BND Abs	8		2	
	GH HANG	120s		1	Relax Mouth
	Pair w/				
	Rollers Quads & Back	120s		1	
	Pair w/				
	LAYING WALL SHAKES	120s		1	Relax Mouth

BLOCK FOUR (2-DAY): High Force at High Velocity Hyperlinks

Day 1	Exercise Hyperlink	Day 2	Exercise Hyperlink
Box 1	Squat Jump Cuban Press INC F8 Ankle Band Work	Box 1	Tea Cup Stuff Calf Raises
Box 2	Back Squat Hip Flex Iso Prone 1 Arm LAT Pull	Box 2	Back Squat Isometric Ball Groin Squeeze Dynamic Lat Pull
Box 3	BENCH PRESS GH HYPER Incline OH LAT Raise	Box 3	Bench Press Ball Leg Curls Dumbbell Rear Delt
Box 4	DB Tri Ext Bicep Shock Curls 90 90 Groin ISO Hold	Box 4	Supinate Pronate Tricep Extention Dumbbell Curl to Press 90 90 Glute ISO Hold
Box 5	H-sq Shi Bi Trap Chest Rev Grip Iso	Box 5	Isometric Glute Hamstring Back Hold Isometric Hindu Squat Trap Shoulder Bicep Hold
Box 6		Box 6	
Box 7	Pike Swiss Ball Abs	Box 7	Partner Band Abs
Box 8	GH Hang Rollers Glutes and Hams Laying Relaxation	Box 8	Glute Ham Hang Laying Wall Shakes

SECTION 6

HIGH VELOCITY PEAKING
(Below 55 Percent)

6.1: TRANSFER OF TRAINING AND DYNAMIC CORRESPONDENCE

The previous blocks are devised to give an athlete a solid foundation of potential athletic ability, strengthening their muscles and tendons to absorb large amounts of force and teaching their nervous system to fire efficiently, violently, to ensure that the energy is unleashed in a controlled, advantageous manner. But understand that I said it only gives an athlete *potential* ability, not direct athletic ability. For athletic potential to transfer to the field, an athlete must learn to harness his new found power and learn to use it quickly, explosively, with a high rate of acceleration and velocity.

Forces that athletes encounter on the field are ten times what they normally experience in the weight room. This isn't due to excessive loads but rather the high accelerations and decelerations that take place to jump, sprint, cut, and throw. This last block—below 55 percent or high velocity peaking—is designed to maximize the transferability of the athletic abilities (speed, strength, and power) that the athlete has gained through his hard work over the past two mesocycles.

The transfer of training gains isn't by any means an easy thing. It has been the quest of many coaches, athletes, and scientists alike to try and find methods that allow the acquisition of a skill in one exercise to transfer positively to another. For example, performing exercise A results in improvements in exercise B. Furthermore, this isn't a situation where you can just throw a lot of stuff at a wall and see what sticks, trying dozens of exercises and variations to improve performance. The transfer can just as likely be negative as it can be positive. In this instance, performing exercise A would result in decreased performance in exercise B.

According to Dr. Anatoly Bondarchuk, there are actually three types of training transfer—positive, negative, and neutral.[39] In his extensive writings on the subject, which you can read in

---

[39] Bondarchuk A (2007) *Transfer of Training in Sports*. Ultimate Athlete Concepts.

his book *Transfer of Training in Sports*, Dr. Bondarchuk concludes that to maximize the transfer of training gains to performance enhancement, the athlete must do two things:

1) Choose specialized developmental exercises that are closely related to the movement patterns and neural firing rates the athlete will find in competition.

2) Perform these exercises at velocities that are slightly slower (light loads) or slightly faster (assisted loads) than those found in competition.[40]

If a progression of these types of exercises isn't used leading up to competition, Dr. Bondarchuk noted that there was little to no transfer observed.[41] It was also noted that excluding specialized developmental exercises during the last mesocycle block led to a loss in the previously achieved physical abilities of the athletes during competition. Not only is it essential to properly peak your athletes to maximize performance, but if the wrong methods are used (or worse, nothing is used at all), their performance will decrease.

Image 6.1 - Dr. Bondarchuk

Figure 6.1 is a table from Dr. Bondarchuk's book that helps explain his findings. It displays the transferability of multiple exercises to throwing the shot. He performed extensive statistical analysis, calculating the correlation coefficients of dozens of exercises from hundreds of elite Russian national team athletes to their respective sports. Very simply, he tried to figure out what exercises made his athletes better and which exercises transferred the best from weight room to field. The column on the far left lists the exercises performed by the athletes. The top row is an athlete classification system. Instead of classifying them by group (world class, elite, or amateur), the athletes were grouped by their performance level, taking their best throw or time to put them in a group. For example, a lower end thrower who had a personal record (PR) throw of 14.25 meters would be placed in the first column to the right of the exercise column. A world

---

[40] Bondarchuk A (2007) *Transfer of Training in Sports*. Ultimate Athlete Concepts.

[41] Image 6.1: Used with permission from Dr. Anatoly Bondarchuk.

class thrower with a PR throw of 20.1 meters would be placed in the far right column. The other numbers in the table are a statistic known as the correlation coefficient (r). In statistics, r is a measure of the relationship between two variables, X and Y. In this case, it is the relationship between a given parameter (exercise) and the resulting performance measure (throwing distance). All values for r are always between -1.0 and +1.0. Numbers closer to +1.0 have a high correlation and thus high transferability to performance. Numbers close to zero don't have any correlation and would be considered to have no transfer; they are neutral. Negative numbers have a negative correlation and a detrimental (decrease) effect on performance.

Exercise	Sports Result, Coefficient of Correlation						
	14-15m	15-16m	16-17m	17-18m	18-19m	19-20m	20-21m
Throwing a 5kg shot	0.768	0.702	0.724	0.564	0.512	0.456	0.365
Throwing a 6kg shot	0.872	0.765	0.689	0.654	0.607	0.582	0.498
Throwing a 8kg shot	0.654	0.669	0.754	0.788	0.845	0.824	0.754
Throwing a 9kg shot	---	---	0.706	0.806	0.765	0.824	0.724
Throwing a 10kg shot	---	---	0.552	0.605	0.786	0.765	0.714
Throwing a 6kg shot from place	0.882	0.786	0.765	0.806	0.776	0.721	0.687
Throwing a 8kg shot from place	0.712	0.687	0.722	0.742	0.825	0.786	0.670
Barbell snatch	0.410	-0.387	0.406	-0.354	0.276	0.211	0.197
Power clean	-0.366	0.324	-0.287	-0.212	0.226	0.268	0.107
Squat with a barbell	0.521	0.605	0.724	0.807	0.657	0.398	0.165
Bench Press	0.574	0.665	0.642	0.786	0.602	0.605	0.126
Standing long jump	0.398	0.344	-0.324	0.245	0.221	0.156	0.127
Triple jump from place	0.345	0.367	0.325	0.214	0.242	-0.198	0.222
Vertical jump	0.566	0.488	0.376	0.324	0.256	0.224	0.178
Throwing a shot forward	-0.367	0.321	0.298	0.246	-0.200	0.242	0.192
Throwing a shot backward	-0.387	0.345	-0.309	0.288	0.244	-0.187	0.156
Running 30m from blocks	0.426	0.367	0.312	0.242	0.212	-0.178	0.198

Figure 6.1: Table showing the results of Dr. Bondarchuk's experiments on the transferability of exercise parameters and performance, looking specifically at throwing distance in shot putters. Relationships shown by statistical analysis of correlation coefficients (r). Table reproduced from *Transfer of Training* with permission from *Ultimate Athlete Concepts*.

When examining figure 6.1, two things pop out. First, as the exercise becomes more similar (specialized) to the competitive movement, the transferability of that exercise increases. In looking at figure 6.1, you see that the highest transferability (correlation) was seen with athletes throwing different weighted shots, both heavier and lighter than competition weight. The next highest transfer exercise is the bench press, which again is a similar motor and neural firing pattern to throwing a shot.

The second thing to note is the change of transferability from left to right seen in the table. Notice that the correlation coefficient (transfer) for a given exercise isn't the same for every level of athlete. In almost every instance, as the level of athlete improves, the transferability of an exercise decreases. Let's look again at the bench press in figure 6.1. The first four athlete classifications, up to 17–18 meters, see large improvements (transfer) in their throws as a result of increasing their bench press (r increasing from 0.57 to 0.78). However, as you continue to move across the line, getting to the 20–21 meter group, their transfer plummets to only 0.126. Why?

There comes a point when the level of athlete quite literally out grows the transferability of an exercise. There is a tipping point where being stronger will no longer help an athlete perform at a higher level. This is due to the time constraints imposed on the athlete by his event or sport. To be able to lift a heavier weight doesn't do him any good because he doesn't have time to transfer that strength into the implement (shot, field).

Let's look at another example. Figure 6.2 outlines the PR loads and distances of 1984 Olympic hammer throw champion, U. Sedykh (yes, he's Russian). Looking at his power clean, squat, and snatch numbers from 1980 to 1984, you should notice something you might think odd. They never increased! Alright, so his snatch went up five kilograms in four years, but other than that, his strength numbers remained exactly the same. Now look at the distances of his 7.296-kg hammer throw during the same time. They increased from 81.8 meters to 86.34 meters! For Sedykh, increasing his strength wouldn't have been advantageous. There came a point when to continue to improve he had to focus on more specialized developmental exercises that more closely resembled the parameters of his sport.

Exercise	Years						
	1980	1981	1982	1983	1984	1985	1986
Throwing the 7.260kg hammer, m	81.80	80.14	81.66	80.94	86.34	80.50	86.74
Throwing the 5kg hammer, m	97.00	95.00	96.00	95.00	99.00	96.00	100
Throwing the 6kg hammer, m	96.00	90.00	93.00	91.00	95.00	90.00	96.00
Throwing the 8kg hammer, m	77.50	74.00	76.00	75.00	80.00	75.50	80.46
Throwing the 9kg hammer, m	72.00	70.00	72.00	71.50	75.00	71.00	75.50
Throwing the 10kg hammer, m	67.00	64.00	67.50	66.50	69.50	65.50	70.2
Throwing the 16kg weight, m	23.70	---	---	---	23.40	---	23.85
Barbell snatch, kg	115	115	110	115	120	120	120
Power clean, kg	155	155	155	155	155	155	155
Squat with a barbell, kg	230	230	230	230	230	230	230
Throwing the shot forward, m	16.00	15.50	16.00	---	---	---	16.00
Throwing the shot backward, m	18.00	18.00	17.50	18.00	---	---	18.00
Long jump from place, m	3.10	3.10	3.10	3.10	3.10	3.15	3.15
Triple jump from place, m	9.00	9.00	9.00	9.00	---	---	---
Vertical Jump, cm	85	85	80	80	80	85	---

Figure 6.2: Table showing the personal records of Olympic champion U. Sedykh in both throwing implement and major assistance lifts by training year from 1980 until 1986. Table reproduced from *Transfer of Training* with permission from *Ultimate Athlete Concepts*.

Now, I'm not saying that you abandon heavy lifting with your athletes and constantly perform specialized developmental exercises. That won't work. An athlete must be at the highest levels physically and mentally before these methods will produce optimal gains. By 1980, Sedykh had already built an impressive strength base, squatting 230 kg. That's a 506-lb squat. The impressive performance gains made by Sedykh and other elite athletes using high velocity peaking methods were obtained after years of proper periodized training building strength and power. If an athlete isn't already strong and powerful, there isn't anything to transfer to competition. Also, keep in mind that Sedykh and other athletes like him don't stop lifting heavy during this time. They continue to lift loads above 80 percent during their yearly macrocycle. However, when lifting during a strength focused mesocycle (such as the high force at low velocity phase), their focus is simply to maintain the parameter rather than increase it. When only looking to maintain a parameter, less time needs to be allocated in training for its maintenance. Instead of spending six to nine weeks training with loads above 80 percent, these athletes only need to spend three to four weeks to maintain their strength levels. As a result, more training time could be allocated for lightened load, high velocity training. This means there's more time training with the methods and parameters that we know improve sport performance!

What you need to take away from these examples is the importance of peaking your athletes with a method that allows for a high level of transferability, preparing them and their bodies for the rigors specific to their sport. In most instances, training occurs at velocities that are considerably lower than the actual competition. For example, a college level thrower releases the shot put with a velocity around 14 meters per second. Conversely, most dynamic effort bench speeds (assuming 50 percent of a 1RM on the bar) only reach 0.9–1.1 meters per second.

To determine the validity of the transferability of an exercise, researchers have developed a set of criteria. These have come to be known as the *criteria of dynamic correspondence*.[42] Determining the transferability of an exercise isn't by any means a science. However, a good coach will always analyze and evaluate the merits of a peaking program based on this criteria.

CRITERIA FOR DYNAMIC CORRESPONDENCE:

- THE AMPLITUDE AND DIRECTION OF MOVEMENT
- THE ACCENTUATED REGION OF FORCE PRODUCTION
- THE DYNAMICS OF THE EFFORT
- THE RATE AND TIME OF MAXIMUM FORCE PRODUCTION
- THE REGIME OF MUSCULAR WORK

The amplitude and direction of movement is a fancy way to saying range of motion (ROM). To meet this criterion, the exercise must exhibit the same general movement pattern and range of motion that an athlete will perform during competition. When selecting or modifying exercises to be performed, it is important to know the starting position, finishing position, and posture of the athlete as well as understand the direction of application with which force is applied during the movement. For example, the degree of knee flexion for a linebacker is different than an offensive lineman at the snap of the ball. A good strength coach who has programmed a back squat into the

---

[42] Verkhoshansky Y, Siff M (2009) *Supertraining*. Sixth edition. Ultimate Athlete Concepts.

high velocity peaking program before camp will take note of this difference and adjust the ROM with which each player performs the back squat to increase transferability to the field.

The accentuated region of force production looks at the importance of building joint angle specific strength for the athlete. Similar to amplitude and direction, this criterion looks at the specific point within the range of motion where the athlete must generate the most force. This point is generally within ten degrees of the athlete's starting position or the lower end of his ROM.

The dynamics of the effort simply means that the effort exerted and the speed produced by the athlete during training must be at a level equal to or greater than those seen in competition. A high velocity of movement is essential. Every repetition of the exercise must be performed with 100 percent effort with the athlete pushing or pulling through the entire ROM.

The rate and time of maximum force production is another way of terming a concept that you're familiar with from earlier sections of this book—the rate of force development (RFD). The focus on every exercise must always be a high RFD to improve the neuromuscular system, enabling maximal force to be produced in a minimal amount of time.

The *regime of muscular work* is stating that the type of "work" performed by the athlete's physiologic structures in competition should be simulated in training. For example, boxers and shot putters can perform the same exercises in training because the amplitude and direction of the movement and the dynamics of effort are very similar.[43] However, because boxing requires quick, unresisted contractions performed in a repetitive manner with the ability to repeat it many times without a significant decrease in force, its regime of muscular work is unique. It must be different than that of a shot putter, who's sport involves single, explosive muscular contractions against a specific resistance with long durations of rest. To accommodate for these differences, the use of time as a parameter for training has proved to be optimal for peaking an athlete.

---

[43] Verkhoshansky Y, Siff M (2009) *Supertraining*. Ultimate Athlete Concepts.

Transferability and the criteria of dynamic correspondence dictate that as the competitive season nears, velocity of training must increase within a specific ROM to make the nervous system more sport-specific and allow transfer of the previously attained physical adaptations. This mesocycle is designed to do just that. Some of the criteria are very similar and overlap. If an exercise meets one criteria from the list, it likely meets one or two more. I have never found an exercise that perfectly meets all five, so I keep a rule of three. If an exercise doesn't meet at least three of the criteria for dynamic correspondence, I won't program it in my peaking phase. To accomplish the high levels of transferability required for sport performance improvement, a coach must take advantage of an antagonistically facilitated specialized method of training (AFSM).

6.2: AFSM

Before I go any further in explaining the antagonistically facilitated specialized method of training (AFSM) and its application to sport performance, I must take a moment to recognize someone who was paramount in its realization. Kevin Kocos, my assistant at the University of Minnesota, has spent countless hours helping me research, decipher, and apply AFSM methods. His efforts have helped me realize this method and turn it into a system that garners amazing results for peaking athletic performance. This high velocity method could have never been realized without his knowledge, research, and expertise.

AFSM is based on Sherrington's Law of Reciprocal Inhibition, a concept we covered in section four. It states that for every neural activation of a muscle (agonist), there is a corresponding inhibition of the opposing muscle (antagonist). For example, if you want to contract your bicep (agonist), your triceps (antagonist) must relax at the same time. This law and its application to sport was studied at length by Leo Matveyev, one of the Soviet's leading sports scientists and originators of modern periodization training. In his research, he found an underlying theme among the top level athletes within the Soviet Union. Those who achieved Master of Sport (the highest level of sports mastery in the Russian system of classification) had the highest speed of muscle relaxation. The speed of relaxation that they showed was nearly 200 percent faster than novice level athletes! Even those who were classified as level four athletes (right below Master of Sport) still exhibited relaxation times about 50 percent slower than Masters of Sport. Elite athletes not only turn muscles on quickly, but they also relax them quickly.

Because Matveyev's data shows that it is crucial for the nervous system to be able to produce contractions and relaxations at high velocities, we must ask ourselves, "How we can enhance this quality in our athletes?" This is where the system of AFSM comes in. AFSM describes a new method used to perform shock, plyometric, or high velocity strength training movements that are specifically designed to help athletes relax and contract at higher velocities, velocities close to those seen in competition. This point, as seen in the work by Dr. Bondarchuk, is essential to the transfer of gains for the athlete from the weight room to competition.

This method of training is very advanced and requires an athlete to not only be experienced in shock, plyometric, and strength training but also trained to the highest physiologic and neural levels to withstand the stress of this method. Just because the loads are light doesn't mean the intensity has decreased. Quite the opposite. From a neurological standpoint, this phase is just as taxing as either of the previous two phases.

Before I can get into the specifics about how to train AFSM, we need to define what I mean by the terms "plyometric," "shock," and "high velocity strength training." All three of these methods are used to take advantage of three things:

1) The body's powerful stretch shortening cycle via the muscle tendon complex

2) A highly trained and adaptable central nervous system

3) Large levels of explosive force focused through raw power development

If you think back, all three are things that were the focal points and goals of the first training phase (triphasic blocks 1–3) and subsequently improved on and reinforced during the second training phase (50–80 percent, block four). The first two phases can be viewed as the athlete setting himself up well for the peaking phase and competition. Without a solid base of strength, power, and neural coordination, what is there left for an athlete to peak? What solid base does he have to stand on when he enters competition? None. Remember, the SSC is used advantageously in sports when the muscles and tendons, which are arranged in a series, are subjected to a powerful stretch or eccentric contraction, creating a large amount of potential kinetic energy. This stored kinetic energy from the eccentric contraction results in a concentric contraction performed with significantly more force than it could have produced without a "pre-stretch" of the muscle tendon series (as I explained in the triphasic loading method), all of which is amplified by a well trained, efficient nervous system resulting in large levels of power.

Plyometrics is a term that was popularized when the Soviet training system made its way to western countries. Plyometric training will refer to any muscle action that uses a SSC in the muscle to enhance the force output of the concentric contraction. Plyometrics, therefore, could be anything from low intensity jump roping to highly intense back squats that approximate up to 55 percent of the athlete's one repetition maximum (this will be explained more in depth in the high velocity strength training method below).

Shock training was developed in the 1960s by Soviet sports scientists such as Yuri Verkhoshansky. The difference between plyometrics and shock training is that shock training will involve a drop from a depth of twelve inches or greater, thereby causing the forces involved to be significantly higher than plyometric training. Ground contact time during true shock training must be as short as possible, ideally under 0.20 seconds. These intense contractions from shock training occur not only in the weight room but also in cyclic sporting actions such as sprinting where elite level athletes can generate over 800 pounds of force on a single limb while the ground contact time often lasts less than 0.10 seconds.[44] There are those out there who claim that potential energy from the SSC can be held for several seconds. This is a half truth. While *some* of the potential energy can be stored within the muscle tendon complex for a second or two, it is a very small percentage of the whole. Research has shown that the resulting power from absorbed energy through the SSC begins to dissipate after approximately 0.20 seconds.[45] Therefore, to simulate competition like conditions and maximize transfer, the method of application must meet the same parameters. This is ideally carried out by using the shock method.

High velocity strength training is a method that takes the principles of plyometric training with external loads that are less than 55 percent of the athlete's one repetition maximum (1RM) in order to maximize the velocity at which the actions are performed. The laws of physics dictate that power is the product of force and velocity. Therefore, it is crucial that you use methods in strength training that employ light resistance with high velocity. When doing so, the athlete is able to produce a high amount of force at a high velocity. Those who use methods with only heavy loads all year long are able to produce a high amount of force but only at very low

---

[44] Ball N, Stock C, Scurr J (2010) Bilateral contact ground reaction forces and contact times during plyometric drop jumping. *Journal of Strength & Conditioning Research* 24(10):2762–69.

[45] Earp JE, Newton RU, Cormie P, Kraemer W J (2011) The influence of muscle-tendon unit structure on rate of force development, during the squat, countermovement, and depth drop jumps. *Journal of Strength & Conditioning Research* 25(5).

velocities. If repetitive low velocity stresses are applied to the athlete at all points of his training, he will adapt and carry that over into the sport. As a result, the athlete will undoubtedly become slower in his competitive endeavors.

Relaxation is paramount in facilitating subsequent contraction of the agonist muscles. The issue isn't how fast the athlete can contract but rather how fast he can *relax!* If an athlete can grasp and train this mechanism, AFSM will bridge the gap between novice and elite athletes. It will allow for increased intermuscular coordination and decreased time of the relaxation/contraction pathway. In addition (and you may not believe me when I tell you this, but you will once you try it with your athletes), AFSM won't only increase the velocity at which the athlete moves lighter loads, but it will also increase his overall RFD and general strength as well!

Two summers ago, I took six athletes from my hockey team (if you haven't realized already, they are my lab rats) and changed their workout parameters to test my AFSM methods. All of these athletes had been in the Gopher strength program for three years, so their conditioning and strength levels were fairly high. In the first two phases of the summer, they performed the same triphasic and 55–80 percent lifting as the rest of the team, just as my teams do every year. For the last six weeks of the off-season, I changed their workout parameters to only use loads equal to 25–55 percent of their 1-RM and had them perform my AFSM methods. When I tested the entire team at the end of the summer, I was shocked. Not only had the AFSM methods made these six athletes more explosive, but they had made them stronger as well! I will use one athlete as an example. At the end of his base phase, he could bench 285 pounds, but it was a strained and slow effort. It looked as if he was competing in a powerlifting meet and going for his last attempt trying to squeeze it out. At the end of the AFSM training, he retested with a bench of 325 pounds that flew off his chest! He literally pulled the bar down to his chest, hit the isometric like a rock hitting concrete, and exploded through the bar like he was throwing a chest pass in a basketball game. It was one of the most impressive things I have ever seen in terms of nervous system adaptation.

6.3: LOADING PARAMETERS

In order to simulate the velocities seen in competition, the loads used during this mesocycle are light—25–55 percent of an athlete's 1RM. When using lighter loads such as these, the emphasis must be placed entirely on getting the athlete to relax and contract the antagonist/agonist complex trained in the movement. Because the loading of the movement is light, the high power stimulus must come from the athlete maintaining a very high average velocity throughout the entire movement, rapidly accelerating and decelerating the bar during both the eccentric and concentric phases. The athlete must constantly push the bar during the concentric phase and rapidly (and intentionally) pull the bar down during the eccentric phase of each repetition. As a result, the loading parameters for this phase are unique from the others. They differ in three ways:

1) Sets are based on time as opposed to performing a prescribed number of reps

2) Loads and times used are static—they don't change for the duration of the phase

3) Progression is derived from increasing work rate within the set rather than altering other parameters

Many coaches have a hard time believing the use of such light loads can yield such dramatic improvements in athletic performance. However, everything I saw in the training of my athletes told me I had to go lighter and faster to reach a level of transferability that would allow for the continued improvement of the athlete through the peaking phase. The results from the first summer that I implemented this method—the four weeks leading up to the season—was proof in the pudding. My hockey players didn't train with a weight on their backs or in their arms that was greater than 55 percent of what they had done the previous spring. The results? Every athlete maintained his strength levels while decreasing his pro-shuttle and 20-yard dash time and increasing his vertical jump height. Light loads improved sport performance. Table 6.1, below, shows the loading scheme (sets/reps/percentages) for my high velocity peaking mesocycle.

TABLE 6.1: BELOW 55% LOADING VARIABLES

PARAMETER	APPLIED FOR SPORT SPECIFIC PEAKING	MONDAY LOADING (IDEAL TIME)		WEDNESDAY LOADING (BELOW IDEAL TIME)		FRIDAY LOADING (ABOVE IDEAL TIME)	
		SET DURATION (SECONDS)	LOAD	SET DURATION (SECONDS)	LOAD	SET DURATION (SECONDS)	LOAD
STRENGTH SPEED	• SHOT PUT • FOOTBALL: LINEMAN • VOLLEYBALL	5	35-40%	3	45-55%	7	25-30%
SPEED STRENGTH	• FOOTBALL: SKILL PLAYERS • BASEBALL • SOFTBALL • 100M SPRINTER	7		5		10	
STRENGTH ENDURANCE	• HOCKEY • BASKETBALL	15		10		17	
ENDURANCE STRENGTH	• SOCCER • MEN'S/WOMEN'S LACROSS • SWIMMING: 50-200M	25		17		32	
ENDURANCE (MODERATE)	• SWIMMING: 200M+ • 400M RUNNER	32		25		40	
ENDURANCE (LONG)	• 800M+ RUNNER • DISTANCE SWIMMER • ROWING	40		32		47	

Sets are no longer defined by a number of prescribed reps. Instead, the athlete performs as many reps as possible in a specified time frame that is either at, above, or below his ideal time for his respective sport (you will notice this in table 6.1 under each daily loading scheme). The underlying goal of this phase is to try and get the athlete to perform work at velocities and forces close to those seen in competition. Again, sport is all about who can do more work in less time. To motivate the athlete to perform as much work as possible, give him a time limit. One of the biggest advantages I have found using AFSM methods with timed parameters is its ability to be energy system specific for the athlete. For example, sports such as football consist of short, intense work bouts followed by moderate rest periods. In looking at table 6.1, you can see that a speed/strength athlete such as a football player would perform sets lasting seven, five, and ten seconds, respectively, on each of the three training days. This not only increases the rate of force development for the athlete by promoting reciprocal inhibition of the agonist/antagonist complex, but it also increases sport-specific work capacity.

If you choose, you can make this more specific by breaking down a sport by position. For example, the above speed/strength parameters (seven, five, and ten seconds) may work better for a skills position player such as a wide receiver or safety. Other players, such as offensive or defensive linemen who typically don't cover as much ground on a play, may be better suited to perform their sets with the strength/speed parameters (five, three, seven seconds). Again, the main goal here is athletic task specificity and transferability. The closer you as a coach can mold the parameters to an athlete's competition, the better the gains and transfer will be.

In addition to time being used instead of reps, the loading parameters change as well. Instead of progressing the loads and sets each week, they will be held constant for the duration of the phase. If the athlete starts the phase on Monday with 40 percent of his 1RM on the bar for three sets of five seconds, he will keep that 40 percent on the bar every Monday and perform three sets for five seconds for the duration of the phase. This is done for two reasons. First, with the use of such light loads, progressing 2.5–5 percent over a three- to five-week period is useless in the sense of promoting adaptation by increased loading. The loads are just too light to accomplish this. Second, by keeping both the load and time constant, you are establishing a marker that shows progression. If the athlete gets seven repetitions in five seconds in the first week but gets nine repetitions in five seconds in the second week, it is clear that the athlete has progressed. During this phase, progression is derived from increasing work rate within the set rather than altering other parameters.

6.4: BELOW 55 PERCENT TRAINING BLOCK

Now that you understand the loading scheme and undulation used within the high velocity peaking phase, let's take a closer look at the actual block that makes up this mesocycle. The chart below shows the loading variables used on each day of the three-day training week. Here lies the last *big* difference between this phase and previous ones. The only training model that I use for this phase is the three-day. I don't use a four-day, five-day, or six-day peaking model when the mesocycle is immediately before the competitive season. (However, there is a two-day in-season model for maintaining these qualities during the season.) In my experience, as athletes approach the competitive season, additional stress from more frequent practice sessions, sport-specific conditioning, the start of a new school year or semester, and/or other variables increases to such a degree that I can only reasonably get three good, hard training days out of the athletes. This allows for two things:

1) It ensures that the athlete isn't overtrained in any capacity going into a competitive season.

2) It ensures that the athlete is fresh and recovered for practice, which allows him to practice at the same speeds and intensities that he'll produce in a game (task specificity and transferability).

That isn't to say that other training day model lengths don't work; they do. They just don't work when you're approaching the season. In the middle of the training year when I'm going through my normal mesocycle progression, I implement a four-day and five-day high velocity training model effectively.

Just as before, the length of the block can be shortened or extended to fit different peaking schedules. Typically, my athletes perform this block for three weeks; this has shown to be optimal. There are times, however, where the block can be extended to as long as five weeks if needed. Thinking back on what you learned about residual training effects, the strength and power gains from the previous two phases can be maintained for 25–35 days or longer, if the athlete returns to the methods that specifically trained those parameters for brief periods within subsequent phases.

TABLE 6.2: BLOCK 5 LOADING VARIABLES (BELOW 55 PERCENT)

BLOCK	DAY	LOAD	REPS	SETS
BLOCK 5 3–5 WEEKS	MONDAY (MEDIUM INTENSITY)	35–40%	PARAMETER BASED ON TIME	3–5
	WEDNESDAY (HIGH INTENSITY)	45–55%		3–5
	FRIDAY (HIGH VOLUME)	25–30%		3–5

Unlike previous phases where we used a progressive loading scheme to constantly spur gains week after week, training with timed sets self-regulates work load by changing the repetitions completed during the time period rather than varying the load on the bar. For example, here an athlete will keep 40 percent of his 1RM on the bar for three straight weeks. However, the number of repetitions he completes for a workout will increase, thus increasing the overall stress placed on the athlete.

TABLE 6.3: PROGRESSIVE LOADING SCHEME FOR BELOW 55 PERCENT

LOADING PARAMETER	TIME PARAMETER	EXERCISE	WEEK	REPS COMPLETED (BEST SET)
35% 1RM	7 SECONDS	BENCH PRESS	1	10
			2	12
			3	13
			4	15

Table 6.3 shows how even though the load and time of the exercise remain constant for the entire four-week training block, the number of repetitions the athlete can complete within those parameters increases from ten to fifteen. The result is that the athlete can complete more work at a very high velocity, raising the stress level, in less time. Does that sound familiar? It's the same thing that defines sport, isn't it? The athletes who can do more work in less time win.

6.5: SPECIALIZED METHODS OF APPLYING TRAINING MEANS

TIMED METHOD OF TRAINING

I had two main questions when implementing time methods into my system—"will the athlete train harder with time?" and "would he accept it as a training method/modality?" Before I switched over to my time system, I ran a brief experiment with my athletes. For several weeks, I secretly timed how long it took them to complete the prescribed number of repetitions for each exercise during their workout. The team was in the middle of their high force at high velocity mesocycle, so many of the exercises were prescribed for eight repetitions. As a general rule, I found that most of the athletes took twelve seconds to complete the eight repetitions.

For the second phase of the experiment, I changed the parameters on their workout sheet to read twelve seconds per set instead of eight repetitions. If you want to see some dumbfounded looks, just give your athletes a workout sheet using time instead of repetitions. The looks are priceless. My athletes are used to me having them do as they call it "weird" stuff, so they went along with it. They were glad they did because it turned out that when using time as the parameter with the instruction of "get as many reps as possible," the athletes completed four additional repetitions on average than before. Instead of doing eight reps in twelve seconds, they were doing twelve reps in twelve seconds! I continued to experiment with timed parameters with other teams and found the same thing to be true across the board. The athletes typically increased their work rate or density of training by 50 percent if the set was completed with time as a parameter as opposed to repetitions. More work in less time—where have I heard that before? Oh yeah, it's the basic principle of sports performance! By training with time, I came to the realization that the athlete will become much more aggressive and train much more intensely over the same period of time by periodizing the duration of the set with seconds instead of repetitions.

This is essential when using lightened loads such as those under 55 percent of an athlete's 1RM. Using a simple set/rep scheme with such light loads is inefficient at stimulating positive adaptation. The loads are so light that an athlete can inadvertently coast through a set if he isn't focused on pushing/pulling every rep as fast as possible. He isn't maximally stressing himself. When using such light loads, maximal stress is elicited by maximal velocity of movement, which in turn creates very high levels of force. Decades of research and training have shown that intensity of exercise is the key to pushing an athlete to the next level. Within that intensity comes volume and work capacity, both key factors for performing at a high level. Switching the sets to be based on a time parameter instead of a repetition based parameter will motivate the aggressive athlete to push himself to train more intensely with the preferred duration. Many times, you'll see a 50 percent increase in volume over the same time that would've been trained using the rep scheme. And you won't just see raw volume but sport-specific volume—high velocity, powerful work.

Time is an excellent way to peak an athlete and measure performance. To do this, I turn each set into a mini competition where the athlete must beat the number of reps that he achieved on a previous set. The athlete's training sheet has a list of exercises with the number and duration of the sets to be completed. On the back side is a replica table with all the exercises listed (figure 6.3). That box is where the athlete will record the highest number of repetitions that he achieved during any of the sets for that given exercise during the workout—his personal best for the day. The next time the athlete comes into train, he tries to beat his previous record.

Every time the athlete trains during the peaking block, he will know what his best repetition was with the particular weight advised and the load, regardless of whether the block was two weeks or four weeks. The athletes often try to push themselves to higher and higher levels by raising the repetitions performed based on the time duration of the set. The downside is that as a strength coach, you may have to purchase digital clocks or handheld stopwatches for the weight room. I have four digital clocks hanging in my weight room of about 4000 square feet. Often, the athletes will need to train with a partner. I believe this is a necessity so that they have someone to watch the clock whether that person is an athlete or a coach. Regardless, someone must always be watching the athlete.

495	Hex Deadlift	T	100 - 125	2	0.0.0.6.10		Hex Deadlift							
	PW/ 15 Rest BB				ISO									
	Cuban PRSS INC F8	5		2			Cuban PRSS INC F8							
	PW/ 15 Rest BB													
	Ankle Band Work	8		2	Each Side		Ankle Band Work							
	Squat Drop Jump	T		2	0.0.0.7.10		Squat Drop Jump							
	PW/ 15 Rest BB				Set Drop off									
	4 way neck	6		2			4 way neck							
					Reactive									
495	Hex Deadlift	T	345 - 370	2	0.0.0.7.10		Hex Deadlift							
215	SL Hex Deadlift	T	65 - 75	3	0.0.0.7.10		SL Hex Deadlift							
	PW/ 30 Rest BB				oc-D									
	Hip Flex Prone oc	T		3	0.0.0.7.10		Hip Flex Prone oc							
	PW/ 30 Rest BB				OC-D									
114	DB BO Row	T	85 - 90	3	0.0.0.7.10		DB BO Row							
325	BENCH PRESS	5,3	165 - 220	1,1			BENCH PRESS							
	PW/ 30 Rest BB													
	Med Ball Pass	5		2			Med Ball Pass							
	PW/ 30 Rest BB				OC-D		BENCH PRESS							
325	BENCH PRESS	T	165 - 180	2	0.0.0.7.10									
325	BENCH PRESS	T	100 - 115	3	0.0.0.7.10		BENCH PRESS							
	PW/ 30 Rest BB				oc-D									
	GH HYPR Incline	5		3	0.0.0.7.10		GH HYPR Incline							
	PW/ 30 Rest BB				OC-A		DB Shoulder Press							
81	DB Shoulder Press	T	25 - 30	3	7 - OC-D									
	Band Tricep Extension	T		2	0.0.0.7.10		Band Tricep Extension							
	PW/ 30 Rest BB				oc-D		Bicep shock curls							
	Bicep shock curls	T		2	0.0.0.7.10									
	PW/ 30 Rest BB						90 90 Grion ISO Hold							
	90 90 Grion ISO Hold	T		2	0.0.0.7.10									

(Matson, Taylor)

Figure 6.3: Example exercise sheet that shows the front and back of a AFSM high velocity peaking workout.

AFSM HIGH VELOCITY STRENGTH METHOD

This method is the most prevalently used throughout the peaking phase. It is a fancy way of saying, "Move the bar as fast as possible all the time." The best coaching cue to give an athlete is to push the bar during the concentric phase of the movement and pull it as hard as possible during the eccentric. This should look violent. The athlete should, if done correctly, throw himself off with the concentric and slam himself back down with the eccentric (see example exercise in table 6.4).

When using high velocity strength training, the athlete uses loads ranging from 25–55 percent of his 1RM. As an example, when teaching the back squat, the coach will instruct the athlete to pull himself down for the eccentric part of the lift using the glutes and hamstrings as rapidly as possible. Because of the force velocity curve, the athlete will put out a greater amount of force with increased speed during the eccentric portion of the lift. While this goes against the conventional advice of a "slow and controlled descent," it is much more specific to the ballistic actions that occurs in sports. Once the athlete reaches the depth that was set by the coach, he must work to abruptly stop the load and reverse it in the opposite direction as explosively as possible. By being able to withstand the load of the barbell and lift it up with an average velocity near or exceeding one meter per second[2] (this can be quantified using a Tendo unit if one is available to the coach), he is truly maximizing the SSC in his strength training. When looking at the workout sheets, assume that every exercise is to be performed with this method unless otherwise noted.

TABLE 6.4: AFSM HIGH VELOCITY STRENGTH TRAINING EXAMPLES		
EXERCISE	CONVENTIONAL METHOD	AFSM METHOD
BACK SQUAT	HYPERLINK	HYPERLINK
BENCH PRESS	HYPERLINK	HYPERLINK

AFSM OSCILLATORY METHOD

Another method that can be employed with high velocity strength training is the use of oscillatory contractions. We talked about these briefly in section four. The main difference here is that they are now performed with the addition of a time parameter. Oscillatory contractions work to enhance the intermuscular coordination of opposing muscle groups. Intermuscular coordination is the efficiency in which different groups of muscle can contract and relax in order to perform a given motor task. This becomes possible because of the principle of reciprocal inhibition where the SSC will excite one group of muscles while relaxing another group of muscles. Being able to efficiently make use of reciprocal inhibition is another method that will then facilitate the high velocity relaxations that are fundamental to Matveyev's research findings.

Oscillatory contractions are performed with light loads in the 20–55 percent 1RM range in order to maintain the high velocity component. The contractions are performed at one of two points in the athlete's range of motion—an advantageous joint angle (specific point in the athlete's range of motion where he is strongest) or a disadvantageous joint angle (specific point in the athlete's range of motion where he is the weakest). When the joint angle is identified, the athlete will bring the weight to that specific joint angle, lift it explosively over a very small range (about 3–4 inches), and then pull the load very explosively in the opposite direction. These contractions are repeated as rapidly as possible for the amount of reps prescribed by the coach.

As an example, when performing a single leg oscillatory squat (table 6.5), the athlete would be using a load of 30 percent of his single leg squat 1RM. The athlete would position the bar on his back with one foot elevated behind him. When performing the single leg oscillatory squat at a disadvantageous point, he would squat so that his femur on the front leg is parallel with the ground. In this position, the athlete would raise and lower the hips as rapidly as possible over the small range of motion (about 4–6 inches) for the duration of the set. The coach will instruct the athlete to "pull himself down with his glutes and hamstrings and drive up through his heel" as fast as he possibly can.

While performing the single leg oscillatory squat in the advantageous position (table 6.5), the athlete would position himself so that his femur sits above parallel at about a 45- to 60-degree angle. The oscillatory contractions would then be performed at the advantageous joint angle where the athlete is strongest. These extremely rapid contractions and relaxations throughout opposing muscle groups help to better enhance intermuscular coordination as well as high velocity relaxation that Masters of Sport have shown.

TABLE 6.5: AFSM OSCILLATORY TRAINING EXAMPLES			
EXERCISE	CONVENTIONAL METHOD	AFSM METHOD	
SINGLE LEG BACK SQUAT	HYPERLINK	ADVANTAGEOUS	HYPERLINK
		DISADVENTAGEOUS	HYPERLINK
BENCH PRESS	HYPERLINK	ADVANTAGEOUS	HYPERLINK
		DISADVENTAGEOUS	HYPERLINK

AFSM Plyometric Method

Performing AFSM plyometric training differs from conventional jump training because in AFSM the powerful eccentric action placed on the muscle tendon series is initiated by a strong contraction of the antagonist muscles. For this to happen, there must be a simultaneous relaxation of the agonist muscle group while the drop is occurring. When performing a squat drop jump in AFSM plyometric training, the athlete would begin standing in an upright position on the ground. The athlete would then forcefully pull his hips down with the glutes and hamstrings, causing them to go into a free fall by lifting the knees and feet in the air. For this to happen, there must be a relaxation of the anterior knee extensors (the agonists of the jump) while the descent is facilitated by the antagonists (glutes and hamstrings) pulling the athlete down. This will bring the athlete into a power position (a knee joint angle of approximately 45–60 degrees, which is more advantageous for force production) while falling through the air. As soon as the athlete strikes the ground, there must be an all out effort to reverse the action as fast and explosively as possible. This will help the athlete achieve maximum height in the vertical portion of his jump.

When performing a squat drop jump, the coach must cue the athlete to pull himself down as forcefully as possible with the hamstrings and glutes, the antagonistic muscles of the jump. The next aspect, which is crucial for the coach to communicate, is that once the athlete strikes the ground, he must drive off it the very instant he hits the floor. I've found that the best cue is to tell the athlete to attack the ground. When properly performed, the agonistic muscles are turned on, causing a forced/facilitated relaxation of the antagonistic muscles (glutes and hamstrings) that were just used to pull the athlete into position.

By comparison, when performing a traditional counter movement jump, an athlete would normally squat down in a fast manner in order to create a SSC from the leg extensors that would aid his ascent into the air. However, this limits the force output because the ground contact lasts too long and doesn't allow for a forceful pre-stretch in the muscle tendon complex. When performed correctly, AFSM can create a higher amount of eccentric force, which in turn can be released in a more forceful concentric action of the jump.

The most crucial aspect of coaching any type of AFSM training is that you are able to tell if the athlete is withstanding the impact of the drop while maintaining joint stiffness (ability to keep the same joint angle when experiencing impact during shock training) and minimizing ground contact time. If the athlete isn't able to maintain joint stiffness, the coach must go back and address the athlete's lack of eccentric and/or isometric strength.

TABLE 6.6: AFSM PLYOMETRIC TRAINING EXAMPLES

EXERCISE	CONVENTIONAL METHOD	AFSM METHOD
SQUAT DROP JUMP	HYPERLINK	HYPERLINK
HURDLE HOP	HYPERLINK	HYPERLINK

AFSM SHOCK METHOD

The methods of AFSM shock training are very similar to those outlined in AFSM plyometric training. However, as indicated earlier, the AFSM shock training methods are significantly more forceful due to the height of the drop and the brief ground contact time. When performing the drop box jump in AFSM shock training, the athlete will begin on a box at a height of at least twelve inches while standing upright. The athlete will then fall off the front of the box, not step off the box. During the athlete's descent, he will pull himself into a power position. Joint stiffness must be maintained with the power position that is achieved while falling through the air. The very instant that the athlete strikes the ground, he must work to reverse the action and jump on to the next box.

It's essential in the shock training that the coach cues the athlete in a similar way to the AFSM plyometric training, telling the athlete to pull himself down while he's falling through the air and to drive off the ground as explosively as possible as soon as he hits. Because the height that the athlete is falling from is greater than that of the AFSM plyometric training, the laws of physics dictate that AFSM shock training will be significantly more forceful than AFSM plyometrics.

The one exception within my below 55 percent high velocity peaking method is that time isn't used as a parameter. Instead, this method is performed using conventional set/rep parameters. Due to the increased time it takes to perform a single repetition of this method (the drop time from the box and the additional time to step down from the box the athlete jumped on to and back on to the box the athlete jumped from), it is impossible to complete quickly while keeping quality height. This method, therefore, is performed typically as 2–8 sets of 2–5 reps.

TABLE 6.7: AFSM SHOCK TRAINING EXAMPLE		
EXERCISE	CONVENTIONAL METHOD	AFSM METHOD
DEPTH JUMP	HYPERLINK	HYPERLINK

6.6: HOW TO READ THE WORKOUT SHEET: PART II

Before we get into the actual below 55 percent high velocity peaking programs, there is one additional piece of information I need to give you so that you can read the workout sheets. Earlier in the book, I explained the four-number system that I placed in the workout programs to convey to the athlete the tempo with which he is to perform an exercise. Each of the four numbers associated with an exercise indicate how long in seconds the specific "phase" (**eccentric**, **isometric**, **concentric**, and **pause time between reps**) should be performed. For example, a squat may have the following tempo—**3:1:0:0**. The first number (**3**) represents the eccentric phase of the movement. The second number (**1**) represents the isometric phase. The third number (**0**) represents the concentric phase. Finally, the last number (**0**) represents the amount of rest between reps. Here it is zero seconds. That should all sound familiar.

For this phase, there are two additional numbers added to the end of the first four. For example, the number sequence will now appear as **0:0:0:0:7:10**. The first four numbers are exactly the same as before, representing the eccentric, isometric, concentric, and pause times, respectively. The fifth number (**7**) represents the time parameter of the set. It tells the athlete how many seconds he is to perform the high velocity reps in with whatever method is prescribed. The final number (**10**)

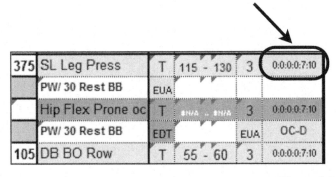

- Figure 6.4

communicates the amount of time the athlete should rest between limbs on a unilateral exercise. For example, in figure 6.4, the athlete would perform repetitions of a single-leg leg press reactively (the first four numbers are all zeros) for seven seconds with one leg, rest for ten seconds, and then perform reps for seven seconds with the other leg. This would be repeated for three sets. If there is ever a number in the sixth slot for a bilateral exercise (both limbs work at the same time), simply ignore it and perform the exercise as prescribed by the other parameters.

6.7: MONDAY, MEDIUM INTENSITY
(SPORT-SPECIFIC TIME: IDEAL)

LOADING

Below is a section from the loading table showing exclusively the loading variables applied on Monday. Remember, the loads and times don't change during the block. The emphasis is placed on the athlete performing more repetitions (high quality work) within the same parameters.

TABLE 6.8: MONDAY LOADING (IDEAL TIME)			
PARAMETER	APPLIED FOR SPORT-SPECIFIC PEAKING	SET DURATION (SECONDS)	LOAD
STRENGTH SPEED	• SHOT PUT • FOOTBALL LINEMEN • VOLLEYBALL	5	35–40%
SPEED STRENGTH	• FOOTBALL SKILL PLAYERS • BASEBALL • SOFTBALL • 100-M SPRINTER	7	
STRENGTH ENDURANCE	• HOCKEY • BASKETBALL	15	
ENDURANCE STRENGTH	• SOCCER • MEN'S/WOMEN'S LACROSSE • SWIMMING 50–200 M	25	
ENDURANCE (MODERATE)	• SWIMMING 200 M+ • 400-M RUNNER	32	
ENDURANCE (LONG)	• OVER 800-M RUNNER • DISTANCE SWIMMER • ROWING	40	

WORKOUTS

On the next page you will find Monday's workout for the three-day below 55 percent high velocity peaking block. The column on the left is the actual workout, using our "imaginary" athlete to calculate the loads used on each exercise. The column on the right labeled "Coaching Points" gives further explanation about exercise sequencing and important coaching queues to use with your athletes. The coaching points are labeled with the respective workout box that they apply to. At the end of this section, you will find additional three-day programs specifically designed to peak football, baseball, basketball, and swimming athletes.

BLOCK FIVE, MONDAY

100%	MONDAY	REPS	LOAD	SETS	NOTES
575	Hex Deadlift	T		2	0:0:0:0:5:10
	PW/ 15 Rest BB	EU		EU	ISO
	Cpress Ext Rot rev Band OC	T	$N/A .. $N/A	2	0:0:0:0:7:10
	PW/ 15 Rest BB	EDT			Each side
	Ankle Band Work	T		2	0:0:0:0:7:10
	Squat Drop Jump	C1T	$N/A .. $N/A	2	2% - Tendo
	PW/ 15 Rest BB	EU		EU	Set Drop off
	4 way neck	6	$N/A .. $N/A	2	
				EUA	Reactive
375	SL Leg Press	T	150 - 170	2	0:0:0:0:7:10
375	SL Leg Press	T	115 - 130	3	0:0:0:0:7:10
	PW/ 30 Rest BB	EUA			
	Hip Flex Prone OC CL	T	$N/A .. $N/A	3	0:0:0:0:7:10
	PW/ 30 Rest BB	EDT		EUA	OC-D
105	DB BO Row	T	55 - 60	3	0:0:0:0:7:10
	Cpress Int Rot Band OC	T	$N/A .. $N/A	2	0:0:0:0:7:10
	PW/ 30 Rest BB	EU			
	Med Ball Pass	5	$N/A .. $N/A	2	ONE ARM
	PW/ 30 Rest BB			ED	OC-D
105	DB BENCH	T	40 - 45	2	0:0:0:0:7:10
105	DB BENCH	T	40 - 45	2	0:0:0:0:7:10
	PW/ 30 Rest BB			ED	oc-D
	GH HYPR Incline	T	$N/A .. $N/A	3	0:0:0:0:7:10
	PW/ 30 Rest BB	EUA		ED	OC-A
38	DB Side Lat Raise	T	15 - 15	3	7 - OC-D
	Band Tricep Extension	T	$N/A .. $N/A	2	0:0:0:0:7:10
	PW/ 30 Rest BB	EDT		EU	oc-D
	Bicep shock curls	T		2	0:0:0:0:7:10
	PW/ 30 Rest BB	EDT			
	OC Ball Grion Sqeeze	T		2	0:0:0:0:7:10
	GH HANG	120S		1	
	Pair w/				
	Rollers Glutes & Hams	120S	$N/A .. $N/A	1	
	Pair w/				
	LAYING RELAXATION	120S		1	

COACHING POINTS AND EXERCISE TUTORIAL

BOX 1
-This hex deadlift is a 5 second isometric in the advantageous position, pulling against the fixed rack with slightly bent knees
-The maximal isometric simulates a hormonal and nervous system response crucial for the rest of the workout
-This cuban press variant stimulates the rotator cuff at higher velocities for more experienced athletes
-For the ankle band work, each side is done for 7 seconds
Hex Deadlift; Cpress Ext Rot Rev Band Oc; Ankle Band Work

BOX 2
-For the squat drop jump, pull into an athletic jumping position forcefully; reverse direction immediately upon impact
-If using a Tendo, a 2% dropoff point is used such that after an athlete drops below 98% of his/her maximal jump, the set is finished
-On the SL leg press, pull the leg down violently (so fast it separates from the machine); the athlete catches the leg press and throws it up reactively
Squat Drop Jump; 4 way neck; SL Leg Press

BOX 3
-The prone hip flex OC CL is a high speed hip flexor movement using contralateral limbs to mimic sports specific hip involvement
-For the dumbbell bent over row, cue the athlete to push and pull the dumbbell with the elbow near the ribs
SL Leg Press; Hip Flex OC Prone CL; DB BO Row

BOX 4
-Perform the DB bench in the disadvantageous position (near the chest); Push and pull the dumbbells as fast as possible (Note: some athletes push so violently they come off of the bench)
Cpress Int Rot Band OC; Med Ball Chest Pass; DB Bench

BOX 5
-The GH hyper incline is done in the advantageous position in the peaking cycle; the torso and knee should form a straight line
-The DB side lat raise educates the deltoids to fire and re-fire
DB Bench; GH HYPR Incline; DB Side Lat Raise

BOX 6
-The band tricep extension utilizes the AFSM principles
Band Tricep Extension; Bicep Shock Curls; OC Ball Groin Squeeze

BOX 8
GH HANG; Rollers Glutes and Hams; Laying Relaxation

√ COACH'S CORNER

TRANSFERRING FORCE AND IMPROVING PERFORMANCE THROUGH THE FOOT AND ANKLE COMPLEX
By: Cal Dietz & Ben Peterson
Edited By: Daniel Raimondi

Over many years of coaching I have witnessed athletes who have made tremendous gains in knee and hip flexion and explosiveness in their training, yet this training time and advancement never seem to transfer into training results for testing. Then one day about 8 years ago I was able to spot the main reason why all this newly developed athletic potential and speed did not transfer over into testing. The question arose with several athletes I made much stronger in the knee and hip joint, along with explosion from those various joints. However, in testing the athletes' 10 and 20-yard dash we didn't see the results that we anticipated based on their gains everywhere else in the weight room and/or vertical jump. When we tested one particular athlete we saw no advancements in the 10 and 20 yd dash, which was a huge concern and misunderstanding on my part. I realized at this point that I must dig into this to its fullest extent.

As I reviewed the tape of the athlete running the starts in the 10 and 20 I was able to spot something that was of key importance. The original reason I was video tapping was to rectify some technical flaws that could improve the 10 and 20 times, but since this athletes was a hockey player, just by practicing the skill he got much better. Anyone that has ever trained a hockey athlete for running realizes how poor the technique often is when they start coming right out of the season. What I saw on this day was that as the athlete's foot struck the ground on the second step I saw that the heel lost 2-3 inches from the point when the toes hit the ground. When I say "lost" I mean there was a reversal of direction of the center of mass in the body and the heel thus, became closer to the ground. This indicated a loss of power being, incapable of helping the athlete run faster.

I then reversed the tape and looked at the first step and the same thing was happening with the athletes out of the initial start. I realized what had taken place: I made the hip and knee joint much more powerful and stronger, but the ankle joint (being a hockey player) couldn't absorb the force from the knee and hip. It was as if all the athletes had been running their times on sand. Since I made the hip and knee stronger the ankle, the weak link in the chain, was unable to absorb the force that dampened the stiffness qualities and those particular testing results By addressing the ankle complex weaknesses that existed to absorb the force and power we were able to within one week make the ankle complex strong enough to withstand the foot striking the ground.

This can often be seen in a number of populations. The aforementioned example of hockey players is obvious because they spend most of the season in the boot. Basketball players are often suspect because their ankles become weakened in the season due to the excessive taping and braces that they wear. I've seen throwers(shotput and/or discus) have this coming across the ring as they change directions. This technique flaw often happens when they start to spin and transfer across the rear of the ring to the front of the ring. You will see their ankle give and at that point many gains can be made in speed and quickness in the ankle and foot.

One must have a full understanding of the foot/ankle complex and its functions many athletes demonstrate dysfunctional patterns in the said area. Hopefully you have a good medical staff that can manipulate the foot (Or are willing to learn if they can't) to better transfer this force into the ground such that performance improves. Fortunately, I have been able to learn a number of techniques to help manipulate the foot so that it functions better. Without functioning correctly you will never get the entire benefits of the training program.

Let's first look at the basic functions of the ankle foot as it's used in sport. As the foot strikes the ground, whether during acceleration or at top speed, near the small toes as it tries to find the ground. What then occurs is a transfer of forces from the small toes over to the big toe at push off. The transference is utilizing the size and strength of the big toe in running; this action must be used in all movements in training. So keep in mind that in every possible action you must use a few key coaching points/actions with your athletes:

1. Focus on pushing through the big toe

You will see a huge improvement in their jumping ability if you add this one component to your jumping/plyometric programs. Also, in any weight lifting movement that applies extension of all three joints (at a slow or high speed) this also must be implemented to transfer weight room performance to the field. So, in your cleans, cue the athletes to push through the big toe at the top of the pull. This is not recommended for Olympic weight lifters; however, for sports performance it would be highly recommended. The walking lunge is another example of how this should be implemented. As an athlete would push and finish off the movement at the top, all the forces must be transferred off the foot to the big toe to strengthen it and emphasize its mobility and strength at the range of motion.

2. Calf raises for sport training should be done explosively with a knee bend.

That knee bend must be timed with the extension of the foot at the top when completing the exercise. The feet sometimes misfire on the timing at the beginning of sporting movements, but remember it is an absolute necessity to transfer all the actions on the joint to the sporting field. Bodybuilders would not want to implement this. Athletes should execute this exercise at the end of the a training cycle in the last 4-6 weeks. Just completing heavy loads without the knee bend would be fine, but keep in mind you must always finish with the explosive knee bend calf raises, being sure to push through the big toe at the top.

No matter what sport you play, if it involves movement with the legs, you must constantly coach the athletes up on these finer points of foot function. Essentially, what happens is they're losing all the potential power from the main two joints of explosion and not transferring it onto the speed on the field. I've seen too many athletes underutilize their potential and have a simple biomechanical problem that can't be transferred over because of one joint in the kinetic chain in applying power and force to the ground. You lose so much potential.

Having your squatting potential transfer to the sporting field to optimize results:
Many athletes and/or coaches use an Olympic or powerlifting style squat when they are performing front and back squats when training for sport. Let's keep in mind that these are all excellent exercises in gaining strength for athletes to become faster and more explosive. Please keep in mind that I use these various techniques throughout the year, but you can't get the greatest sport results by not changing up these methods once your athletes have become strong enough. When making this statement one must realize that you can't keep squatting heavier and heavier and have performance keep improving. This has never been the case with any athlete that I've seen. You must have a level of strength that is high enough to perform the task at hand. Once the strength has been developed one must use more sports specific methods to transfer the gains made from the Olympic and power-lifting squat over to the field.

This is where the "sport back squat" comes into play. The sport back squat essentially is taking your wider stance squat and moving the feet of the athlete to a very narrow position (shoulder width or slightly within/outside based on size). The reason for this is that during the majority of performances the athlete completes the feet will be in this position. To facilitate the transfer and strength gains from the Olympic and power lifting style back squat, the last 4 to 6 weeks of training (potentially longer during the in season) would use the sport back squat to get the most specific position of your feet when squatting. Some things change in this particular style of squat, especially with athletes that have a long thigh bone; they will not be able to go as deep as before as in the Olympic or power lifting style back squat. Keep in mind when you switch from the Olympic or power lifting style back squat to the sport back squat that you most likely wont have your athletes go as deep for biomechanical reasons. So realizing that your athletes wont go as deep you must increase the glute and hamstring work in your programming because you will not be utilizing the hamstring and glutes as much as you would in the deeper Olympic and power squats.

Many people often ask, "Well is not squatting deep the ideal thing for my athletes?" I would say unless they are going into some type of squatting competition not to worry about it because in sport they rarely ever get into that deep of a position; also, they will not lose much strength in regard to squatting during the transition time utilizing the sport back squat, which again should be the last 4 to 6 weeks of your training cycles to get optimal transfer of sports performance. Dr. Bondarchuck rarely ever squatted his athletes that deep because they never went into those deep positions in their throwing movements. He felt that squatting at the angles that they would compete at was optimal and got the best results. His results speak for themselves, being arguably the greatest coach in the history of the summer games. Just remember when utilizing the sport back squat one can also come up with some very specific glute and hamstring exercises to help your athletes transfer into their sporting event.

6.8: WEDNESDAY, HIGH INTENSITY
(SPORT SPECIFIC TIME: BELOW IDEAL)

LOADING

Below is a section from the loading table showing exclusively the loading variables and set durations applied on Wednesday. Remember, the loads and times don't change during the block. The emphasis is placed on the athlete performing more repetitions (high quality work) within the same parameters.

TABLE 6.9: WEDNESDAY LOADING (BELOW IDEAL TIME)			
PARAMETER	APPLIED FOR SPORT-SPECIFIC PEAKING	SET DURATION (SECONDS)	LOAD
STRENGTH SPEED	• SHOT PUT • FOOTBALL LINEMEN • VOLLEYBALL	3	45–55%
SPEED STRENGTH	• FOOTBALL SKILL PLAYERS • BASEBALL • SOFTBALL • 100-M SPRINTER	5	
STRENGTH ENDURANCE	• HOCKEY • BASKETBALL	10	
ENDURANCE STRENGTH	• SOCCER • MEN'S/WOMEN'S LACROSSE • SWIMMING 50–200 M	17	
ENDURANCE (MODERATE)	• SWIMMING 200 M+ • 400-M RUNNER	25	
ENDURANCE (LONG)	• 800-M+ RUNNER • DISTANCE SWIMMER • ROWING	32	

WORKOUT

On the next page you will find Wednesday's workout for the three-day below 55 percent high velocity peaking block. Coaching points with their respective hyperlinks to the exercises are in the right-hand column.

BLOCK FIVE, WEDNESDAY

100%	WENDESDAY	REPS	LOAD	SETS	NOTES
575	Hex Deadlift	T		2	0:0:0:0:5:10
	PW/ 40 Rest BB			EU	ISO
	Cpress Ext Rot rev Band	T	$N/A .. $N/A	2	0:0:0:0:5:10
	PW/ 40 Rest BB	EUA			
	Calf Raises	T		2	0:0:0:0:5:10
	Squat Drop Jump	T	$N/A .. $N/A	2	0:0:0:0:5:10
	PW/ 40 Rest BB	ED		EU	
	OC Ball Grion Sqeeze	T	$N/A .. $N/A	2	0:0:0:0:5:10
				EU	Reactive
575	Hex Deadlift	T	290 - 315	2	0:0:0:0:5:10
575	Hex Deadlift	T	290 - 315	3	Reactive
	PW/ 40 Rest BB	ED		EU	0:0:0:0:5:10
	Hip Flex Prone oc	T	$N/A .. $N/A	3	0:0:0:0:5:10
	PW/ 40 Rest BB			EUA	OC-D
105	DB BO Row	T	55 - 60	3	0:0:0:0:5:10
300	BENCH PRESS	5,3	150 - 200	1,1	
	PW/ 40 Rest BB	EU		ED	
	Med Ball Pass	3		2	ONE ARM
				ED	OC-D+1
300	Bench Press	T	150 - 165	2	0:0:0:0:5:10
300	Bench Press	T	150 - 165	2	0:0:0:0:5:10
	PW/ 40 Rest BB	EU		ED	OC-D+1
500	Glute Bar Lift	T	250 - 275	3	0:0:0:0:5:10
	PW/ 40 Rest BB	EUA			
	Delt BO Lat Reb Drop	T		3	0:0:0:0:5:10
	Tri PRess Band ASFM	T	$N/A .. $N/A	2	0:0:0:0:5:10
	PW/ 40 Rest BB	EU			0:0:0:0:5:10
	Curl Band ASFM	T		2	oc-A
	PW/ 40 Rest BB	EDT		ED	SL - OC
	STR Leg OC Glute Lifts	T		2	0:0:0:0:5:10
					#N/A
	Pair w/				
	GH HANG	120S		1	Relax Mouth
	Pair w/				
	Rollers Quads & Back	120S	$N/A .. $N/A	1	#REF!
	Pair w/				
	LAYING WALL SHAKES	120S		1	Relax Mouth

COACHING POINTS AND EXERCISE TUTORIAL

Box 1
-This hex deadlift is a 5 second isometric in the advantageous position, pulling against the fixed rack with slightly bent knees
-For the calf raises, cue the athlete to push through the big toe and use a slight knee bend
Hex Deadlift; Cpress Ext Rot rev Band; Calf Raises

Box 2
-For the squat drop jump, pull into an athletic jumping position forcefully; reverse direction immediately upon impact
-With a Swiss ball between the knees, powerfully contract and relax the groin for the prescribed time
-In the standard hex deadlift, keep the butt down and chest up, completing as many reps as possible in the prescribed time
Squat Drop Jump; OC Ball Groin Squeeze; Hex Deadlift

Box 3
-The hip flex prone is done reactively while oscillating
Hex Deadlift; Hip Flex Prone OC; DB BO Row

Box 4
-For the med ball pass, face the wall, turn towards one hip, and throw the ball as hard as possible
-The bench press is done with the bar near the chest with submaximal loads; push and pull the bar as hard as possible; finish the set on a full repetition
Bench Press; Med Ball Chest Pass; Bench Press

Box 5
-When doing the glute bar lift, athletes may or may not touch the ground on each rep; the goal should be to perform as many reps as possible in the prescribed time
-The delt BO lat reb drop is designed to improve the explosiveness of the shoulder
Bench Press; Glute Bar Lift; Delt BO Lat Reb Drop

Box 6
-For the curl band AFSM, the hand must supinate(palm up) at the top, and pronate(palm down) at the bottom. After curling the band, the athlete should try to press it back to the floor
-The straight leg OC glute lifts are used to fire and re-fire the glutes in a very fast manner
TriPress Band ASFM; STR Leg OC Glute Lifts

Box 8
GH HANG; Rollers Quads and Back; Laying Wall Shakes

√ COACH'S CORNER

RECOVERY PROTOCOLS AFTER HEAVY LOADING OF THE POSTERIOR CHAIN
BY: CAL DIETZ

Inversion is a recovery method that helps by decompressing the spinal column and elongating the spinal discs. There is also some evidence that it can help with CNS recovery by decreasing the amount of time it takes an athlete to return to a parasympathetic state. This proves to be especially important during phases of intense, heavy, posterior chain loading. The following protocols can be performed on either an inversion table or a glute ham machine. In all cases, the key points are to make sure you relax your mouth and tongue, and focus on taking deep belly breaths in through your nose and out through your mouth. This method was first brought to my attention by Dr. Michael Yessis.

1) Used for spinal de-loading. (Total time = 5min)

- 5 minutes of continuous inversion

2) Used for CNS recovery. (Total time = 7—9min)

- 1 minute inverted
- 30 to 60 upright
- 1 minute inverted
- 30 to 60 upright
- 1 minute inverted
- 30 to 60 upright
- 1 minute inverted
- 30 to 60 upright
- 1 minute inverted

3) Used for CNS recovery. (Total time = 7—9min)

- 1 minute Glute ham hang
- 30 to 60 seconds Laying Wall Shakes
- 1 minute Glute ham hang
- 30 to 60 seconds Laying Wall Shakes
- 1 minute Glute ham hang
- 30 to 60 seconds Laying Wall Shakes
- 1 minute Glute ham hang
- 30 to 60 seconds Laying Wall Shakes
- 1 minute Glute ham hang

6.9: FRIDAY, LOW INTENSITY
(SPORT-SPECIFIC TIME: ABOVE IDEAL)

LOADING

Below is a section from the loading table showing exclusively the loading variables and set durations applied on Friday. Remember, the loads and times don't change during the block. The emphasis is placed on the athlete performing more repetitions (high quality work) within the same parameters.

TABLE 6.10: FRIDAY LOADING (ABOVE IDEAL TIME)			
PARAMETER	APPLIED FOR SPORT-SPECIFIC PEAKING	SET DURATION (SECONDS)	LOAD
STRENGTH SPEED	• SHOT PUT • FOOTBALL LINEMEN • VOLLEYBALL	7	25–30%
SPEED STRENGTH	• FOOTBALL SKILL PLAYERS • BASEBALL • SOFTBALL • 100-M SPRINTER	10	
STRENGTH ENDURANCE	• HOCKEY • BASKETBALL	17	
ENDURANCE STRENGTH	• SOCCER • MEN'S/WOMEN'S LACROSSE • SWIMMING 50–200 M	32	
ENDURANCE (MODERATE)	• SWIMMING 200 M+ • 400-M RUNNER	40	
ENDURANCE (LONG)	• 800-M+ RUNNER • DISTANCE SWIMMER • ROWING	47	

WORKOUT

On the next page you will find Friday's workout for the three-day below 55 percent high velocity peaking block. Coaching points with their respective hyperlinks to the exercises are in the right-hand column.

BLOCK FIVE, FRIDAY

100%	FRIDAY	REPS	LOAD	SETS	NOTES
575	Hex Deadlift	T	115 - 145	2	0:0:0:5:10
	PW/ 15 Rest BB			EU	ISO
	Delt BO OH Reb Drop	T	SHA - SHA	2	0:0:0:0:10:10
	PW/ 15 Rest BB				
	Calf Raises	T		2	0:0:0:0:10:10
	Squat Drop Jump	T	SHA - SHA	2	0:0:0:0:10:10
	PW/ 15 Rest BB				
	OC Ball Grion Sqeeze	T		2	0:0:0:0:10:10
		OC			
	BAL SNGL LG SQ	T		2	0:0:0:0:10:10
575	Hex Deadlift	T	290 - 315	3	0:0:0:0:10:10
	Pair w/				
	OC Ball Sqeeze	T	SHA - SHA	3	0:0:0:0:10:10
	Pair w/				
105	DB BO Row	T	55 - 60	3	0:0:0:0:10:10
300	BENCH PRESS	5,3	150 - 200	1,1	0:0:0:0:10:10
	Pair w/				
	Med Ball Pass	3	SHA - SHA	2	one arm
		OC			
105	DB BENCH	T	55 - 60	2	0:0:0:0:10:10
105	DB BENCH	T	55 - 60	2	0:0:0:0:10:10
	Pair w/	OC			
500	Glute Bar Lift	T	250 - 275	3	0:0:0:0:10:10
	Pair w/	OC			
	Delt BO Lat Reb Drop	T		3	0:0:0:0:10:10
	Tri PRess Band ASFM	T	SHA - SHA	2	
	Pair w/				
	Curl Band ASFM	T		2	
	Pair w/				
	STR Leg OC Glute Lifts	T		2	
	Pair w/				
	GH HANG	120S		1	Relax Mouth
	Pair w/				
	Rollers Quads & Back	120S		1	
	Pair w/				
	LAYING WALL SHAKES	120S		1	Relax Mouth

COACHING POINTS AND EXERCISE TUTORIAL

Box 1
-This hex deadlift is a 5 second isometric in the advantageous position, pulling against the fixed rack with slightly bent knees
-The delt BO OH reb drop improves reactive ability of the shoulder
-For the calf raises, cue the athlete to push through the big toe and use a slight knee bend
Hex Deadlift; Delt BO OH Reb Drop; Calf Raises

Box 2
-For the squat drop jump, pull into an athletic jumping position forcefully; reverse direction immediately upon impact
-With a Swiss ball between the knees, powerfully contract and relax the groin for the prescribed time
-The balance single leg squat is a controlled movement in which the athlete lowers the unsupported foot towards the ground, keeping the foot on the bench flat
Squat Drop Jump; OC Ball Groin Squeeze; BAL SNGL LG SQ

Box 3
-In the standard hex deadlift, keep the butt down and chest up, completing as many reps as possible in the prescribed time
-Perform the DB BO row through a full range of motion
Hex Deadlift; OC Ball Groin Squeeze; DB BO Row

Box 4
-The bench press and med ball pass are performed as described on previous days
-Perform the DB Bench through a full range of motion
Bench Press; Med Ball Chest Pass; DB Bench

Box 5
-The glute bar lift is perfumed as an oscillatory movement near the top of the lift to contract and relax the glutes as fast as possible
- The delt BO lat reb Drop is designed to improve the explosiveness of the shoulder
DB Bench; Glute Bar Lift; Delt BO Lat Reb Drop

Box 6
-The tricep band press AFSM is performed as a press and curl in which the athlete presses the band down (palm down) and curling the band (palm up) to the start
-The Curl band ASFM and straight leg OC glute Lifts are performed as described on previous days
TriPress Band ASFM; Curl Band AFSM; STR Leg OC Glute Lifts

Box 8
GH HANG; Rollers Quads and Back; Laying Wall Shakes

6.10: THREE-DAY HIGH VELOCITY PEAKING PROGRAM OVERVIEW

The importance of choosing the correct exercises along with the proper methods and parameters in their application is clear. Choosing specialized developmental exercises closely related to the movement patterns and neural firing rates that an athlete will find in competition is imperative if you want to see gains from the weight room transfer to the field. This last phase, the peaking phase, is the most important part of an athlete's training year and the most difficult part of a coach's job. Peaking an athlete isn't an exact science. Yes, scientists have created great methods and parameters that definitely help athletes. However, every athlete is unique. What is an ideal method for peaking one athlete or type of athlete is likely detrimental to another. While the criteria of dynamic correspondence serve as great guides, it often takes a coach years of experience working with thousands of athletes to truly find what works best to draw out their maximum potential.

To help speed up this process and give you a jump on other coaches and athletes, I have added several peaking programs for different sports (chapter 6.11). These are programs I've developed over the years using specialized exercises that I've found to have a very high correlation (r) to the respective sport. Below, you will find tables that give the general overview and outline the lifting and conditioning parameters for the three-day high velocity peaking phase (tables 6.11 and 6.12).

TABLE 6.11: UNDULATING BLOCK MODEL							
TRAINING WEEK:		DAY 1	DAY 2	DAY 3	DAY 4	DAY 5	DAY 6
THREE-DAY MODEL	FOCUS	TOTAL BODY	OFF	TOTAL BODY	OFF	TOTAL BODY	OFF
	LOAD	35–40%		45–55%		25–30%	
	MEANS APPLIED	AFSM		AFSM		AFSM	

		TABLE 6.12: BELOW 55 PERCENT THREE-DAY CONDITIONING MODEL		
TRAINING DAY	CONDITIONING GOAL	SPECIAL INSTRUCTIONS		EXAMPLE WORKOUT
DAY 1	**Long Sprints** *or* **Short Sprints with Reduced Rest** (Speed Conditioning)	• Sprints over 15 seconds or • Sprints under 10 seconds and recovery under 20 seconds.		• High Quality Lactic Anaerobic Power Training Builder • Metabolic Injury Prevention Runs
DAY 2	**Short Sprints** (High Quality Speed)	• Sprints under 10 seconds • Full recovery; rest 90–120 seconds.		• Alactic High Quality Workout • Flying 60s • 16-Week Short Sprint Workouts • Cone Agility
DAY 3	**Longer Sprints** *or* **Continuous Running** (Oxidative Conditioning)	This day is purely work capacity focused.		• Aerobic Work Capacity Training Builder • Game Speed Conditioning • Bike Conditioning • Trash Ball

Be sure to notice in the programs that as the metabolic and neural demands of a sport change, the timed parameters of the exercises—not just the exercises—change as well. It doesn't do a lineman any good to perform sets over twenty seconds. Their plays are completed in 1–3 seconds. Below are two hyperlinks to a conference talk I gave at the University of Richmond in 2011, about my high velocity peaking method. It will serve as a great review, as well as give some additional insights into how to peak your athletes.

HIGH VELOCITY PEAKING METHODS AND TECHNIQUES IN SPORT SPECIFICITY: PART I

HIGH VELOCITY PEAKING METHODS AND TECHNIQUES IN SPORT SPECIFICITY: PART II

BLOCK FIVE (3-DAY): HIGH VELOCITY PEAKING FOR GENERAL ATHLETE

MONDAY

100%	Exercise	REPS	LOAD	SETS	NOTES
575	Hex Deadlift	T		2	0:0:0:0.5:10
	PW/ 15 Rest BB	EU		EU	ISO
	Cpress Ext Rot rev Band OC	T		2	
	PW/ 15 Rest BB	EDT			Each side
	Ankle Band Work	T		2	0:0:0:0.7:10
	Squat Drop Jump	CIT			2% - Tendo
	PW/ 15 Rest BB	EU		EU	Set Drop off
	4 way neck	6		EUA	Reactive
375	SL Leg Press	T	150 - 170	2	0:0:0:0.7:10
375	SL Leg Press	T	115 - 130	3	0:0:0:0.7:10
	Hip Flex Prone OC CL	EUA		3	0:0:0:0.7:10
	PW/ 30 Rest BB	EDT		EUA	OC-D
105	DB BO Row	T	55 - 60	2	0:0:0:0.7:10
	Cpress In Rot Band OC	EU		EU	ONE ARM
	Med Ball Pass	5		ED	OC-D
105	DB BENCH	T	40 - 45	2	0:0:0:0.7:10
105	DB BENCH	T	40 - 45	2	0:0:0:0.7:10
	GH HYPR Incline	T		3	oc-D
	PW/ 30 Rest BB	EUA		ED	OC-A
38	DB Side Lat Raise	T	15 - 15	3	7 - OC-D
	Band Tricep Extension	T		2	0:0:0:0.7:10
	PW/ 30 Rest BB	EDT		EU	oc-D
	Bicep shock curls	T		2	0:0:0:0.7:10
	PW/ 30 Rest BB	EDT			
	OC Ball Grion Sqeeze	T		2	0:0:0:0.7:10
	GH HANG	120S		1	
	Pair w/				
	Rollers Glutes & Hams	120S		1	
	Pair w/				
	LAYING RELAXATION	120S		1	

WENDESDAY

100%	Exercise	REPS	LOAD	SETS	NOTES
575	Hex Deadlift	T		2	0:0:0:0.5:10
	PW/ 40 Rest BB	EU		EU	ISO
	Cpress Ext Rot rev Band	T		2	0:0:0:0.5:10
	PW/ 40 Rest BB	EUA			0:0:0:0.5:10
	Calf Raises	T		2	0:0:0:0.5:10
	Squat Drop Jump	T		EU	0:0:0:0.5:10
	PW/ 40 Rest BB	ED			0:0:0:0.5:10
	OC Ball Grion Sqeeze	T		EU	Reactive
575	Hex Deadlift	T	290 - 315	3	0:0:0:0.5:10
575	Hex Deadlift	T	290 - 315	3	Reactive
	Hip Flex Prone oc	ED		3	0:0:0:0.5:10
	PW/ 40 Rest BB	EU		EUA	OC-D
105	DB BO Row	T	55 - 60	3	0:0:0:0.5:10
300	BENCH PRESS	5,3	150 - 200	1,1	0:0:0:0.5:10
	PW/ 40 Rest BB	EU		ED	0:0:0:0.5:10
	Med Ball Pass	3		2	ONE ARM
300	Bench Press	T	150 - 165	2	OC-D+1
300	Bench Press	T	150 - 165	2	0:0:0:0.5:10
	PW/ 40 Rest BB	EU		ED	OC-D+1
500	Glute Bar Lift	T	250 - 275	3	0:0:0:0.5:10
	PW/ 40 Rest BB	EUA			0:0:0:0.5:10
	Det BO Lat Reb Drop			3	0:0:0:0.5:10
	TriPPress Band ASFM	T		2	0:0:0:0.5:10
	PW/ 40 Rest BB	EU		ED	oc-A
	Curl Band ASFM	T		2	0:0:0:0.5:10
	PW/ 40 Rest BB	EDT		ED	SL - OC
	STR Leg OC Glute Lifts	T			0:0:0:0.5:10
	Pair w/				
	GH HANG	120S		1	Relax Mouth
	Pair w/				
	Rollers Quads & Back	120S		1	#REF!
	Pair w/				
	LAYING WALL SHAKES	120S		1	Relax Mouth

FRIDAY

100%	Exercise	REPS	LOAD	SETS	NOTES
575	Hex Deadlift	T	115 - 145	2	0:0:0:0.5:10
	PW/ 15 Rest BB			EU	ISO
	Deft BO OH Reb Drop			2	0:0:0:10:10
	PW/ 15 Rest BB				0:0:0:10:10
	Calf Raises	T			0:0:0:10:10
	Squat Drop Jump	T			0:0:0:10:10
	PW/ 15 Rest BB			2	0:0:0:10:10
	OC Ball Grion Sqeeze				0:0:0:10:10
	BAL SNGL LG SQ	OC		2	0:0:0:10:10
575	Hex Deadlift	T	290 - 315	3	0:0:0:10:10
	OC Ball Grion Sqeeze	T		3	0:0:0:10:10
	Pair w/				0:0:0:10:10
105	DB BO Row	T	55 - 60	3	0:0:0:10:10
300	BENCH PRESS	5,3	150 - 200	1,1	0:0:0:10:10
	Pair w/				
	Med Ball Pass	3		2	one arm
105	DB BENCH	OC	55 - 60	2	0:0:0:10:10
105	DB BENCH	T	55 - 60	2	0:0:0:10:10
	Pair w/	OC			
500	Glute Bar Lift	T	250 - 275	3	
	Pair w/	OC			
	Det BO Lat Reb Drop			3	
	TriPPress Band ASFM	T		2	
	Curl Band ASFM	T			
	STR Leg OC Glute Lifts	T			
	Pair w/				
	GH HANG	120S		1	Relax Mouth
	Pair w/				
	Rollers Quads & Back	120S		1	
	Pair w/				
	LAYING WALL SHAKES	120S		1	Relax Mouth

BLOCK FIVE (3-DAY): HIGH VELOCITY PEAKING FOR GENERAL ATHLETE HYPERLINKS

Day 1	Exercise Hyperlink	Day 2	Exercise Hyperlink	Day 3	Exercise Hyperlink
Box 1	Hex Deadlift Cpress Ext Rot Rev Band Ankle Band Work	Box 1	Hex Deadlift Cpress Ext Rot rev Band Calf Raises	Box 1	Hex Deadlift Delt BO OH Reb Drop Calf Raises
Box 2	Squat Drop Jump 4 way neck SL Leg Press	Box 2	Squat Drop Jump OC Ball Groin Squeeze Hex Deadlift	Box 2	Squat Drop Jump OC Ball Groin Squeeze BAL SNGL LG SQ
Box 3	SL Leg Press Hip Flex OC Prone CL DB BO Row	Box 3	Hex Deadlift Hip Flex Prone OC DB BO Row	Box 3	Hex Deadlift OC Ball Groin Squeeze DB BO Row
Box 4	Cpress Int Rot Band OC Med Ball Chest Pass DB Bench	Box 4	Bench Press Med Ball Chest Pass Bench Press	Box 4	Bench Press Med Ball Chest Pass DB Bench
Box 5	DB Bench GH HYPR Incline DB Side Lat Raise	Box 5	Bench Press Glute Bar Lift Delt BO Lat Reb Drop	Box 5	DB Bench Glute Bar Lift Delt BO Lat Reb Drop
Box 6	Band Tricep Extension Bicep Shock Curls OC Ball Groin Squeeze	Box 6	TriPress Band ASFM STR Leg OC Glute Lifts	Box 6	TriPress Band ASFM Curl Band AFSM STR Leg OC Glute Lifts
Box 7		Box 7		Box 7	
Box 8	GH HANG Rollers Glutes and Hams Laying Relaxation	Box 8	GH HANG Rollers Quads and Back Laying Wall Shakes	Box 8	GH HANG Rollers Quads and Back Laying Wall Shakes

6.11: SPORT SPECIFIC PEAKING PROGRAMS

Below you will find six specialized peaking programs to enhance the training of:

1) Football linemen (p. 340)

2) Football skill players (backs and receivers) (p. 342)

3) Baseball position players (p. 344)

4) Hockey players (p. 346)

5) Swimmers (200–400 meter) (p. 348)

6) Volleyball players (p. 350)

BLOCK FIVE (3-DAY): HIGH VELOCITY PEAKING FOR FOOTBALL (LINEMAN)

MONDAY

100%	Exercise	REPS	LOAD	SETS	NOTES
	Hex Deadlift Iso	T	EU	2	0:0:0:5:10 ISO
	PW/ 15 Rest BB	EU		2	
	Cpress Ext Rot rev Band OC	T		2	Each side
	PW/ 15 Rest BB	EDT		2	
	Ankle Band Work	T		2	
	Squat Drop Jump	C11		2	2½ - Tendo
	PW/ 15 Rest BB	EU		2	Set Drop off
	4-W Neck OC Ball	6	EUA		Reactive
225	Single Leg Squat	T	70 - 80	2	0:0:0:5:10
225	Single Leg Squat	T	70 - 80	3	
	Hip Flex Prone oc	EUA		3	
	PW/ 30 Rest BB	EDT		3	OC-D
105	DB BO Row	T	55 - 60	3	
	Cpress Inr Rot Band OC	EU	EUA	2	OC-A
	PW/ 30 Rest BB	T		2	7 - OC-D
	Med Ball Pass	4	ED		ONE ARM
	PW/ 30 Rest BB			2	OC-D
105	DB BENCH	T	30 - 35	2	0:0:0:5:10
105	DB BENCH	T	30 - 35		
	GH HYPR Incline	EDT		3	oc-D
	PW/ 30 Rest BB	T		3	
	Inc Delt Lat Reb Drop	EUA		2	OC-A
	Band Tricep Extension	T		2	7 - OC-D
	PW/ 30 Rest BB	EDT	EU	2	oc-D
	Bicep shock curls				
	PW/ 30 Rest BB	EDT			
	OC Ball Grion Sqeeze	T		2	
	GH HANG	120S		1	
	Pair w/				
	Rollers Glutes & Hams	120S		1	
	Pair w/				
	LAYING RELAXATION	120S		1	

WENDESDAY

100%	Exercise	REPS	LOAD	SETS	NOTES
	Hex Deadlift Iso	T		2	EU · ISO
	PW/ 15 Rest BB	EU		2	0:0:0:3:10
	Cpress Ext Rot rev Band	T		2	0:0:0:3:10
	PW/ 15 Rest BB	EUA		2	0:0:0:3:10
	Calf Raises	T		2	0:0:0:3:10
	Squat Drop Jump	ED		EUA	0:0:0:3:10
	PW/ 15 Rest BB	T		3	OC-D
	Hip Flex Prone OC CL			3	0:0:0:3:10
375	SL Leg Press	T	190 - 205	2	OC-Reactive
375	SL Leg Press	ED	190 - 205	3	OC Reactive
	OC Ball Grion Sqeeze	T		3	0:0:0:3:10
	Pair w/			EUA	OC-D
105	DB BO Row	T	30 - 35	3	0:0:0:3:10
300	BENCH PRESS	5,3	150 - 200	1,1	
	Pair w/	EU		ED	
	Med Ball Pass	3		2	ONE ARM
		ED		2	OC-D+1
300	Bench Press	T	90 - 105	2	0:0:0:3:10
300	Bench Press	T	90 - 105	3	OC-D+1
500	Glute Bar Lift	EU	150 - 175	3	0:0:0:3:10
	Pair w/	T		EUA	OC
	Delt BO Lat Reb Drop	EUA		3	0:0:0:3:10
	Tri PRess Band ASFM	T		10	0:0:0:3:10
	Pair w/	EU		2	oc-A
	Curl Band ASFM	EDT		ED	SL - OC
	Pair w/	T		2	0:0:0:3:10
	STR Leg OC Glute Lifts				
	Pair w/				
	GH HANG	120S		1	
	Pair w/				Relax Mouth
	Rollers Quads & Back	120S		1	#RET
	Pair w/				
	LAYING WALL SHAKES	120S		1	Relax Mouth

FRIDAY

100%	Exercise	REPS	LOAD	SETS	NOTES
	Hex Deadlift Iso	T		2	0:0:0:5:10
	PW/ 15 Rest BB		EU	2	ISO
	Cpress Ext Rot rev Band	T		2	0:0:0:7:10
	PW/ 15 Rest BB	T		2	0:0:0:7:10
	Calf Raises	8		2	0:0:0:7:10
	Squat Drop Jump	T		2	0:0:0:7:10
	PW/ 15 Rest BB	T		2	0:0:0:7:10
	Hip Flex Prone OC CL			2	0:0:0:7:10
250	SL Hex Deadlift	T	75 - 90	3	0:0:0:7:10
250	SL Hex Deadlift	T	75 - 90	3	0:0:0:7:10
	Pair w/				
	OC Ball Grion Sqeeze	T		2	0:0:0:7:10
105	DB BO Row	T	30 - 35	3	0:0:0:7:10
300	BENCH PRESS	5,3	150 - 200	1,1	0:0:0:7:10
	Pair w/				
	Med Ball Pass	5		2	
300	Bench Press	T	90 - 105	2	0:0:0:7:10
300	Bench Press	T	90 - 105	2	0:0:0:7:10
	Pair w/				
500	Glute Bar Lift	T	150 - 175	3	0:0:0:7:10
	Pair w/				
	Delt BO Lat Reb Drop	T		3	0:0:0:7:10
	Tri PRess Band ASFM	10		2	0:0:0:7:10
	Pair w/				
	Curl Band ASFM	T		2	0:0:0:7:10
	Pair w/				
	STR Leg OC Glute Lifts	T		2	0:0:0:7:10

BLOCK FIVE (3-DAY): High Velocity Peaking For Football (Lineman) Hyperlinks

Day 1	Exercise Hyperlink	Day 2	Exercise Hyperlink	Day 3	Exercise Hyperlink
Box 1	Hex Deadlift Cpress Ext Rot Rev Band Ankle Band Work	Box 1	Hex Deadlift Cpress Ext Rot rev Band Calf Raises	Box 1	Hex Deadlift Cpress Ext Rot rev Band Calf Raises
Box 2	Squat Drop Jump 4-way Neck OC Ball Single Leg Squat	Box 2	Squat Drop Jump Hip Flex OC Prone CL SL Leg Press	Box 2	Squat Drop Jump Hip Flex OC Prone CL SL Hex Deadlift
Box 3	Single Leg Squat Hip Flex Prone OC DB BO Row	Box 3	SL Leg Press OC Ball Groin Squeeze DB BO Row	Box 3	SL Hex Deadlift OC Ball Groin Squeeze DB BO Row
Box 4	Cpress Int Rot Band OC Med Ball Chest Pass DB Bench	Box 4	Bench Press Med Ball Chest Pass Bench Press	Box 4	Bench Press Med Ball Chest Pass Bench Press
Box 5	DB Bench GH HYPR Incline Inc Delt Lat Reb Drop	Box 5	Bench Press Glute Bar Lift Delt BO Lat Reb Drop	Box 5	Bench Press Glute Bar Lift Delt BO Lat Reb Drop
Box 6	Band Tricep Extension Bicep Shock Curls OC Ball Groin Squeeze	Box 6	TriPress Band ASFM Curl Band AFSM STR Leg OC Glute Lifts	Box 6	TriPress Band ASFM Curl Band AFSM STR Leg OC Glute Lifts
Box 7		Box 7		Box 7	
Box 8	GH HANG Rollers Glutes and Hams Laying Relaxation	Box 8	GH HANG Rollers Quads and Back Laying Wall Shakes	Box 8	GH HANG Rollers Quads and Back Laying Wall Shakes

BLOCK FIVE (3-DAY): HIGH VELOCITY PEAKING FOR FOOTBALL (SKILL)

MONDAY — 100%

Exercise	REPS	LOAD	SETS	NOTES
Hex Deadlift Iso	T		2	0:0:0:0.5:10
PW/ 15 Rest BB	EU		EU	ISO
Cpress Ext Rot rev Band OC	T	$NA - $NA	2	0:0:0:0.7:10
PW/ 15 Rest BB	EDT			Each side
Ankle Band Work	T		2	0:0:0:0.7:10
Squat Drop Jump	C1T	$NA - $NA	2	2/- Tendo
PW/ 15 Rest BB	EU		EU	Set Drop off
4-W Neck OC Ball	6		2	0:0:0:0.7:10
	EUA		EUA	Reactive
Single Leg Squat	225 T	70 - 80	2	0:0:0:0.7:10
Single Leg Squat	225 T	70 - 80	3	0:0:0:0.7:10
PW/ 30 Rest BB	EUA	$NA - $NA	3	
Hip Flex Prone oc	T		3	OC-D
PW/ 30 Rest BB	EDT		EUA	0:0:0:0.7:10
DB BO Row	105 T	55 - 60	3	OC-D
Cpress In Rot Band BB	T	$NA - $NA	2	0:0:0:0.7:10
PW/ 30 Rest BB	EU			ONE ARM
Med Ball Pass	4		2	ED / OC-D
DB BENCH	105 T	30 - 35	2	0:0:0:0.7:10
DB BENCH	105 T	30 - 35	ED	oc-D
PW/ 30 Rest BB	EU		EU	
GH HYPR Incline	T	$NA - $NA	2	0:0:0:0.7:10
PW/ 30 Rest BB	EUA		ED	OCA
Inc Delt Lat Reb Drop	T		2	7 - OC-D
Band Tricep Extension	T		2	0:0:0:0.7:10
PW/ 30 Rest BB	EDT		EU	oc-D
Bicep shock curls	T	$NA - $NA	2	0:0:0:0.7:10
PW/ 30 Rest BB	EDT			
OC Ball Groin Sqeeze	T		2	0:0:0:0.7:10
GH HANG	120S		1	
Pair w/				
Rollers Glutes & Hams	120S	$NA - $NA	1	
Pair w/				
LAYING RELAXATION	120S		1	

WENDESDAY — 100%

Exercise	REPS	LOAD	SETS	NOTES
Hex Deadlift Iso	T		2	0:0:0:0.5:10
PW/ 15 Rest BB	EU		EU	ISO
Cpress Ext Rot rev Band	T	$NA - $NA	2	0:0:0:0.5:10
PW/ 15 Rest BB	EUA			0:0:0:0.5:10
Calf Raises	T		2	0:0:0:0.5:10
Squat Drop Jump	T	$NA - $NA	2	0:0:0:0.5:10
PW/ 15 Rest BB	ED		EU	
Hip Flex Prone OC CL	T		2	0:0:0:0.5:10
			EU	OC Reactive
SL Leg Press	375 T	190 - 205	2	0:0:0:0.5:10
SL Leg Press	375 T	190 - 205	3	OC Reactive
PW/ Pair w/	ED	$NA - $NA	EU	0:0:0:0.5:10
OC Ball Groin Sqeeze	T		3	0:0:0:0.5:10
	EUA		EUA	OC-D
DB BO Row	105 T	30 - 35	3	0:0:0:0.5:10
BENCH PRESS	300 5,3	150 - 200	1,1	0:0:0:0.5:10
Med Ball Pass	3		ED	ONE ARM
Bench Press	300 T	90 - 105	ED	OC-D+1
Bench Press	300 T	90 - 105	2	0:0:0:0.5:10
Pair w/	EU		ED	OC-D+1
Glute Bar Lift	500 T	150 - 175	3	0:0:0:0.5:10
Pair w/	EUA			OC
Delt BO Lat Reb Drop	T		3	0:0:0:0.5:10
Tri PPress Band ASFM	10		2	0:0:0:0.5:10
Pair w/	EU		2	oc-A
Curl Band ASFM	T	$NA - $NA	ED	SL - OC
Pair w/	EDT		2	0:0:0:0.5:10
STR Leg OC Glute Lifts	T			
Pair w/				
GH HANG	120S		1	Relax Mouth
Rollers Quads & Back	120S	$NA - $NA	1	PREP
Pair w/				
LAYING WALL SHAKES	120S		1	Relax Mouth

FRIDAY — 100%

Exercise	REPS	LOAD	SETS	NOTES
Hex Deadlift Iso	T		2	0:0:0:0.5:10
PW/ 15 Rest BB			EU	ISO
Cpress Ext Rot rev Band	T	$NA - $NA	2	0:0:0:0.10:10
PW/ 15 Rest BB				0:0:0:0.10:10
Calf Raises	8		2	0:0:0:0.10:10
Squat Drop Jump	T	$NA - $NA	2	0:0:0:0.10:10
PW/ 15 Rest BB				0:0:0:0.10:10
Hip Flex Prone OC CL	T		2	0:0:0:0.10:10
SL Hex Deadlift	250 T	75 - 90	2	0:0:0:0.10:10
SL Hex Deadlift	250 T	75 - 90	3	0:0:0:0.10:10
OC Ball Groin Sqeeze	T	$NA - $NA	3	0:0:0:0.10:10
DB BO Row	105 T	30 - 35	3	0:0:0:0.10:10
BENCH PRESS	300 5,3	150 - 200	1,1	0:0:0:0.10:10
Med Ball Pass	5		2	0:0:0:0.10:10
Bench Press	300 T	90 - 105	2	0:0:0:0.10:10
Bench Press	300 T	90 - 105	2	0:0:0:0.10:10
Pair w/				0:0:0:0.10:10
Glute Bar Lift	500 T	150 - 175	3	0:0:0:0.10:10
Pair w/				
Delt BO Lat Reb Drop	T		3	0:0:0:0.10:10
Tri PPress Band ASFM	10		2	0:0:0:0.10:10
Pair w/		$NA - $NA		0:0:0:0.10:10
Curl Band ASFM	T		2	0:0:0:0.10:10
Pair w/				
STR Leg OC Glute Lifts	T			
Pair w/				
GH HANG	120S		1	Relax Mouth
Pair w/				
Rollers Quads & Back	120S		1	
LAYING WALL SHAKES	120S		1	Relax Mouth

BLOCK FIVE (3-DAY): High Velocity Peaking For Football (Skill Player) Hyperlinks

Day 1	Exercise Hyperlink	Day 2	Exercise Hyperlink	Day 3	Exercise Hyperlink
Box 1	Hex Deadlift Cpress Ext Rot Rev Band Ankle Band Work	Box 1	Hex Deadlift Cpress Ext Rot rev Band Calf Raises	Box 1	Hex Deadlift Cpress Ext Rot rev Band Calf Raises
Box 2	Squat Drop Jump 4-way Neck OC Ball Single Leg Squat	Box 2	Squat Drop Jump Hip Flex OC Prone CL SL Leg Press	Box 2	Squat Drop Jump Hip Flex OC Prone CL SL Hex Deadlift
Box 3	Single Leg Squat Hip Flex Prone OC DB BO Row	Box 3	SL Leg Press OC Ball Groin Squeeze DB BO Row	Box 3	SL Hex Deadlift OC Ball Groin Squeeze DB BO Row
Box 4	Cpress Int Rot Band OC Med Ball Chest Pass DB Bench	Box 4	Bench Press Med Ball Chest Pass Bench Press	Box 4	Bench Press Med Ball Chest Pass Bench Press
Box 5	DB Bench GH HYPR Incline Inc Delt Lat Reb Drop	Box 5	Bench Press Glute Bar Lift Delt BO Lat Reb Drop	Box 5	Bench Press Glute Bar Lift Delt BO Lat Reb Drop
Box 6	Band Tricep Extension Bicep Shock Curls OC Ball Groin Squeeze	Box 6	TriPress Band ASFM Curl Band AFSM STR Leg OC Glute Lifts	Box 6	TriPress Band ASFM Curl Band AFSM STR Leg OC Glute Lifts
Box 7		Box 7		Box 7	
Box 8	GH HANG Rollers Glutes and Hams Laying Relaxation	Box 8	GH HANG Rollers Quads and Back Laying Wall Shakes	Box 8	GH HANG Rollers Quads and Back Laying Wall Shakes

BLOCK FIVE (3-DAY): HIGH VELOCITY PEAKING FOR BASEBALL (POSITION)

Day 1

100%	Exercise	REPS	LOAD	SETS	NOTES
500	Sport Back Squat	5,3	250 - 335	1,1	Pw/ Delba F8
	No Rest/B-Breath	EU			I band Rollers
500	Sport Back Squat	3	390 - 400	1	pw/cuban 18
	No Rest/B-Breath	EU			I band Rollers
	1/2 SQ JMP Weighted	T		3	0:0:0:7:10
	Hurdle Hop	EU		3	Pull Down
	15 rest- BB	T		3	0:0:0:7:10
	1/2 SQ JMP Weighted	EU		3	0:0:0:7:10
	15 rest- BB	T		3	0:0:0:7:10
	15 Yard Starts	T		3	
300	BENCH PRESS	5,3	150 - 200	1,1	Ext Shock
	No Rest/B-Breath	ED			Ext Shock
300	Bench Press	3	- 240	1	coach see
	No Rest/B-Breath	ED			
300	BENCH PRESS	T	120 - 135	3	20C-d+1
	One Leg MB Side Toss	5			
	25 rest- BB	EUA		EDT	
105	DB BO Row	T	40 - 45	3	Elbow wide
	25 rest- BB	EDT		3	0:0:0:7:10
	90 90 Jump Twist	T		3	
500	Glute Bar Lift	T	200 - 225	3	OC
	25 rest- BB	EU		ED	0:0:0:7:10
	Cuban PFSS OC Band	T		3	0:0:0:7:10
	25 rest- BB	EUA		3	0:0:0:7:10
105	DB BO Row	T	40 - 45	3	Each Arm
	GH HYPR	T		3	oc-D+1
	25 rest- BB	ED		ED	0:0:0:7:10
	OC Ball Grion Sqeeze	T		3	0:0:0:7:10
	25 rest- BB	ED		3	0:0:0:7:10
	Plate Pincher	T		3	Each Arm
75	DB Shoulder Press	T	30 - 35	2	oc-D+1
	25 rest- BB	ED		EDT	0:0:0:7:10
	Hip Flex OC Prone CL	T		2	
	25 rest- BB	ED		2	0:0:0:7:10
	Iso Bi Recip	T		2	0:0:0:7:10
	Iso Tri Recip	EU		ED	0:0:0:7:10
	Iso Bi Recip	T		2	0:0:0:7:10
	25 rest- BB	EU		2	0:0:0:7:10
	Jobes ECC	T		2	0:0:0:7:10

Day 2

100%	Exercise	REPS	LOAD	SETS	NOTES
500	Back Squat	5,3	250 - 335	1,1	
	No Rest/B-Breath	EU			
500	Back Squat	3	- 400	1	
	No Rest/B-Breath	EU			
	1/2 SQ JMP Weighted	T		3	0:0:0:5:10
	Stding SQ Drop Jump	T		3	0:0:0:5:10
	25 rest- BB	EU		EUA	
	Delt BO Lat Reb Drop	T		3	0:0:0:5:10
	25 rest- BB	ED		3	0:0:0:5:10
	Plate Pincher	T		3	
300	BENCH PRESS	5,3	150 - 200	1,1	One Arm
	No Rest/B-Breath	ED			
300	Bench Press	3	235 - 240	1	
	No Rest/B-Breath	ED			
300	BENCH PRESS	T	150 - 165	3	
	Med Ball Chest Pass	5		3	One Arm
	25 rest- BB	EUA		3	0:0:0:5:10
105	DB BO Row	T	55 - 60	3	Elbow wide
	25 rest- BB	EU		3	0:0:0:5:10
	Ball Pike Drop	T		3	Drops
	Lunge OC Hops	T		3	Each Leg
	Pair w/	EU		EUA	0:0:0:5:10
	Delt BO OH Reb Drop	T		3	0:0:0:5:10
	Pair w/	EUA		3	0:0:0:5:10
105	DB BO Row	T	55 - 60	3	Each Arm
	GH HYPR	T		3	oc-A
	Pair w/	ED		ED	0:0:0:5:10
	OC Ball Grion Sqeeze	T		3	0:0:0:5:10
	Pair w/	ED		3	0:0:0:5:10
	Plate Pincher	T		3	Each Arm
75	DB Shoulder Press	T	40 - 40	3	oc-D+1
	25 rest- BB	EU		EDT	0:0:0:5:10
	Russian Switch lunge	T		3	
	25 rest- BB	ED		3	0:0:0:5:10
	Iso Tri Recip	T		3	
	25 rest- BB	EU		ED	0:0:0:5:10
	Bicep shock curls	T		2	Bands
	25 rest- BB	EU		2	0:0:0:5:10
	Band Lying Int Rot	EU		2	OC

Day 3

100%	Exercise	REPS	LOAD	SETS	NOTES
225	Single Leg Squat	12	80 - 100	3	OC+1
	15 Rest-BB	EUA		ED	0:0:0:10:10
	Hip Flex OC Prone CL	8		3	0:0:0:10:10
	15 Rest-BB	ED			0:0:0:10:10
90	Ball LG Curl	15		3	OC-A
	DB INCLINE BENCH	12	30 - 40	3	oc-D+1
	15 Rest-BB	EU		ED	0:0:0:10:10
	1 Arm DB Row Reactive	12		3	Speed
	15 Rest-BB	ED		3	0:0:0:10:10
	Jobes	6		3	0:0:0:10:10
	Speed Switch Lunge with jump	8		3	0:0:0:10:10
75	DB Fly	8	40 - 45	3	Each Way
	15 Rest-BB	EU		ED	0:0:0:10:10
	Delt Lat Rebound Drop	8		3	0:0:0:10:10
500	Glute Bar Lift	12	175 - 225	3	0:0:0:10:10
	15 Rest-BB	EU		Oc	
	Rope Circles	15		3	Each Way
	15 Rest-BB	ED		3	0:0:0:10:10
180	Gripper	15	115 - 125	3	0:0:0:10:10
	Iso Bi Recip	8		2	0:0:0:10:10
	15 Rest-BB	ED		EU	0:0:0:10:10
	Iso Tri Recip	8		2	0:0:0:10:10
	15 Rest-BB	EDT		2	0:0:0:10:10
	OC Ball Grion Sqeeze	10		2	OC-A
	Iso Bi Recip	6	60 - 70	2	Each Leg
	15 Rest-BB	ED		EUA	0:0:0:10:10
	Speed Abduction	8		2	0:0:0:10:10
	15 Rest-BB	EU		2	0:0:0:10:10
240	Close Grip Bench	6	60 - 70	2	OC-A
	Lunge OC Hops	12		2	Each Leg
	15 Rest-BB	EUA		ED	0:0:0:10:10
	Rope Vertical	15		2	0:0:0:10:10
	15 Rest-BB	ED		2	0:0:0:10:10
	GH Supine CL Shock Abc	8		2	Each Side

BLOCK FIVE (3-DAY): High Velocity Peaking For Baseball Hyperlinks

Day 1	Exercise Hyperlink	Day 2	Exercise Hyperlink	Day 3	Exercise Hyperlink
Box 1	Sport Back Squat Sport Back Squat 1/2 SQ JMP Weighted	Box 1	Back Squat Back Squat 1/2 SQ JMP Weighted	Box 1	Single Leg Squat Hip Flex OC Prone CL Ball LG Curl
Box 2	Hurdle Hop 1/2 SQ JMP Weighted 15 Yard Starts	Box 2	Stnding Squat Drop Jump Delt BO Lat Reb Drop Plate Pincher	Box 2	DB Incline Bench 1 Arm DB Row Reactive Jobes
Box 3	Bench Press Bench Press Bench Press	Box 3	Bench Press Bench Press Bench Press	Box 3	Speed Switch Lunge with Ju DB Fly Delt BO Lat Reb Drop
Box 4	One Leg MB Side Toss DB BO Row 90 90 Jump Twist	Box 4	Med Ball Chest Pass DB BO Row Ball Pike Drop	Box 4	Glute Bar Lift Rope Circles Gripper
Box 5	Glute Bar Lift Cuban Press OC Band DB BO Row	Box 5	Lunge OC Hops Delt BO OH Reb Drop DB BO Row	Box 5	Iso Bi Recip Iso Tri Recip OC Ball Groin Squeeze
Box 6	GH HYPR OC Ball Groin Squeeze Plate Pincher	Box 6	GH HYPR OC Ball Groin Squeeze Plate Pincher	Box 6	Iso Bi Recip Speed Abduction Close Grip Bench
Box 7	DB Shoulder Press Hip Flex OC Prone CL Iso Bi Recip	Box 7	Inc Delt Lat Reb Drop Russian Switch Lunge DB Shoulder Press	Box 7	Lunge OC Hops Rope Vertical GH Supine CL Shock Abs
Box 8	Iso Tri Recip Iso Bi Recip Jobes ECC	Box 8	Iso Tri Recip Bicep Shock Curls Band Lying Int Rot	Box 8	

BLOCK FIVE (3-DAY): HIGH VELOCITY PEAKING FOR HOCKEY

MONDAY (100%)

Exercise	REPS	LOAD	SETS	NOTES
Hex Deadlift Iso	T		2	0:0:0:0:5:10
PW/ 15 Rest BB	EU		EU	ISO
Cpress Ext Rot rev Band OC	T	#NA	2	0:0:0:0:10:10
PW/ 45 Rest BB	EDT			Each side
Ankle Band Work	T		2	0:0:0:0:10:10
Squat Drop Jump	C1T	#NA	2	2x - Tendo
PW/ 15 Rest BB	EU		EU	Set Drop off
4-W Neck OC Ball	6		2	Reactive
375 SL Leg Press	T	115 - 130	2	0:0:0:0:15:10
375 SL Leg Press	T	115 - 130	3	0:0:0:0:15:10
PW/ 30 Rest BB	EUA		EUA	
Hip Flex Prone oc	T	#NA	3	0:0:0:0:15:10
PW/ 30 Rest BB	EDT		EUA	OC-D
105 DB BO Row	T	55 - 60	3	0:0:0:0:15:10
Cpress Int Rot Band OC	EU		ED	OC-A
Med Ball Pass	4		2	ONE ARM
PW/ 30 Rest BB			ED	OC-D
105 DB BENCH	T	30 - 35	2	0:0:0:0:15:10
105 DB BENCH	T	30 - 35	ED	oc-D
PW/ 30 Rest BB			ED	
GH HYPR Incline	T	#NA	2	0:0:0:0:15:10
PW/ 30 Rest BB	EUA		ED	OC-A
Inc Delt Lat Reb Drop	T		2	7 - OC-D
Band Tricep Extension	T	#NA	2	0:0:0:0:15:10
PW/ 30 Rest BB	EDT		EU	oc-D
Bicep shock curls	T	#NA	2	0:0:0:0:15:10
PW/ 30 Rest BB	EDT			
OC Ball Grion Sqeeze	T		2	0:0:0:0:15:10
GH HANG	120S		1	
Pair w/				
Rollers Glutes & Hams	120S		1	
Pair w/				
LAYING RELAXATION	120S			

WENDSDAY (100%)

Exercise	REPS	LOAD	SETS	NOTES
Hex Deadlift Iso	T		2	0:0:0:0:5:10
PW/ 15 Rest BB	EU		EU	ISO
Cpress Ext Rot rev Band	T	#NA	2	0:0:0:0:10:10
PW/ 15 Rest BB	EUA		2	0:0:0:0:10:10
Calf Raises	T		2	0:0:0:0:10:10
Squat Drop Jump	T	#NA	2	0:0:0:0:10:10
PW/ 15 Rest BB	ED		EU	
OC Ball Grion Sqeeze	T		2	Reactive
575 Hex Deadlift	T	175 - 200	2	0:0:0:0:10:10
575 Hex Deadlift	T	175 - 200	3	Reactive
OC Ball Grion Sqeeze	T	#NA	3	0:0:0:0:10:10
Pair w/	ED		EU	OC-D
105 DB BO Row	T	30 - 35	3	OC-D
300 BENCH PRESS	5,3	150 - 200	1,1	
Med Ball Pass	EU		ED	ONE ARM
	3		ED	OC-D+1
300 Bench Press	T	90 - 105	2	0:0:0:0:10:10
300 Bench Press	T	90 - 105	ED	OC-D+1
Pair w/	EU		3	0:0:0:0:10:10
500 Glute Bar Lift	T	150 - 175	3	0:0:0:0:10:10
Pair w/	EUA			OC
Delt BO Lat Reb Drop	T		3	0:0:0:0:10:10
Tri PRess Band ASFM	10	#NA	2	0:0:0:0:10:10
Pair w/	EU		2	oc-A
Curl Band ASFM	T	#NA	ED	SL - OC
Pair w/	EDT		2	0:0:0:0:10:10
STR Leg OC Glute Lifts	T			
Pair w/				
GH HANG	120S		1	Relax Mouth
Rollers Quads & Back	120S	#NA	1	#REP?
LAYING WALL SHAKES	120S		1	Relax Mouth

FRIDAY (100%)

Exercise	REPS	LOAD	SETS	NOTES
Hex Deadlift Iso	T		2	0:0:0:0:5:10
PW/ 15 Rest BB	EU		EU	ISO
Cpress Ext Rot rev Band	T	#NA	2	0:0:0:17:10
PW/ 15 Rest BB			2	0:0:0:17:10
Calf Raises	8		2	0:0:0:17:10
Squat Drop Jump	T		2	0:0:0:17:10
PW/ 15 Rest BB				
OC Ball Grion Squeeze	T		2	0:0:0:17:10
575 Hex Deadlift	T	175 - 200	2	0:0:0:17:10
575 Hex Deadlift	T	175 - 200	3	0:0:0:17:10
OC Ball Grion Sqeeze	T	#NA	3	0:0:0:17:10
Pair w/				
105 DB BO Row	T	30 - 35	3	0:0:0:17:10
300 BENCH PRESS	5,3	150 - 200	1,1	
Pair w/				
Med Ball Pass	5		2	0:0:0:17:10
300 Bench Press	T	90 - 105	2	0:0:0:17:10
300 Bench Press	T	90 - 105	2	0:0:0:17:10
Pair w/				
500 Glute Bar Lift	T	150 - 175	3	0:0:0:17:10
Pair w/				
Delt BO Lat Reb Drop	T		3	0:0:0:17:10
Tri PRess Band ASFM	10	#NA	2	0:0:0:17:10
Pair w/				
Curl Band ASFM	T		2	0:0:0:17:10
Pair w/				
STR Leg OC Glute Lifts	T			
Pair w/				
GH HANG	120S		1	Relax Mouth
Rollers Quads & Back	120S		1	
LAYING WALL SHAKES	120S		1	Relax Mouth

BLOCK FIVE (3-DAY): HIGH VELOCITY PEAKING FOR HOCKEY HYPERLINKS

Day 1	Exercise Hyperlink	Day 2	Exercise Hyperlink	Day 3	Exercise Hyperlink
Box 1	Hex Deadlift Cpress Ext Rot Rev Band Ankle Band Work	Box 1	Hex Deadlift Cpress Ext Rot rev Band Calf Raises	Box 1	Hex Deadlift Cpress Ext Rot rev Band Calf Raises
Box 2	Squat Drop Jump 4-way Neck OC Ball SL Leg Press	Box 2	Squat Drop Jump Isometric Ball Groin Squeeze Hex Deadlift	Box 2	Squat Drop Jump OC Ball Groin Squeeze Hex Deadlift
Box 3	SL Leg Press Hip Flex OC Prone CL DB BO Row	Box 3	Hex Deadlift Isometric Ball Groin Squeeze DB BO Row	Box 3	Hex Deadlift OC Ball Groin Squeeze DB BO Row
Box 4	Cpress Int Rot Band OC Med Ball Chest Pass DB Bench	Box 4	Bench Press Med Ball Chest Pass Bench Press	Box 4	Bench Press Med Ball Chest Pass Bench Press
Box 5	DB Bench GH HYPR Incline Inc Delt Lat Reb Drop	Box 5	Bench Press Glute Bar Lift Delt BO Lat Reb Drop	Box 5	Bench Press Glute Bar Lift Delt BO Lat Reb Drop
Box 6	Band Tricep Extension Bicep Shock Curls OC Ball Groin Squeeze	Box 6	TriPress Band ASFM Curl Band AFSM STR Leg OC Glute Lifts	Box 6	TriPress Band ASFM Curl Band AFSM STR Leg OC Glute Lifts
Box 7		Box 7		Box 7	
Box 8	GH HANG Rollers Glutes and Hams Laying Relaxation	Box 8	GH HANG Rollers Quads and Back Laying Wall Shakes	Box 8	GH HANG Rollers Quads and Back Laying Wall Shakes

BLOCK FIVE (3-DAY): HIGH VELOCITY PEAKING FOR SWIMMING (200-400M)

MONDAY

100%	MONDAY	REPS	LOAD	SETS	NOTES
250	Squat Jump	C:T	140 - 150	2	2% - Tendo
	PW/ 21 Rest BB	T		EU	0:0:0:3
	Dual Action Bar Rows	T		2	Speed/Drop
	PW/ 21 Rest BB	EUA		ED	0:0:0:32:10
	Leg Press Calf Raise	T		2	0:0:0:32:10
575	Hex Deadlift	T		2	0:0:0:5:10
	PW/ 27 Rest BB	EU		EU	Iso
	Cuban PRSS INC F8	3		2	0:5:0:0
575	Hex Deadlift	ED		EU	
225	Single Leg Squat	T	175 - 200	3	0:0:0:32:10
	PW/ 32 Rest BB	T	70 - 80	EUA	
	Hip Flex Prone CL	T		3	0:0:0:32:10
	PW/ 32 Rest BB	EDT		ED	0:0:0:32:10
225	Lat Pull Chin Grip	T	180 - 190	3	0:0:0:32:10
120	DB BENCH	T	35 - 40	3	0:0:0:32:10
	PW/ 32 Rest BB	ED		ED	
	GH HYPR Incline	T		3	0:0:0:32:10
	PW/ 32 Rest BB	ED		ED	
75	DB Shoulder Press	T	25 - 25	3	0:0:0:32:10
60	DB Tri Ext	T	20 - 20	3	0:0:0:32:10
	PW/ 18 Rest BB	EU		EU	
225	Lat Pull Down	T	70 - 80	2	0:0:0:32:10
	PW/ 18 Rest BB	EUA		ED	
	Band Push Back	T		2	
			40% -	EU	
		EU	-		120S
		EU			120S
	GH HANG	120S		1	Relax Mouth
	Pair w/	EU		1	
	Rollers Glutes & Hams	120S		1	
	Pair w/	EU		1	
	LAYING RELAXATION	120S		1	

WENDESDAY

100%	WENDESDAY	REPS	LOAD	SETS	NOTES
	Squat Drop Jump	C:T		2	2% - Tendo
	PW/ 21 Rest BB			EU	0:0:0:10
	Prone Rings Figure 8	5		2	Speed/Drop
	PW/ 21 Rest BB	EUA			0:0:0:25:10
	Calf Raises	8		2	Knee Bend
575	Hex Deadlift	T		2	0:0:0:5:10
	PW/ 27 Rest BB	EDT		EU	Iso
	Hip Flex Prone OC	T		2	0:0:0:25:10
		EU			
750	Leg Press	T	150 - 190	2	0:0:0:25:10
750	Leg Press	T	150 - 190	2	0:0:0:25:10
	Defl BO OH Reb Drop	EU		EUA	
	PW/ 32 Rest BB	T		3	0:0:0:25:10
105	DB BO Row	T	20 - 25	3	0:0:0:25:10
300	BENCH PRESS	5,3	150 - 200	1,1	oc-D
	PW/ 32 Rest BB			EUA	
	Inc Delt Lat Reb Drop	ED		3	0:0:0:25:10
	PW/ 32 Rest BB	ED		ED	
300	Bench Press	T	60 - 75	2	0:0:0:25:10
300	BENCH PRESS	T	60 - 75	3	0:0:0:25:10
	PW/ 18 Rest BB	ED		EU	
500	Glute Bar Lift	T	100 - 125	3	0:0:0:25:10
	PW/ 18 Rest BB	ED		ED	
210	DB Shrug	T	65 - 75	2	0:0:0:25:10
240	Dips	T	70 - 85	2	0:0:0:25:10
180	Chin up	EU	55 - 65	ED	
	PW/ 18 Rest BB	T		2	
	Side to Side supine Row	EDT			
	Pair w/	5	65% - 70%	1	
	Pair w/	EU			
	Pair w/	1	80% - 80%	1	
		EU			
		3	90% - 95%	3	
	GH HANG	120S		1	Relax Mouth
	Pair w/				
	Rollers Quads & Back	120S		1	
	Pair w/				
	LAYING WALL SHAKES	120S		1	Relax Mouth

FRIDAY

100%	FRIDAY	REPS	LOAD	SETS	NOTES
250	Squat Jump	T	100 - 115	2	0:0:0:2:40:20
	PW/ 18 Rest BB	EU		EUA	
	STR LG Iso Glue Lifts	T		2	0:0:0:40:20
	PW/ 18 Rest BB	EUA			0:0:0:40:20
	Calf Raises	T		2	0:0:0:40:20
750	Leg Press	T	150 - 190	3	0:0:0:40:20
	PW/ 18 Rest BB	EU			
	4 w/Y BND Ankle Kick	T		3	0:0:0:10:10
	PW/ 18 Rest BB	ED			
225	Lat Pull Down	T	45 - 55	3	0:0:0:40:20
60	DB Fly	T	35 - 35	3	0:0:0:40:20
	PW/ 18 Rest BB	EU		EU	
	Ball LG Curl	T		3	0:0:0:40:20
	PW/ 18 Rest BB	ED			
38	DB Rear Delt	T	10 - 10	3	0:0:0:40:20
	Tricep Band Press	x			0:0:0:40:20
	PW/ 18 Rest BB	EU		ED	
180	Chin up	x	125 - 145	2	0:0:0:40:20
		ED			
		180s		1	
	Pair w/	180s	60% -	1	
		ED			
		120S		1	
		EU			
	Pair w/	5	65% - 70%	1	
		EU			
	Pair w/	1	80% - 80%	1	
	Pair w/	6	65% - 70%	3	
		ED			
		8		2	OC
		EUA			
	GH HANG	120S		1	Relax Mouth
	Pair w/				
	Rollers Quads & Back	120S		1	
	Pair w/				
	LAYING WALL SHAKES	120S		1	Relax Mouth

BLOCK FIVE (3-DAY): HIGH VELOCITY PEAKING FOR SWIMMING (200-400M) HYPERLINKS

Day 1	Exercise Hyperlink	Day 2	Exercise Hyperlink	Day 3	Exercise Hyperlink
Box 1	Squat Jump Dual Action Bar Rows Leg Press Calf Raise	Box 1	Squat Drop Jump Prone Rings Figure 8 Calf Raises	Box 1	Squat Jump STR LG Iso Glute Lifts Calf Raises
Box 2	Hex Deadlift Cuban Press Incline Figur Hex Deadlift	Box 2	Hex Deadlift Hip Flex Prone OC Leg Press	Box 2	Leg Press 4 wy BND Ankle Kick Lat Pull and Press
Box 3	Single Leg Squat Hip Flex Prone CL Lat Pull Chin Grip	Box 3	Leg Press Delt BO OH Reb Drop DB BO Row	Box 3	DB Fly Ball LG Curl DB Rear Delt
Box 4	DB Bench GH HYPR Incline DB Shoulder Press	Box 4	Bench Press Inc Delt Lat Reb Drop Bench Press	Box 4	Tricep Band Press Chin up
Box 5	DB Tri Ext Lat Pull Down Band Push Back	Box 5	Bench Press Glute Bar Lift DB Shrug	Box 5	
Box 6		Box 6	Dips Chin up Side to side supine row	Box 6	
Box 7		Box 7		Box 7	
Box 8	GH HANG Rollers Glutes and Hams Laying Relaxation	Box 8	GH HANG Rollers Quads and Back Laying Wall Shakes	Box 8	GH HANG Rollers Quads and Back Laying Wall Shakes

BLOCK FIVE (3-DAY): HIGH VELOCITY PEAKING FOR VOLLEYBALL

Day one

%	Day one	REPS	LOAD	SETS	NOTES
	Black Burn Series	T		2	0:10:0:0
	No Rest/B-Breath	EU		EU	
	Scarecrow	5	BHA	2	0:0:0:7:10
		ED		ED	
105	DB BENCH	T	30 – 35	3	2OC-d+1
	One Leg MB Side Toss	5	BHA	2	
	25 rest- BB	EUA		EDT	
105	DB BO Row	T	30 – 35	3	0:0:0:7:10
	25 rest- BB	EDT			Elbow Wide
	90 90 Jump Twist	T		3	0:0:0:7:10
	Band Push Back	T	BHA	2	one Arm
	25 rest- BB	EUA		EDT	0:0:0:7:10
	Hip Flex OC Prone CL	T	BHA	3	0:0:0:7:10
	25 rest- BB	EDT			0:0:0:7:10
	Band Lying Int Rot	T		2	OC
250	SL Hex Deadlift	5,3	25 – 170	1,1	Pwl Cubar F8
	No Rest/B-Breath	T			1band Rollers
	SL Hex Deadlift	T	– 90	3	1band Rollers
	No Rest/B-Breath	EU			
	1/2 SQ JMP Weighted	T		3	0:0:0:7:10
	Hurdle Hop	5		3	Pull Down
	15 rest- BB	EU			
	1/2 SQ JMP Weighted	T	BHA	3	reactive
	25 rest- BB	EU			
	15 Yard Starts	T		3	OC
45	DB Tri Pro Sup	T	15 – 15	2	oc-D+1
	25 rest- BB	EU		ED	0:0:0:7:10
	Iso Bi Recip	T		2	OC
	25 rest- BB	EU			
	Jobes ECC	EU		2	0:0:0:7:10
500	Glute Bar Lift	EU	150 – 175	3	OC
	25 rest- BB	EU		ED	
	CubPr Ext Rot Flex Band	T	BHA	3	OC-D
	25 rest- BB	EDT			
105	DB BO Row	T	30 – 35	3	OC-A
	GH HYPR	T		ED	oc-A
	Pair w/	ED		3	0:0:0:7:10
	Iso Ball Grion Sqeeze	T		3	OC
	25 rest- BB	ED			
	Plate Pincher	T		3	Each Arm

Day 2

%	Day 2	REPS	LOAD	SETS	NOTES
	Jobes	T		2	0:0:0:0
	No Rest/B-Breath	EU		EU	
	Prone Ring F8	6	BHA	2	0:0:0:5:10
		ED		ED	
90	DB INCLINE BENCH	T	35 – 40	3	OC
	Med Ball Chest Pass	5	BHA	3	One Arm
	25 rest- BB	EU		EUA	
	1 Arm DB Row	T		3	Reactive
	25 rest- BB	ED			
	Pike Abs Strap Drop	T	BHA	3	0:0:0:5:10
	Inc Delt Lat Reb Drop	T		EDT	0:0:0:5:10
	25 rest- BB	EUA			
	Hip Flex OC Prone CL	T	BHA	3	0:0:0:5:10
	25 rest- BB	EUA			
	CubPr Ext Rot Rev Band	T		2	OC
500	Back Squat	5,3	250 – 335	1,1	0:0:0:5:10
	No Rest/B-Breath	T			Band
500	Back Squat	3	390 – 400	1	Band
	No Rest/B-Breath	EU			
	1/2 SQ JMP Weighted	T		3	0:0:0:5:10
	Stding SQ Drop Jump	T		3	
	25 rest- BB	EU		EUA	
	Delt BO Lat Reb Drop	T		3	0:0:0:5:10
	25 rest- BB	ED			
	Plate Pincher	T		3	Each Arm
	Iso Tri Recip	T		EDT	Band
	25 rest- BB	EUA		2	0:0:0:5:10
	Iso Bi Recip	T		2	Band
	25 rest- BB	EU			
	Cub P in Rot Rev Band OC	T		2	0:0:0:5:10
	Lunge OC Hops	T		3	Each Leg
	25 rest- BB	EU		EU	0:0:0:5:10
	Band Lying Int Rot	EUA		3	oc-A
	Pair w/	EUA			0:0:0:5:10
105	DB BO Row	T	40 – 45	3	OC
	GH HYPR	T		ED	0:0:0:5:10
	Pair w/	ED		3	dc-A
	OC Ball Grion Sqeeze	T		3	OC
	Pair w/	ED			0:0:0:5:10
	Plate Pincher	T		3	0:0:0:5:10

Day 3 — 9-Dec-11

%	Day 3	REPS	LOAD	SETS	NOTES
90	DB INCLINE BENCH	T	25 – 30	3	oc-D+1
	15 Rest-BB	ED		ED	0:0:0:10:10
	1 Arm DB Row Reactive	T	BHA	3	0:0:0:10:10
	15 Rest-BB	ED			
	Jobes	T		3	0:0:0:10:10
	Iso Bi Recip	ED	BHA	2	EU
	Iso Tri Recip	T		2	0:0:0:10:10
	15 Rest-BB	EDT			
	OC Ball Grion Sqeeze	T	BHA	2	0:0:0:10:10
225	Single Leg Squat	EUA	70 – 80	3	OC+1
	15 Rest-BB	T	BHA	3	0:0:0:10:10
	Hip Flex OC Prone CL	T		3	0:0:0:0:10
	15 Rest-BB	ED			
	Ball LG Curl	T		3	OC-A
	Iso Bi Recip	8		3	0:0:0:10:10
	15 Rest-BB	T	BHA		Each Way
	90 90 Jump Twist	8		2	0:0:0:10:10
	15 Rest-BB	EUA			
	Iso Tri Recip	6	BHA	2	0:0:0:10:10
	Lunge OC Hops	T		3	Each Leg
	15 Rest-BB	EU		ED	0:0:0:10:10
	Reactive Bench Toss	T	BHA	3	
	15 Rest-BB	EUA			
	Delt Lat Rebound Drop	T		3	0:0:0:10:10
500	Glute Bar Lift	T	150 – 175	3	OC
	15 Rest-BB	EU		OC	0:0:0:10:10
	Rope Circles	15		3	0:0:0:10:10
	15 Rest-BB	ED			
	Plate Pincher	15		3	Each Hand
	Sqwat Squat Lunge with Jump	6			0:0:0:10:10
	15 Rest-BB	EUA			
	Rope Vertical	15	BHA	2	0:0:0:10:10
	15 Rest-BB	ED			
	GH Supine CL Shock Abs	T		2	0:0:0:10:10

BLOCK FIVE (3-DAY): HIGH VELOCITY PEAKING FOR VOLLEYBALL HYPERLINKS

Day 1	Exercise Hyperlink	Day 2	Exercise Hyperlink	Day 3	Exercise Hyperlink
Box 1	Black Burn Series Scarecrow DB Bench	Box 1	Jobes Prone Rings Figure 8 DB Incline Bench	Box 1	DB Incline Bench DB BO Row Jobes
Box 2	One Leg MB Side Toss DB BO Row 90 90 Jump Twist	Box 2	Med Ball Chest Pass 1 Arm DB Row Pike Abs Strap Drop	Box 2	Iso Bi Recip Iso Tri Recip OC Ball Groin Squeeze
Box 3	Band Push Back Hip Flex OC Prone CL Band Lying Int Rot	Box 3	Inc Delt Lat Reb Drop Hip Flex OC Prone CL CubPr Ext Rot Rev Band	Box 3	Single Leg Squat Hip Flex OC Prone CL Ball LG Curl
Box 4	SL Hex Deadlift SL Hex Deadlift 1/2 SQ JMP Weighted	Box 4	Back Squat Back Squat 1/2 SQ JMP Weighted	Box 4	Iso Bi Recip 90 90 Jump Twist Iso Tri Recip
Box 5	Hurdle Hop 1/2 SQ JMP Weighted 15 Yard Starts	Box 5	Stnding SQ Drop Jump Delt BO Lat Reb Drop Plate Pincher	Box 5	Lunge OC Hops Reactive Bench Toss Delt BO Lat Reb Drop
Box 6	DB Tri Pro Sup Iso Bi Recip Jobes ECC	Box 6	Iso Tri Recip Iso Bi Recip CubPr In Rot Rev Band	Box 6	Glute Bar Lift Rope Circles Plate Pincher
Box 7	Glute Bar Lift CubPr Ext Rot Rev Band DB BO Row	Box 7	Lunge OC Hops Band Lying Int Rot DB BO Row	Box 7	Speed Switch Lunge with Ju Rope Vertical GH Supine CL Shock Abs
Box 8	GH HYPR Isometric Ball Groin Sque Plate Pincher	Box 8	GH HYPR OC Ball Groin Squeeze Plate Pincher	Box 8	

6.12: BELOW 55 PERCENT TWO-DAY IN-SEASON PROGRAM

Last but not least, table 6.13 shows how to take what you learned about the three-day model and convert it to a two-day in-season program. In table 6.13, day one loading parameters are in white, day two loading parameters are in light gray, and day three loading parameters are in dark gray. Remember, whenever athletes are in-season, all their volume work comes from practice. Additional volume in the weight room or through conditioning will likely lead to an overtrained, underperforming athlete. Remember, *don't do any additional conditioning in-season outside of organized practice!*

TABLE 6.13: BELOW 55 PERCENT THREE-DAY VERSUS TWO-DAY IN-SEASON MODEL							
TRAINING WEEK:		DAY 1	DAY 2	DAY 3	DAY 4	DAY 5	DAY 6
THREE-DAY MODEL	FOCUS	TOTAL BODY	OFF	TOTAL BODY	OFF	TOTAL BODY	OFF
	LOAD	35–40%		45–55%		25–30%	
	MEANS APPLIED	AFSM		AFSM		AFSM	
TWO-DAY MODEL	FOCUS	TOTAL BODY	OFF	TOTAL BODY	OFF	OFF	OFF
	LOAD	35–40%		45–55%			
	MEANS APPLIED	AFSM		AFSM			

TWO-DAY IN SEASON BELOW 55 PERCENT VIDEO

BLOCK FIVE (2-DAY IN-SEASON): HIGH VELOCITY PEAKING GENERAL ATHLETE

MONDAY

100%	MONDAY	REPS	LOAD	SETS	NOTES
575	Hex Deadlift	T	115 - 145	2	0:0:0:0:5:10
	PW/ 15 Rest BB	EU		EU	ISO
	Cuban PRSS INC F8	5	#N/A - #N/A	2	
	PW/ 15 Rest BB	EDT			
	Ankle Band Work	8		2	Each Side
	Squat Drop Jump	C1T	#N/A - #N/A	2	2x- Tendo
	PW/ 15 Rest BB	EU		EU	Set Drop off
	4 way neck	6		2	Reactive
375	SL Leg Press	T	115 - 130	2	0:0:0:0:7:10
375	SL Leg Press	T	115 - 130	3	0:0:0:0:7:10
	PW/ 30 Rest BB	EUA		EUA	
	Hip Flex Prone oc	T		3	OC-D
	PW/ 30 Rest BB	EDT			0:0:0:0:7:10
105	DB BO Row	T	55 - 60	3	0:0:0:0:7:10
	Prone Rings Figure 8	8	#N/A - #N/A	2	
	PW/ 30 Rest BB	EU		EU	
	Med Ball Pass	5			
	PW/ 30 Rest BB			ED	OC-D
105	DB BENCH	T	30 - 35	2	0:0:0:0:7:10
105	DB BENCH	T	30 - 35	2	oc-D
	PW/ 30 Rest BB	EDT		ED	
	GH HYPR Incline	5	#N/A - #N/A	3	OC-A
	PW/ 30 Rest BB	EUA		ED	
38	DB Side Lat Raise	T	10 - 15	3	7 - OC-D
	Band Tricep Extension			EU	OC-D
	PW/ 30 Rest BB	EDT		2	0:0:0:0:7:10
	Bicep shock curls	T			oc-D
	PW/ 30 Rest BB	EDT			0:0:0:0:7:10
	90 90 Grion ISO Hold	T		2	
		6	75% - 80%	2	
	GH HANG	120S		1	
	Pair w/				
	Rollers Glutes & Hams	120S		1	
	Pair w/				
	LAYING RELAXATION	120S		1	

WENDESDAY

100%	WENDESDAY	REPS	LOAD	SETS	NOTES
575	Hex Deadlift	T	115 - 145	2	0:0:0:0:5:10
	PW/ 15 Rest BB		EU	EU	ISO
	Cpress Ext Rot rev Band	T	#N/A - #N/A	2	0:0:0:0:5:10
	PW/ 15 Rest BB	EUA			
	Calf Raises	8		2	
	Squat Drop Jump	T	#N/A - #N/A	2	0:0:0:0:5:10
	PW/ 15 Rest BB	ED		EU	
	Iso Ball Grion Sqeeze	T			0:5:0:0
575	Hex Deadlift	T	175 - 200	2	0:0:0:0:5:10
575	Hex Deadlift	T	175 - 200	3	Reactive
	Pair w/	ED		EU	0:0:0:0:5:10
	Iso Ball Grion Sqeeze	T	#N/A - #N/A	3	0:0:0:0:5:10
	Pair w/	T		EUA	OC-D
105	DB BO Row	T	30 - 35	3	
300	BENCH PRESS	5,3	150 - 200	1,1	
	Pair w/	EU		ED	
	Med Ball Pass	3			
				ED	OC-D+1
300	Bench Press	T	90 - 105	2	0:0:0:0:5:10
300	Bench Press	T	90 - 105	3	OC-D+1
	Pair w/	EU		EUA	0:0:0:0:5:10
500	Glute Bar Lift	T	150 - 175	3	
	Pair w/	EUA		3	0:0:0:0:5:10
	Delt BO Lat Reb Drop	10		3	0:0:0:0:5:10
	Band Tricep Extension	EU		ED	
	Pair w/	T	35 - 40	2	oc-A
120	Bar Curl	EDT		ED	0:0:0:0:5:10
	Pair w/	T		2	0:0:0:0:5:10
	90 90 Glute ISO Hold				
	Pair w/				
	GH HANG	120S		1	Relax Mouth
	Pair w/				
	Rollers Quads & Back	120S		1	
	Pair w/				
	LAYING WALL SHAKES	120S		1	Relax Mouth

BLOCK FIVE (2-DAY IN-SEASON): HIGH VELOCITY PEAKING FOR GENERAL ATHLETE HYPERLINKS

Day 1	Exercise Hyperlink	Day 2	Exercise Hyperlink
Box 1	Hex Deadlift Cuban Press Incline Figure 8 Ankle Band Work	Box 1	Hex Deadlift Cpress Ext Rot rev Band Calf Raises
Box 2	Squat Drop Jump 4 way neck SL Leg Press	Box 2	Squat Drop Jump Isometric Ball Groin Squeeze Hex Deadlift
Box 3	SL Leg Press Hip Flex OC Prone CL DB BO Row	Box 3	Hex Deadlift Isometric Ball Groin Squeeze DB BO Row
Box 4	Prone Rings Figure 8 Med Ball Chest Pass DB Bench	Box 4	Bench Press Med Ball Chest Pass Bench Press
Box 5	DB Bench GH HYPR Incline DB Side Lat Raise	Box 5	Bench Press Glute Bar Lift Delt BO Lat Reb Drop
Box 6	Band Tricep Extension Bicep Curl Shock 90 90 Groin ISO Hold	Box 6	Band Tricep Extension Bar Curl 90 90 Glute ISO Hold
Box 7		Box 7	
Box 8	GH HANG Rollers Glutes and Hams Laying Relaxation	Box 8	GH HANG Rollers Quads and Back Laying Wall Shakes

SECTION 7

PUTTING IT ALL TOGETHER

7.1: THE BIG PICTURE

Back in the first chapter, I used the analogy that coaches are mechanics and athletes are the cars they work on. Our goal as mechanics is simple — get the cars to produce as much horsepower as possible, in as short a time as possible. But before coaches can do this proficiently, before they can consider themselves master mechanics, they need to know the tools of the trade and the parts of the car that need to be worked on to improve performance. Do you think that NASCAR mechanics know anything about how to install a plush leather interior? How about installing a 6-disc CD changer? They might have an idea, but I promise you they aren't proficient at it. And why would they be? Neither of those things improve the performance of the car. Their focus is narrow (the engine) and their goal is simple (more power).

Just as master mechanics know their way around an engine, strength coaches must know their way around an athlete. Both must have a solid understanding of how their "vehicles" work, their moving parts, and how to adjust or enhance those parts to improve performance. I hope that this book has given you the tools and methods to confidently go and work with your athletes – a step-by-step guide to sport performance. First, we looked at the importance of stress. We then examined the ideal way in which a coach can maximize the application of stress to optimize performance gains through a modified undulated model. We looked not only at general stress, but the specific ways that the neuromuscular system must be stimulated to promote maximal positive adaptation by the use of triphasic training. And finally, we looked at how coaches could combine all of these parameters in a structured, block template to ensure the continuous adaptation of their athletes through a progressive mesocycle training program.

Now it's time to take what you have learned and view it in a macrocycle, off-season training context. In the pages that follow, you will find tables (7.1—7.4) that give a bird's eye view in the application and sequencing of the means, methods, and parameters you learned throughout *Triphasic Training*. This is all mainly a review. However, seeing it laid out will help you better grasp how you layer the blocks, methods, and parameters on top of each other to optimize training in the varying lengths of off-seasons you encounter.

TABLE 7.1: PROGRESSIVE LOADING VARIABLES FOR TRIPHASIC OFF-SEASON MACROCYCLE

PHASE	BLOCK	DAY	LOAD	TIME	REPS	SETS
PHASE ONE	BLOCK ONE (ECCENTRIC) 2-3 WEEKS	MONDAY (MEDIUM INTENSITY)	82-87%	5-6 SECONDS	1-3	2-4
		WEDNESDAY (HIGH INTENSITY)	ECCENTRIC MEANS NOT APPLIED; REACTIVE			
		FRIDAY (HIGH VOLUME)	75-80%	6-7 SECONDS	2-4	2-4
	BLOCK TWO (ISOMETRIC) 2-3 WEEKS	MONDAY (MEDIUM INTENSITY)	82-87%	2-3 SECONDS	1-3	4-5
		WEDNESDAY (HIGH INTENSITY)	ISOMETRIC MEANS NOT APPLIED; REACTIVE			
		FRIDAY (HIGH VOLUME)	75-80%	3-4 SECONDS	3-4	4-5
	BLOCK THREE (CONCENTRIC) 2-3 WEEKS	MONDAY (MEDIUM INTENSITY)	82-87%	REACTIVE	2-3	3-4
		WEDNESDAY (HIGH INTENSITY)	90-97%		1	1-4
		FRIDAY (HIGH VOLUME)	75-80%		3-4	3-5
PHASE TWO	BLOCK FOUR 3-4 WEEKS	MONDAY (MEDIUM INTENSITY)	62-70%	REACTIVE	2-3	4-6
		WEDNESDAY (HIGH INTENSITY)	72-80%		1-3	4-5
		FRIDAY (HIGH VOLUME)	75-80%		5-8	4-6
PHASE THREE	BLOCK FIVE (AFSM) 3-5 WEEKS	MONDAY (MEDIUM INTENSITY)	35-40%	IDEAL TIME	PARAMETER BASED ON TIME	3-5
		WEDNESDAY (HIGH INTENSITY)	45-55%	BELOW IDEAL TIME		3-5
		FRIDAY (HIGH VOLUME)	25-30%	ABOVE IDEAL TIME		3-5

TABLE 7.2: PEAKING SCHEDULE FOR ANAEROBIC TEAM SPORTS

STRENGTH RANKING	PERFORMANCE RANKING	12 WEEKS OUT	11 WEEKS OUT	10 WEEKS OUT	9 WEEKS OUT	8 WEEKS OUT	7 WEEKS OUT	6 WEEKS OUT	5 WEEKS OUT	4 WEEKS OUT	3 WEEKS OUT	2 WEEKS OUT	1 WEEK OUT
STRENGTH EMPHASIS FOR SPORTS													
8/10	5/10										92-80%	92-80%	92-80%
SPEED EMPHASIS FOR SPORTS													
5/10	8/10										50-25%	50-25%	50-25%
5/10	8/10										80-55%	50-25%	50-25%
6/10	8/10										92-80%	80-55%	50-25%
4/10	9/10									50-25%	50-25%	50-25%	50-25%
6/10	8/10									80-55%	80-55%	50-25%	50-25%
6/10	8/10								80-55%	80-55%	50-25%	50-25%	50-25%
6/10	8/10								80-55%	80-55%	LIGHT	50-25%	50-25%
6/10	8/10							80-55%	80-55%	80-55%	50-25%	50-25%	50-25%
STRENGTH AND SPEED EMPHASIS FOR SPORTS													
6/10	8/10							92-80%	92-80%	80-55%	80-55%	50-25%	50-25%
5/10	9/10						92-80%	92-80%	80-55%	80-55%	50-25%	50-25%	50-25%
7/10	7/10						92-80%	92-80%	92-80%	80-55%	80-55%	80-55%	50-25%
7/10	7/10						92-80%	92-80%	80-55%	LIGHT	80-55%	50-25%	50-25%
8/10	7/10					92-80%	92-80%	92-80%	80-55%	LIGHT	80-55%	50-25%	50-25%
8/10	7/10					92-80%	92-80%	92-80%	80-55%	50-25%	50-25%	50-25%	50-25%
8/10	7/10					92-80%	92-80%	92-80%	80-55%	LIGHT	LIGHT	50-25%	50-25%
8/10	7/10				92-80%	92-80%	92-80%	80-55%	80-55%	80-55%	50-25%	50-25%	50-25%
8/10	7/10				92-80%	92-80%	92-80%	80-55%	LIGHT	LIGHT	50-25%	50-25%	50-25%

Emphasis placed on Eccentric Means

Emphasis placed on Isometric Means

Emphasis placed on Concentric/Reactive Means

*The strength and performance rankings are a scale that show where the emphasis in the peaking schedule lies. Remember, a solid foundation of strength is paramount, however only in so much as the athlete can produce in the time limits of their sport. It is up to the coach to know where an athlete is in their training, and determine how much emphasis must be placed on raw strength and how much placed on speed and performance.

TABLE 7.1: PEAKING SCHEDULE FOR ANAEROBIC TEAM SPORTS

STRENGTH AND SPEED EMPHASIS FOR SPORTS

STRENGTH RANKING	PERFORMANCE RANKING	12 WEEKS OUT	11 WEEKS OUT	10 WEEKS OUT	9 WEEKS OUT	8 WEEKS OUT	7 WEEKS OUT	6 WEEKS OUT	5 WEEKS OUT	4 WEEKS OUT	3 WEEKS OUT	2 WEEKS OUT	1 WEEK OUT
7/10	8/10			92-80%	92-80%	80-55%	92-80%	LIGHT	80-55%	80-55%	80-55%	50-25%	50-25%
7/10	8/10			92-80%	92-80%	92-80%	LIGHT	80-55%	80-55%	80-55%	50-25%	50-25%	50-25%
7/10	8/10			92-80%	92-80%	80-55%	80-55%	50-25%	50-25%	80-55%	80-55%	50-25%	50-25%
9/10	9/10			92-80%	92-80%	92-80%	LIGHT	80-55%	80-55%	80-55%	80-55%	50-25%	50-25%
9/10	9/10			92-80%	92-80%	80-55%	80-55%	50-25%	92-80%	92-80%	80-55%	50-25%	50-25%
9/10	9/10			92-80%	92-80%	80-55%	80-55%	50-25%	92-80%	80-55%	80-55%	50-25%	50-25%
9/10	9/10			92-80%	92-80%	80-55%	80-55%	LIGHT	92-80%	80-55%	80-55%	50-25%	50-25%
8/10	8/10		92-80%	92-80%	92-80%	LIGHT	80-55%	80-55%	80-55%	LIGHT	50-25%	50-25%	50-25%
9/10	9/10		92-80%	92-80%	80-55%	80-55%	50-25%	50-25%	80-55%	80-55%	80-55%	50-25%	50-25%
8/10	8/10		92-80%	92-80%	92-80%	92-80%	92-80%	LIGHT	80-55%	80-55%	50-25%	50-25%	50-25%
8/10	8/10		92-80%	92-80%	92-80%	92-80%	92-80%	LIGHT	80-55%	80-55%	80-55%	50-25%	50-25%
9/10	9/10		92-80%	92-80%	92-80%	92-80%	92-80%	80-55%	80-55%	80-55%	80-55%	50-25%	50-25%
9/10	9/10		92-80%	92-80%	92-80%	92-80%	92-80%	LIGHT	80-55%	80-55%	80-55%	50-25%	50-25%
9/10	9/10	92-80%	92-80%	92-80%	92-80%	92-80%	92-80%	LIGHT	80-55%	80-55%	50-25%	50-25%	50-25%
9/10	9/10	92-80%	92-80%	92-80%	LIGHT	92-80%	92-80%	80-55%	80-55%	50-25%	50-25%	50-25%	50-25%
10/10	10/10	92-80%	92-80%	92-80%	92-80%	92-80%	80-55%	80-55%	LIGHT	50-25%	50-25%	50-25%	50-25%
10/10	10/10	92-80%	92-80%	92-80%	92-80%	LIGHT	80-55%	80-55%	80-55%	80-55%	80-55%	50-25%	50-25%
8/10	9/10	92-80%	92-80%	92-80%	80-55%	50-25%	50-25%	92-80%	92-80%	80-55%	80-55%	50-25%	50-25%
7/10	9/10	92-80%	92-80%	92-80%	50-25%	92-80%	80-55%	80-55%	50-25%	92-80%	80-55%	50-25%	50-25%
6/10	10/10	80-55%	80-55%	50-25%	50-25%	80-55%	50-25%	50-25%	50-25%	80-55%	50-25%	50-25%	50-25%

Emphasis placed on Eccentric Means

Emphasis placed on Isometric Means

Emphasis placed on Concentric/Reactive Means

TABLE 7.2: YEAR LONG TRAINING PROGRAM OUTLINE FOR COLLEGIATE FOOTBALL TEAM

WEEK 1	WEEK 2	WEEK 3	WEEK 4	WEEK 5	WEEK 6	WEEK 7	WEEK 8	WEEK 9	WEEK 10	WEEK 11	WEEK 12
1/2	1/9	1/16	1/23	1/30	2/6	2/13	2/20	2/27	3/5	3/12	3/19
WORK CAPACITY @ HOME	80-55%	80-55%	80-55%	92-80%	92-80%	92-80%	92-80%	92-80%	92-80%	80-55%	BREAK

WINTER BREAK/TRAIN AT HOME — WINTER WORKOUTS

WEEK 13	WEEK 14	WEEK 15	WEEK 16	WEEK 17	WEEK 18	WEEK 19	WEEK 20	WEEK 21	WEEK 22	WEEK 23	WEEK 24
3/26	4/2	4/9	4/16	4/23	4/30	5/7	5/14	5/21	5/28	6/4	6/11
80-55%	80-55%	80-55%	80-55%	80-55%	80-55%	80-55%	80-55%	80-55%	92-80%	92-80%	92-80%

SPRING BALL — FINALS — SUMMER WORKOUTS

WEEK 25	WEEK 26	WEEK 27	WEEK 28	WEEK 29	WEEK 30	WEEK 31	WEEK 32	WEEK 33	WEEK 34	WEEK 35	WEEK 36
6/18	6/25	7/2	7/9	7/16	7/23	7/30	8/6	8/13	8/20	8/27	9/3
92-80%	92-80%	92-80%	80-55%	80-55%	50-25%	50-25%	65-40 %	65-40 %	65-40 %	65-40 %	65-40 %

SUMMER WORKOUTS — HOME TRAINING — TRAINING CAMP

WEEK 37	WEEK 38	WEEK 39	WEEK 40	WEEK 41	WEEK 42	WEEK 43	WEEK 44	WEEK 45	WEEK 46	WEEK 47	WEEK 48
9/10	9/17	9/24	10/1	10/8	10/15	10/22	10/29	11/5	11/12	11/19	11/26
80-55%	80-55%	80-55%	50-25%	50-25%	80-55%	80-55%	50-25%	50-25%	50-25%	50-25%	80-55%

2012 FOOTBALL SEASON

WEEK 49	WEEK 50	WEEK 51	WEEK 52
12/3	12/10	12/17	12/24
80-55%	50-25%	50-25%	50-25%

BOWL PRACTICE

Legend:
- EMPHASIS PLACED ON ECCENTRIC MEANS
- EMPHASIS PLACED ON ISOMETRIC MEANS
- EMPHASIS PLACED ON CONCENTRIC/REACTIVE MEANS
- EMPHASIS PLACED ON PEAKING/AFSM MEANS

TABLE 7.4: POSSIBLE VARIATIONS FOR EXERCISE SEQUENCING					
TRAINING PHASE	PHASE ONE: ABOVE 80% (HIGH FORCE AT LOW VELOCITY)			PHASE TWO: 80-55% (HIGH FORCE AT HIGH VELOCITY)	PHASE THREE: BELOW 55% (HIGH VELOCITY PEAKING)
BLOCK	BLOCK ONE	BLOCK TWO	BLOCK THREE	BLOCK FOUR	BLOCK FIVE
BACK SQUAT	BACK SQUAT ECCENTRIC	BACK SQUAT ISOMETRIC	BACK SQUAT WITH CHAINS	BACK SQUAT	BACK SQUAT WITH BANDS
	BACK SQUAT WEIGHT RELEASERS	BACK SQUAT ISOMETRIC	BACK SQUAT WITH BANDS	BACK SQUAT	BACK SQUAT WITH BANDS
	BACK SQUAT WEIGHT RELEASERS	BACK SQUAT WITH PAUSE	BACK SQUAT WITH CHAINS	BACK SQUAT	SQUAT JUMP WITH WEIGHT
SINGLE LEG SQUAT	SINGLE LEG DUMBBELL SQUAT ECCENTRIC	SINGLE LEG DUMBBELL SQUAT PAUSE	SINGLE LEG DUMBBELL SQUAT OSCILLATORY	SINGLE LEG DUMBELL SQUAT DROP	SINGLE LEG DUMBBELL REACTIVE SQUAT
	SINGLE LEG DUMBBELL SQUAT ECCENTRIC	SINGLE LEG DUMBBELL SQUAT PAUSE	SINGLE LEG DUMBELL SQUAT DROP	SINGLE LEG DUMBBELL REACTIVE SQUAT	SINGLE LEG DUMBBELL SQUAT OSCILLATORY
	SINGLE LEG DUMBBELL SQUAT ECCENTRIC	SINGLE LEG DUMBBELL SQUAT PAUSE	SINGLE LEG DUMBBELL SQUAT OSCILLATORY	SINGLE LEG DUMBBELL SQUAT 2POC	SINGLE LEG DUMBBELL REACTIVE SQUAT
FRONT SQUAT	FRONT SQUAT ECCENTRIC	FRONT SQUAT ISOMETRIC	FRONT SQUAT	DUMBBELL SINGLE LEG FRONT SQUAT REACTIVE	DUMBBELL SINGLE LEG FRONT SQUAT OSCILLATORY REACTIVE
LUNGE	DUMBBELL WALKING LUNGE WITH PAUSE	DUMBBELL WALKING LUNGE	DUMBBELL WALKING LUNGE SWITCH	WALKING LUNGE JUMPS	WALKING DROP LUNGE JUMPS
	WALKING LUNGE WITH BAND	WALKING BAND LUNGE JUMPS	WALKING DROP BAND LUNGE JUMP	BOX DROP LUNGE	BOX DROP REACTIVE LUNGE JUMP

TABLE 7.4: POSSIBLE VARIATIONS FOR EXERCISE SEQUENCING					
TRAINING PHASE	PHASE ONE: ABOVE 80% (HIGH FORCE AT LOW VELOCITY)			PHASE TWO: 80-55% (HIGH FORCE AT HIGH VELOCITY)	PHASE THREE: BELOW 55% (HIGH VELOCITY PEAKING)
BLOCK	BLOCK ONE	BLOCK TWO	BLOCK THREE	BLOCK FOUR	BLOCK FIVE
	DUMBBELL WALKING LUNGE WITH PAUSE	DUMBBELL WALKING LUNGE	DUMBBELL WALKING LUNGE SWITCH	SPEED SWITCH JUMP LUNGE	SPEED CYCLE JUMP LUNGE
RDL	RDL DUMBBELL ECCENTRIC	RDL DUMBBELL ISOMETRIC	RDL DUMBBELL	RDL DUMBBELL OSCILLATORY	RDL DUMBBELL SINGLE LEG BENCH HOP
	IN LINE RDL ECCENTRICS	IN LINE RDL ISOMETRIC	IN LINE RDL	RDL DUMBBELL OSCILLATORY	RDL DUMBBELL SINGLE LEG BENCH HOP
	RDL ECCENTRIC	RDL ISOMETRIC	RDL	IN LINE RDL	RDL OSCILLATORY
LEG PRESS	LEG PRESS SINGLE LEG ECCENTRIC	LEG PRESS SINGLE LEG ISOMETRIC	SINGLE LEG PRESS	LEG PRESS SINGLE LEG DROP PAUSE	LEG PRESS SINGLE LEG REACTIVE
GLUTE HAM	ECCENTRIC GLUTE HAM	GLUTE HAM HYPER	GLUTE HAM HYPER	SPEED GLUTE HAM DROP	GLUTE HAM OC ADVANTAGE POSITION
HIP FLEXOR	HIP FLEXOR ECCENTRIC PRONE	HIP FLEXOR ISOMETRIC PULL	HIP FLEXOR PRONE CONTRALATERAL	HIP FLEXOR PRONE OC CONTRALATERAL	HIP FLEXOR SPEED SWITCH LUNGE
	HIP FLEXOR PRONE ECCENTRIC CONTRALATERAL	HIP FLEXOR PRONE ISOMETRIC CONTRALATERAL	HIP FLEXOR PRONE CONTRALATERAL	HIP FLEXOR PRONE OC CONTRALATERAL	HIP FLEXOR SPEED SWITCH LUNGE
PLYOS	SWITCH LUNGE PAUSE SAND BAG	SWITCH LUNGE WITH JUMP	SWITCH JUMP LUNGE REACTIVE	LUNGE DROP REACTIVE JUMP	BOX DROP REACTIVE LUNGE JUMP
	SQUAT JUMP PAUSE	SQUAT DROP PAUSE JUMP	SQUAT DROP JUMP	ACCELERATED BAND SQUAT JUMP PAUSE	ACCELERATED BAND SQUAT JUMP

7.2: WRAP-UP

For a long time I thought it would be easy to come up with an ending for this book. But, odd as it may seem, the more I thought about how I wanted to bring this all to a close, the further away I felt I got from coming up with a good conclusion. Then it dawned on me why a conclusion is so elusive — I was trying to bring closure to something that is continuous. Sure, this is the end of the book in a physical sense, but from a philosophical perspective it is only the beginning. For most of you, this has been your first exposure to triphasic training. For others, you may have been familiar with the basic principles but were shown a new approach to their application, or had a "I never thought of it that way" moment. What all of you will hopefully take away from this book are new ideas and methods to try with your athletes. This book is only the starting point. The real learning will begin when you walk into the gym and start using what you found in this book.

I have learned quite a bit as well. This book has forced me to reexamine my own methods, to truly look at and question my own principles and see if I still value them as I have in the past. We all get stuck in mental ruts. We form certain paths of thinking that, after awhile, are hard to get out of. And while it is good to be rooted in beliefs, it can be detrimental if those roots prevent you from seeing and changing to a better path. I believe that discovery and innovation in the world of strength and conditioning are the reckless abandonment of assumed facts in the pursuit of better training methods. Don't take that to mean that we throw the baby out with the bath water, but I definitely throw out the bathwater regularly to clear the way for new, fresh ideas. Remember, science is never fully proven. Science simply shows associations between two variables. Don't ever be afraid to challenge those associations.

In that spirit I have decided to leave you with two example programs of my latest triphasic training method. I don't even have a name for it yet, but it is the culmination of the most advanced training ideals and methodologies I have seen and learned over the past seventeen years of coaching. It is without question the most advanced method I have ever seen and has shown amazing results with my athletes. Look at it. Question it. Think about it. But most of all, try it! How else would you end a book about applied sport performance training?

ADVANCED TRIPHASIC (3-DAY): ECCENTRIC PHASE

MONDAY — 100%

Exercise	REPS	LOAD	SETS	NOTES
Stdng SQ Drop P-Jump	C1T	ENA	2	3:X: - Tendo
PW/ 30 Rest BB	EU			0:2:0:6
Cuban PRSS INC F8	T	ENA	2	5:0:0:25:12
PW/ 30 Rest BB	EU			
Leg P Calf Raise KB	EU		2	3:0:0:25:12
500 Back Squat	T	250 - 275	3	5:0:0:25:12 — Box
Np 2:15-HR 105	EU			
Hip Flex Ecc Prone	T	ENA	3	5:0:0:25:12 — Bench
PW/ 30 Rest BB	EUA	EDT		
1 Arm LAT Pull	T	ENA	3	3:0:0:25:12
105 DB BENCH	ED		3	5:0:0:25:12 — Bench
PW/ 30 Rest BB	EU			
GH HYPR Incline	T	ENA	3	5:0:0:25:12
PW/ 30 Rest BB	EU			+ Shrug
30 OH LAT Raise	T	20 - 20	3	5:0:0:25:12
64 JM DB Press	T	50 - 55	2	5:0:0:25:12
PW/ 30 Rest BB	ED			
120 BAR CURL	T	95 - 100	2	5:0:0:25:12
PW/ 30 Rest BB	EDT			
Bench Abd Groin ECC	EDT		2	25:0:0:0:25:12
H-Sq Sh Bi Trap	180s	ENA		25 on 35 off
1:00 R B-Breath	ED			
Chest Rev Grip Iso	180s	ENA	1	25 on 35 off
GH HANG	120s		1	
Pair w/				
Rollers Glutes & Hams	120s		1	
Pair w/				
LAYING RELAXATION	120s			

WEDNESDAY — 100%

Exercise	REPS	LOAD	SETS	NOTES
Stdng SQ Drop Jump	C1T	ENA	2	2:X: - Tendo
PW/ 30 Rest BB	ED			0:0:0:3
Tea Cup Stuff	T	ENA	2	X:0:X:0:17:10
PW/ 30 Rest BB	EU			
Calf Raises	T		2	3:0:0:17:10
750 Leg Press	T	565 - 600	3	3:0:0:0:17:10
Np 2:15-HR 105	EU		ED	
Iso Ball Groin Sqeeze	T	ENA	3	0:3:0:17:10
PW/ 30 Rest BB	EU			
165 Dynamic Lat Pull	T	130 - 140	3	3:0:0:17:10
300 BENCH PRESS	ED	95 - 210	3	3:0:0:17:10
Np 2:15-HR 105	T			
500 Glute Bar Lift	T	350 - 375	3	3:0:0:17:10
PW/ 30 Rest BB	EU			
38 DB Rear Delt	T	25 - 30	2	3:0:0:17:10
45 DB Tri Pro Sup	T	35 - 35	2	3:0:0:17:10
PW/ 30 Rest BB	EU			
60 DB Curl to Press	T	40 - 45	1	3:0:0:17:10
PW/ 30 Rest BB	EUA			
Bench Abd Groin ECC	15S		2	
Glute Ham Back Cav Iso	180s	ENA	1	17 on 43 off
1:00 R B-Breath	EU			
H-Sq Sh Bi Trap	120s		1	17 on 43 off
	ED			
	8	70% - 75%	2	
GH HANG	120s	ENA	1	Relax Mouth
Pair w/				
Rollers Quads & Back	120s	ENA	1	EDT
Pair w/				
LAYING WALL SHAKES	120s		1	Relax Mouth

FRIDAY — 100%

Exercise	REPS	LOAD	SETS	NOTES
750 Leg Press	T	490 - 525	4	5:0:0:0:32:30
Np 2:15-HR 105	EU		ED	
Iso Ball Groin Sqeeze			4	0:5:0:32:30
PW/ 30 Rest BB	EU			
GH HYPR Incline	T		4	5:0:0:0:32:30
Piston Squat Band	T		4	5:0:0:32:30
PW/ 30 Rest BB	EU		ED	
Assist Nordic Ham Curl	T		4	5:0:0:32:30
PW/ 30 Rest BB	ED			
Pike SWB Abs	T		4	6:0:0:32:30
300 BENCH PRESS	EU	195 - 210	4	5:0:0:0:32:30
Np 2:15-HR 105	T			
Cuban PRSS			4	5:0:0:32:30
PW/ 30 Rest BB	ED			
180 Gripper	T	110 - 115	4	5:0:0:0:32:30
60 DB Tri Floor Press	ED	40 - 45	4	5:0:0:32:30
PW/ 30 Rest BB	EU		EUA	
38 DB Side Lat Raise	ED	30 - 30	4	5:0:0:32:30
PW/ 30 Rest BB	ED			
180 Chin up	T		4	5:0:0:0:32:30
H-Sq Sh Bi Trap	180s		1	30 on 30 off
PW/ 30 Rest BB	EU			
Glute Ham Back Cav Iso	180s		1	30 on 30 off
	EU			

ADVANCED TRIPHASIC (3-DAY): ISOMETRIC PHASE

MONDAY (100%)

Exercise	REPS	LOAD	SETS	NOTES
Squat Jump Pause	C1T		2	2¼ - Tendo
Pair w/	EU			
Cuban PRSS INC F8	T		2	Set Drop off
Pair w/	EU		ED	3:0:0:0:17:10
GH HYPR				
Pair w/	T			0:3:0:0:17:10
500 Back Squat	5	225 - 275	1	Cuban F8
Pair w/	EU			
500 Back Squat	3	295 - 325	1	
Pair w/	EU			
500 Back Squat	3	- 400	1	
Pair w/	EU			
500 Back Squat	T	350 - 375	3	0:5:0:0:17:10
Pair w/	EU			0:5:0:0:17:10
Hip Flex Iso Prone	T		3	Bands
Pair w/	ED		EU	0:3:0:0:17:10
1 Arm LAT Pull	T		3	Pause mid
Pair w/	EU		Eu	0:3:0:0:17:10
105 DB BENCH	T	75 - 80	3	0:3:0:0:17:10
Pair w/	EU			
500 Glute Bar Lift	T	350 - 375	3	0:3:0:0:17:10
Pair w/	EU		Eu	
30 OH LAT Raise	T	20 - 25	3	0:3:0:0:17:10
Pair w/	EU			
60 DB Tri Floor Press	T	50 - 50	3	0:0:0:0:17:10
Pair w/	EU		ED	
Dual Action Bicep Curls	T		2	0:0:3:0:17:10
Pair w/	ED		ED	
Iso Adduction Hold	T		2	0:0:0:0:17:10
Pair w/	ED			
Stadium Step Running	3		1	Rest 45
Belly Breath				
Full BCH Curl Up	T		2	0:3:0:0:17:10
Pair w/	ED		EU	Pause BM
Calf Raises KB	T		2	0:2:0:0:17:10
Pair w/	EU			
Glute Ham Back Cav Iso	180s		1	17 on 43 off
Pair w/	EU			
Chest Rev Grip Iso	180s		1	17 on 43 off
Pair w/	ED			
GH HANG	120S		1	
Pair w/				
Rollers Glutes & Hams	120S		1	
Pair w/				
LAYING RELAXATION	120S		1	

WENDESDAY (100%)

Exercise	REPS	LOAD	SETS	NOTES
Squat Drop Jump	C1T		2	2¼ - Tendo
Pair w/	EU			Set Drop off
Cpress Ext Rot for Band OC	5		2	0:0:0:0:10:10
Pair w/	EU		ED	
250 Glute Bar SL	T	175 - 190	2	0:0:0:0:10:10
Pair w/	EU			
750 Leg Press	T	565 - 600	3	0:0:0:0:10:10
Pair w/	EU			
Bench Abd Groin OC			3	
Pair w/	ED		EU	
165 Dynamic Lat Pull	T	125 - 130	3	0:0:0:0:10:10
Pair w/	EU			
300 BENCH PRESS	T	225 - 240	3	0:0:0:0:10:10
Pair w/	ED			
Ball BND LG Curls	T		3	0:0:0:0:10:10
Pair w/	EU		EU	
38 DB Rear Delt	T	30 - 30	3	0:0:0:0:10:10
45 DB Tri Pro Sup	T	35 - 35	3	0:0:0:0:10:10
Pair w/	EU			
60 DB Curl to Press	T	45 - 50	3	0:0:0:0:10:10
Pair w/	ED		ELA	
Bench Add Glute OC			3	0:0:0:0:10:10
Stadium Step Running	3		1	Rest 45
Pair w/	ED			
SWB Up TW	T		3	0:0:0:0:10:10
Pair w/	ED		EU	
Leg P Calf Raise KB				
180 Gripper	T	135 - 145	3	0:0:0:0:10:10
Pair w/	EU			
Ball Pike Drop	T		3	
Pair w/	ED			
	8	70% - 75%	2	
GH HANG	120S		1	Relax Mouth
Pair w/				
Rollers Quads & Back	120S		1	
Pair w/				
LAYING WALL SHAKES	120S		1	Relax Mouth

FRIDAY (100%)

Exercise	REPS	LOAD	SETS	NOTES
750 Leg Press	T	490 - 525	4	0:3:0:0:32:30
P/W R-55/HR120	EU			
Acc Band Jump	T		4	0:2:0:0:32:30
P/W R-35/HR120	EU		ED	1/2 Squat
GH HYPR Incline	T		4	0:2:0:0:32:30
Piston Squat Band			4	0:0:0:0:32:30
P/W R-35/HR120	EU			
200 DB RDL Shrug	T	130 - 140	4	0:3:0:0:32:30
P/W R-35/HR120	ED		ED	
Gopher U Abs			4	0:2:0:0:32:30
300 BENCH PRESS	T	90 - 225	4	0:0:0:0:32:30
P/W R-35/HR120	ED			2-2/2-2
Cuban PRSS			4	0:2:4:4:32:30
P/W R-35/HR120	EU			
180 Gripper	T	115 - 125	4	0:2:0:0:32:30
60 DB Tri Floor Press	T	40 - 40	4	0:2:0:0:32:30
P/W R-35/HR120	EU			
38 DB Side Lat Raise	T	25 - 25	4	0:2:0:0:32:30
P/W R-35/HR120	EUA		ED	
180 Chin up	T	115 - 125	4	0:2:0:0:32:30
H-Sq Sh Bi Trap	180s		1	32 on 28 off
P/W R-35/HR120	EU			
Glute Ham Back Cav Iso	180s		1	32 on 28 off
P/W R-35/HR120	EU			
Pair w/				
Pair w/				Relax Mouth
Pair w/				
Pair w/				Relax Mouth

ADVANCED TRIPHASIC (3-DAY): CONCENTRIC PHASE

MONDAY

100%	Exercise	REPS	LOAD	SETS	NOTES
250	Squat Jump	C1T	140 - 150	2	2% - Tendo
	PW/ 30 Rest BB	EU		EU	Set Drop off
	CP Ext Por rev B and OC	T		2	Each Side
	PW/ 30 Rest BB	Edt			
	Ankle Band Work	T		2	0.0.0.0.7.10
500	Back Squat	5,3	250 - 335	1,1	
	PW/ 30 Rest BB	EU		EU	
	4 way neck	6		2	
500	Back Squat	EU		EU	
250	SL Hex Deadlift	T	375 - 400	3	0.0.0.0.7.90
	PW/ 30 Rest BB	EDT	75 - 90	EUA	oc-D
	Hip Flex Prone OC CL	T		3	0.0.0.0.7.90
	PW/ 30 Rest BB	EU		EU	
225	Lat Pull Down	T	170 - 180	3	0.0.0.0.7.10
300	BENCH PRESS	5,3	150 - 200	1,1	
	PW/ 30 Rest BB	ED		EU	
	Med Ball Pass	5			1/2 Range
	PW/ 30 Rest BB	ED		ED	0.0.0.0.7.10
300	BENCH PRESS	T	225 - 240	3	oc-D
	PW/ 30 Rest BB	EU		ED	OC-A
300	BENCH PRESS	T	90 - 105	3	7 - OC-D
	PW/ 30 Rest BB	EU		EU	0.0.0.0.7.10
75	GH HYPR Incline	T	25 - 25	3	oc-D
60	DB Shoulder Press	T	20 - 20	2	0.0.0.0.7.10
	DB Tri Ext	EU		EU	oc-D
	Bicep shock curls	T		2	0.0.0.0.7.10
	PW/ 30 Rest BB	ED		EDT	
	Bench Add Groin OC			2	0.0.0.0.7.10
	H-Sq Sh Bi Trap	EU			
	PW/ 30 Rest BB	EU		EU	
	Chest Rev Grip Iso	ED			
	GH HANG	120S		1	
	Pair w/				
	Rollers Glutes & Hams	120S		1	
	Pair w/				
	LAYING RELAXATION	120S		1	

WENDESDAY

100%	Exercise	REPS	LOAD	SETS	NOTES
	Vertimax DS 2 Band	C1T		2	2% - Tendo
	Pair w/			EU	Set Drop off
	Tea Cup Stuff	5		2	
	Pair w/	EU			
	Calf Raises	8			
500	Sport Back Squat	5,3	250 - 335	1,1	
	Pair w/	EU		ED	
	OC Ball Grion Speeze	T		2	
		EU			
500	Sport Back Squat	1	440 - 465	2	0.0.0.0.5.10
575	Hex Deadlift	T	175 - 200	3	Reactive
	Pair w/	ED		EUA	0.0.0.0.5.10
	OC Ball Grion Speeze	T		3	0.0.0.0.5.10
		EU		EUA	OC-D
105	DB BO Row	T	30 - 35	3	OC-D
300	BENCH PRESS	5,3	150 - 200	1,1	
	Pair w/	ED		EU	
	Med Ball Pass	3			0.0.0.0.5.10
	Pair w/	ED		ED	0.0.0.0.5.10
300	BENCH PRESS	1	265 - 280	2	0.0.0.0.5.10
300	BENCH PRESS	T	90 - 105	3	OC-D
	Pair w/	EU		ED	OC-D
500	Glute Bar Lift	T	250 - 275	3	0.0.0.0.5.10
	Pair w/	EUA		EUA	
105	Delt BO Lat Reb Drop	T		3	0.0.0.0.5.10
105	Ez Throat Press	10	75 - 80	2	0.0.0.0.5.10
	Pair w/			EU	OC-D
120	Bar Curl	T	35 - 40	2	oc-A
	Pair w/	EDT		ED	0.0.0.0.5.10
	Bench Add Glute OC			2	0.0.0.0.5.10
	Glute Ham Back Cav Iso				#N/A
	H-Sq Sh Bi Trap	EU			#N/A
	Pair w/	ED			
	GH HANG	120S		1	Relax Mouth
	Pair w/				
	Rollers Quads & Back	120S		1	#Rest
	Pair w/				
	LAYING WALL SHAKES	120S		1	Relax Mouth

FRIDAY

100%	Exercise	REPS	LOAD	SETS	NOTES
750	Leg Press	T	490 - 525	4	0.0.0.0.15.20
	Pair w/	EU		EU	
250	Squat Jump	T	165 - 175	4	0.0.0.0.15.20
	Pair w/	ED			
	GH HYPR Incline	T		4	0.0.0.0.15.10
	Piston Squat Band	T		4	0.0.0.0.15.10
	Pair w/	EUA		ED	
	Ball LG Curl			4	0.0.0.0.15.10
		ED			
300	Gopher U Abs			4	0.0.0.0.15.10
300	BENCH PRESS	T	195 - 210	4	0.0.0.0.15.10
	Pair w/	ED		EU	2-2/2-2
	Cuban PRSS	T		4	0.0.0.0.15.10
	Pair w/	ED			
180	Gripper	T	115 - 125	4	0.0.0.0.15.10
60	DB Tri Floor Press	T	40 - 40	4	
	Pair w/	EU		EUA	
38	DB Side Lat Raise	T	25 - 25	4	
	Pair w/	ED			
180	Chin up	T	115 - 125	4	0.0.0.0.15.10
	H-Sq Sh Bi Trap			EU	
	Pair w/	EU			
	Glute Ham Back Cav Iso	120S		1	
		EU			

ADVANCED TRIPHASIC (5-DAY): ECCENTRIC PHASE, LOWER BODY ONLY

MONDAY (100% = 550)

Exercise	REPS	LOAD	SETS	NOTES
Neural Speed Activation	T		1	Fly 60
BACK SQUAT	3	305 - 330		Roll I-band
	2	360 - 385		Spine Rolls
	1	440 - 455		Coach Watch
Pair Below	3	400 - 425		6:0:0:0
Pair Below	3	400 - 425		6:0:0:0
Pair Below	3	400 - 425		6:0:0:0
French Contrast	3	400 - 425		6:0:0:0
Hurdle Hop	4		4	Height
Pair w/NO REST				
SQ Jump Weighted	4		4	0:2:0:0
Pair w/NO REST				
Acc Band Jump Pause	4		4	
4 way neck	T		4	3:0:0:0.20.20
PW / 45 rest/BB/RT				10 sec 2-way
Wrist Flexion	4		4	3:0:0:0.20.20
PW / 45 rest/BB/RT	Set - Hr 110			
ANT TIB BND	T		4	2:0:0:0.20.20
DB Walking Lunge (220)	T	145 - 155	3	Bands
PW / 45 rest/BB/RT				0:2:0:0.20.20
Cuban PRSS INC F8	T		3	3:0:0:0.20.20
PW / 45 rest/BB/RT	Set - Hr 110			Each Leg
Ankle Band Work	T		3	3:0:0:0.20.20
Glute Bar Lift (550)	T	415 - 440	3	3:0:0:0.20.20
PW / 45 rest/BB/RT				3:0:0:0.20.20
Hip Flex Prone Eccentric CL				
PW / 45 rest/BB/RT	Set - Hr 110			
Bench Abd Groin			3	3:0:0:0.20.20
Hip Traction	300S		1	Belly Breath
Pair w/				No Rest
Partner Leg Walks				No Rest
Pair w/				
GH HANG	60S		1	Relax Mouth

WEDNESDAY (100% = 550)

Exercise	REPS	LOAD	SETS	NOTES
Hormonal Strain Release	T		1	0:6:0:6:10
BACK SQUAT	3	305 - 330		Roll I-band
	2	360 - 385		Spine Rolls
	1	440 - 455		Coach Watch
Death Ground	1	480 - 510		Rest 1:00
Death Ground	1	480 - 510		Rest 1:00
Death Ground	1	480 - 510		Rest 1:00
Death Ground	1	480 - 510		Rest 1:00
Death Ground	1	480 - 510		Rest 1:00
Death Ground	1	480 - 510		Rest 1:00
SL Leg Press (413)	T	330 - 350	3	0:0:0:0.5.10
PW / 55 rest/BB/RT	OC			Single Leg
RDL (605)	T	485 - 515	3	0:0:0:0.5.10
PW / 55 rest/BB/RT	OC		OC	Same Leg
Hip Flex Prone OC CL	T		3	0:0:0:0.5.10
SNGL LG ISO Deadlift	T		3	0:5:0:0.5.10
PW / 55 rest/BB/RT			3	
Nordic HAM Curls	T		3	0:0:0:0.5.10
PW / 55 rest/BB/RT	Set - Hr 105		3	OC
Bench Abd Groin OC	T		3	0:0:0:0.5.10
Glute Bar Lift (550)	T	525 - 550	3	0:0:0:0.5.10
PW / 55 rest/BB/RT			3	
SL Reverse Hyper (193)	T	185 - 195	3	0:0:0:0.5.10
PW / 55 rest/BB/RT	Set - Hr 105		3	
PRTNR Abs	T		3	0:0:0:0.5.10
Hip Traction	180s		1	belly Breath
GH HANG	120S		1	Relax Mouth
				Relax Mouth

FRIDAY (100% = 440)

Exercise	REPS	LOAD	SETS	NOTES
Neural Speed Activation	T		1	Fly 60
FRONT SQUAT	3	240 - 265		Roll I-band
	2	285 - 310		Spine Rolls
	1	350 - 365		Coach Watch
	3	285 - 310		6:0:0:0
	3	285 - 310		6:0:0:0
	3	285 - 310		6:0:0:0
	3	285 - 310		6:0:0:0
Hurdle Hop	3		4	Height
PW / no Rest				
USSR Plyo Box	3		4	Pause
PW / no Rest				Rest
Acc Band Jump Pause	3		4	Rest HR 110
Bench Abd Groin ECC	T		3	0:3:0:0.25.30
PW / 35 rest/BB/RT			3	3:0:5:0.25.20
CP Ext Rot rev Band			3	
PW / 35 rest/BB/RT	Set - Hr 115		3	2:0:0:0.25.25
Ankle Band Work				
DB RDL Shrug (248)	T	125 - 135	3	5:0:0:0.25.30
PW / 35 rest/BB/RT			3	
Hip Flex Ecc Prone	T		3	5:0:0:0.25.30
PW / 35 rest/BB/RT	Set - Hr 115		3	3:0:0:0.25.30
Single Leg Squat (248)	T	125 - 135	3	
BENCH PRESS (360)			4	12:0:0:0.25.35
PW / 120 rest/BB/RT			OC	
DB Shoulder Press (90)			3	12:0:10:0.25.35
PW / 120 rest/BB/RT				12:0:10:0.25.35
Rev Grip Tri Push (180)	FFF	125 - 70	3	
GH HANG	120S		1	Relax Mouth
Partner Leg Walks	120S		1	
Pair w/				
Hip Traction	300S		1	Belly Breath

371

BONUS VIDEO

ACKNOWLEDGEMENTS

When we began working on this project a year ago, neither of us could have imagined the amount of work it would ultimately require to bring our vision to fruition. Looking back, the quality and depth of this book would not be what it is without the hard work and dedication from a small group of people.

A special thanks must go to Kevin Kocos and Tommy Miller. They were both there from the beginning, selflessly giving their time and insight. They were also great resources to bounce off and kick around ideas, helping immensely with focusing the vision of the book. We also want to make sure to thank Kyle Ochsner, Tad Johnson, and Daniel Raimondi. They were phenomenal resources for us, helping with tracking down additional sources, hyperlinking, and filming videos, and serving as test readers to experiment with different versions and layout ideas. The quality of the interactive material of the book is a testament to their hard work and dedication over the past six months.

In addition, we want to thank the coaches, teachers, and friends who have shared their time, knowledge, and abilities with us over the years: Adam Kadela, Phil Lundin, Chuck Lobe, Neil Rampe, Karl Erickson, Andy Zalaiskalns, Kevin Ziegler, Bob Rohde, Sara Wiley, Jim Snider, Ryan Feek, Jon Janz, Mike Malone, Buddy Morris, Brad Kligora, Dr. Micheal Yessis, Joe Warpeha, John Fitzgerald, Sam Johnson, Mario Sategna, Don Lucia, Dennis Dale, Kelly Kramer, Dan Simerall, John Anderson, Shawn Nelson, Tubby Smith, Dan Monson, Paul Thorton, Casey Curson, Brad Frost, J Robinson, Laura Halderson, Brad James, Steve Plasencia, Doug Coate, John Means, Dick Strahm, Jim Macintosh, John Jeffire, Curtis Davidson, Don Akers, Miron Kharchilava, Kurt Leonard, Roger Ebersole, Jeff Love, Ron Stepsis, Gary Dvorak, Eric Helland, Todd Hamer, Jeff Dillman, Chad Wagner, Mike Nelson, Sarah Hayes, Tom Myslinski, Don Van Fleet, Chris Hartman, Yosef Johnson, Dr. Mel Siff, and the thousands of athletes we have been lucky to work with over the years. Their contributions to our own knowledge ultimately led to the creation of this book.

Finally, our acknowledgments would not be complete if we did not thank our families for putting up with us over the last year. Writing a book while having a full time time job coaching or going to school places a burden, not just on us an authors, but on our families as well. Their understanding of our minimal free time and willingness to help with the book throughout the entire process has been amazing. Cal would like to thank his wife, Karyn, his two children, Tatum and Brody, as well as Mike, Tommy, Ken, Troy, Nate, Duke, and many other Roughnecks and Oilers. Ben wants to especially thank his parents, Wayne and Jackie, as well as his sister, Katie, and his girlfriend, Michelle. We would like to thank our families for putting up with us over the past twelve months and want you to know how lucky we are to have such great support at home. You are the ones that truly made this book possible.

ABOUT THE AUTHORS

Cal Dietz, M.Ed.
Head Olympic Strength Coach, University of Minnesota

Cal Dietz has been the Head Olympic Strength and Conditioning coach at the University of Minnesota since 2000. He has developed the Strength and Conditioning Programs and overseen the daily progress in Men's Hockey, Men's' Basketball, Women's Hockey, Men's and Women's Golf, Men's Swimming, Track and Field, Baseball, and Wrestling.

During his tenure, Dietz has trained a Hobey Baker Award winner, two Big Ten Athletes of the Year, over 400 All-Americans, 28 Big Ten/WCHA championships teams and 7 NCAA National Team Champions, and 13 teams finish in the top four in the nation. He has consulted with Olympic and World Champions in various sports and professional athletes in the NHL, NFL, NBA, MLB, and Professional Boxing. Also, during his time at the university help founded and chairs the Sport Biomechanics Interest Group with its purpose to explore the physiological and biomechanical aspects of advanced human performance encompassing the various aspects of kinesiology, biomechanics, neuro-mechanics and physics.

The Shelby, Ohio, native earned his bachelor's degree in physical education from the University of Findlay in 1996 and his master's degree from Minnesota in kinesiology in May, 2000. During his athletic career at the University of Findlay Dietz won three National team championships, two in football and one in wrestling. Highlights of his career was earning 2 All-American honors in Football and winning the NAIA National Duals MVP in wrestling. In 1995 he received the NAIA College Sports Magazine Athlete of the year and was inducted into the University's of Findlay's Hall of Fame in 2005.

Ben Peterson, M.Ed., CSCS
Ph.D. Candidate, University of Minnesota

Ben is a graduate of Northwestern University where he played football for the Wildcats. During his tenure he developed a passion for discovering what makes the human body tick -- creating and implementing new methods to train, develop and improve sport performance. Ben started his career working for the Minnesota Twins as an assistant strength and conditioning coach in 2008. Over the past four years, Ben's passion and creativity have allowed him to work with hundreds of professional athletes in the NFL, NHL, and MLB; helping them maximize the limits of their athletic potential. Most recently, Ben has been a consultant for Octagon Hockey, spending the NHL off-season working with their athletes in the Minneapolis area.

Ben is currently pursuing his Doctorate in Kinesiology and Exercise Physiology at the University of Minnesota. At the university he helps run the Sport Performance Lab while assisting to teach two courses within the kinesiology department; *Strength/Power Development* and *Health and Wellness*. His research looks at repeated sprint ability in anaerobic athletes, specifically as it pertains to energy system efficiency and fatigue. His research also looks heavily at power and rate of force development in athletes and its dynamic correspondence and transferability to sport.

Made in the USA
Coppell, TX
06 January 2020